Penguin Books

Towards the Mountain

Alan Paton was born at Pietermaritzburg, Natal, in 1903. He attended Pietermaritzburg College, at which he afterwards taught, and the Natal University College, at which he took his B.Sc. degree in mathematics and physics and the Diploma in Education. After teaching for some years, he was appointed Principal of Diepkloof Reformatory in the Transvaal, a post he held for thirteen years. In 1947  and reformatories in I America. It was while bestselling novel that b *Country* (Penguin), w dramatized and filmed. life for non-whites in S of art' by Francis Bret_____ in the *Sunday Times*. Dame Sybil Thorndike wrote that she had been 'profoundly moved by its sincerity and deep beauty'.

In 1953 Alan Paton's second novel *Too Late the Phalarope* (Penguin) was published. The same year he began to devote himself fully to the newly formed Liberal Party, of which he subsequently became President. The Party was finally outlawed by the South African Government's Prohibition of Political Interference Bill and disbanded in May 1968. In 1960 Alan Paton's passport was confiscated on his return from New York, where he had been presented with the annual Freedom Award.

His other publications include *Apartheid and the Archbishop*, a biography of Geoffrey Clayton, *Ah, But Your Land is Beautiful*, the first part of a projected trilogy, and *Debbie Go Home* (Penguin), a collection of stories. His writing and public work have been recognized by Yale University (Hon. L.H.D.), Kenyon College, Ohio (Hon. D.Litt.) and his own Alma Mater (Hon D. Litt.).

Alan Paton, who has two sons, lives in Natal.

Alan Paton

Towards the Mountain

An Autobiography

Penguin Books

Penguin Books Ltd, Harmondsworth, Middlesex, England
Viking Penguin Inc., 40 West 23rd Street, New York, New York 10010, U.S.A.
Penguin Books Australia Ltd, Ringwood, Victoria, Australia
Penguin Books Canada Limited, 2801 John Street, Markham, Ontario, Canada L3R 1B4
Penguin Books (N.Z.) Ltd, 182–190 Wairau Road, Auckland 10, New Zealand

First published simultaneously in the U.S.A. and Canada by Charles Scribner's Sons 1980
First published in Great Britain by Penguin Books 1986

Reproduced, printed and bound in Great Britain by
Hazell Watson & Viney Limited,
Member of the BPCC Group,
Aylesbury, Bucks

To my sisters, Eunice and Ailsa,

and to the memory of my brother Atholl,

all three of whom were also born and

brought up in Pietermaritzburg,

the lovely city

They shall not hurt or destroy in all my holy

mountain;

for the earth shall be full of the knowledge of

the Lord, as the waters cover the sea.

ISAIAH 11 : 9

Chapter 1

Pietermaritzburg, the lovely city. It lies in a basin of hills, in the valley of the Umsindusi River, which enters from the west and leaves in the east, where it will soon join the Umgeni on its journey to the sea.

The hills to the north, though we would not call them mountains, are big ones, and the trains from Durban to Johannesburg have to climb them. In my boyhood this was done with much puffing and whistling, and later with that electric sound which is louder than a hum and more musical than a growl. Above that would be the sound of the sirens which the growing boy at first compared unfavourably with the whistles, but later accepted fully. He would lie awake at night and listen to the sound of the trains in the hills above his city, with feelings of pride and exaltation.

In these days the city had a population of 30,000 people, while the town and port of Durban, seventy miles away by rail, had about 60,000. It was his hope that one day Pietermaritzburg would overtake the sister town, and each new house built in his city would renew this hope. But today she has a population of 100,000, while Durban has over 700,000. The boy was then probably about ten years old, and he no longer cherishes such a hope.

My hometown was paradise. It was founded by the Voortrekkers (then called Dutch, now called Afrikaners) in 1838. It was named after Piet Retief and Gerrit Maritz, and was called Pietermaritzburg. It remained a trekker town for about seven years, when the British

Government annexed Natal and appointed the first Lieutenant-Governor. Many of the trekkers left Natal for the Orange Free State and the Transvaal, and Pietermaritzburg became a British city.

I did not realise when I was a boy that my home was a Voortrekker city. We British shortened the name to "Maritzburg," and pronounced it in English fashion. Nor did I have any idea that the street names of Burger, Loop, Berg, Greyling, Retief, and Boshoff were Dutch. I did not hear anyone speak Afrikaans (the new language which succeeded Dutch and was largely a simplification of Dutch) until I was twenty-one years of age, and then I heard it in the station yard at Volksrust in the Transvaal, on my way to the graduation ceremony which was then held in Pretoria. We graduates, with a smattering of Afrikaans, shouted jokes at the white labourers. The jokes were not obscene, but the exhibition was unmannerly. It aroused intense anger. It was an example of British arrogance and contempt at their worst. Of the potential harm that we were doing, we had no conception whatsoever.

Pietermaritzburg, being a Voortrekker foundation, was a rectangular city of parallel streets crossing other parallel streets at right angles. It confined itself to the rectangle except for the outgrowths of the Town Hill, Mountain Rise, Scottsville, Alexandra Road, and Prestbury. Access to unspoiled nature was immediate. From our house in Pine Street we crossed the road and were at once in the country. A small stream, the Dorp Spruit, ran below the steeply ascending hills, which were covered in summer with waving grass that became brown in winter, and when set alight caused those spectacular nocturnal fires, the memory of which is inseparably bound up with my boyhood.

My reaction to nature was intense.

I cannot describe my early response to the beauty of hill and stream and tree as anything less than an ecstasy. A tree on the horizon, a line of trees, the green blades of the first grass of spring, showing up against the black ashes of the burnt hills, the scarlet of the fire-lilies among the black and the green, the grass birds that whirred up at one's feet, all these things filled me with an emotion beyond describing. And then in the fold of all south-facing hills were patches of indigenous trees and undergrowth, which we called, hardly ever, the forest, but more often the bush, probably under the influence of the Dutch "bosch," which later became the Afrikaans "bos." These folds were the kloofs, another word of Afrikaans origin, still retained in American English as "clove." As often as not a small stream ran down the kloof, and on its banks grew ferns and the wild begonia whose soft stems we would chew for their acid juice. A rare joy was to find the magnificent orange clivia, now protected, then rapidly disappearing. A glade of clivias in flower, in one of the larger stretches of bush that might be called a forest, is a sight not to be forgotten. The stream would run over black stones, descending rapidly, sometimes with little waterfalls. And one might, though perhaps only once in a lifetime, catch a glimpse of the small mpithi antelope, shy and delicate. If the expanse of bush were large, one might hear the call of the green-spotted wood dove—"my father is dead, my mother is dead, all my relations are dead"—and its melancholy ending, "and my heart goes du-du-du-du-du-du." Or the equally liquid but not melancholy call of the fukwe, also with the refrain, "du-du-du-du-du-du," dropping continuously down the scale. And the whippoorwill, the piet-my-vrou, a bird seldom seen but abundantly heard, arriving from the north in October and returning north in March, and calling night and day while it is here. And the purple-crested loerie. When it is in flight, in its colours of red, green, and purple, it is one of the most beautiful sights in nature, and can evoke from the watcher cries of wonder.

I was much older before I responded, and no less intensely, to the beauty of plain and sky and distant lines of mountains. When I first saw the expanse of the Transvaal highveld and the desolate stretches of the Karoo I did not at once acknowledge that they were beautiful. The qualities of harshness, starkness, and seeming endlessness did not seem to me to be compatible with beauty.

Pietermaritzburg, like all South Africa except the Western Cape, has a summer rainfall, although it can every few years experience a winter downpour of ten to twenty inches, which turns the Umsindusi into a mighty river and the Dorp Spruit into a raging torrent. The annual rainfall is in the region of thirty-five inches, which means that the hills surrounding the city are green and luxuriant in summer. Mist often lies on the tops of the hills. Robert Louis Stevenson expressed my deepest feelings in those lines from his poem "To S.R. Crockett":

> Be it granted to me to behold you again in dying,
> Hills of Home! and to hear again the call;
> Hear about the graves of the martyrs the peewees crying,
> And hear no more at all.

The peewee, or peewit, is a member of the plover family. So is the titihoya. I do not remember that I ever heard it in the hills of Pietermaritzburg, but I certainly heard it on the top of Natal's Table

Mountain in my student years, and in the hills of Ixopo when I was a young schoolmaster. And when one heard it in the mist and rain, the bird itself unseen, it caught at one somewhere—shall we say it plucked the strings of the heart?—as it must have plucked at the heart of Robert Louis Stevenson on some Scottish hill.

The intensity of these experiences I concealed from others. I do not know why. And whether there was some reason for it, whether I had ever revealed too much and been rebuffed, or more likely laughed at, I cannot now remember. One of the effects of this concealment was to create a private world of the self. In that sense I could have been described as a lonely child. But not as an unhappy one. I was too much in love with the world into which I had been born. Of its political and racial realities I knew exactly nothing. I had no idea that before I turned twelve the world would be plunged into the most terrible war of all history, and that the young men of Britain, France, Germany, and Russia would die in the mud for nothing. Nor had I any idea that I lived in a country where almost no child of colour could hope to aspire to the richness of the life that I was going to lead.

No, my world was the world of hills and grass and rain and mist, and of birds seen and unseen, and of the crying of the trains on their way to Johannesburg. Pietermaritzburg was to me the lovely city, and in calling it thus I was not, as one critic has suggested, practising the arts of the beautician. A beautician presumably tries to create, or at least tries to imitate beauty. But my beauty was already created, in that place where I was born.

Chapter 2

On January 11, 1903, my mother gave birth to her first child in the house at 19 Pine Street. My parents called him Alan Stewart.

My father, James Paton, was a Scot from the Glasgow area and came to South Africa in 1901 during the Anglo-Boer War. He did not come to fight, being a Christadelphian and therefore a conscientious objector. He went first to Johannesburg and then to Pietermaritzburg, where he found a place to sleep on the floor of the cobbler's shop of two bachelor brothers, in Church Street. This street had originally been Kerkstraat, but its name was changed after the British annexation of Natal; and still more recently, both names have been recognised.

My father was then about twenty-eight years of age. I do not know how he made his living at first, but I never knew him to have any other post than that of shorthand writer to the Supreme Court. This post he kept until he was pensioned in 1928. He was a man of intelligence, devoted to writing and to literature, but not highly schooled. His father had died when he was fourteen, and he had had to go to work and become the breadwinner of the family. He often wrote poetry for the newspapers, sometimes over his own name, sometimes over noms de plume. It was essentially topical verse, and could be very witty, and he enjoyed a limited and local fame. At home he was an autocrat, but outside he was diffident. Whether he was ambitious I cannot say. But he must have felt a deep sense of frustration at never having been able to progress beyond the machinelike work of a court reporter.

My mother, Eunice Warder James, a schoolteacher, was a few years younger than my father. Her father, Thomas Warder James, had come to South Africa from Bristol about 1850, and when I was old enough to know that he was my grandfather, he was a senior clerk in the well-known firm of wagonmakers, Merryweather and Son, whose works were at the corner of Church and Boshoff streets. He was a faithful Methodist, strict in all moral and therefore business matters, and intensely proud of his firm, which sent wagons all over the world and was known for the quality of its workmanship. My grandmother had been a Miss Mason, and together they brought up four daughters and three sons, of whom my mother was the eldest. My grandfather was not of the gentry, but he was what in those days one would have called a gentleman. My mother both loved him and stood in awe of him.

Our own home, if not poor, was certainly simple. We were not high in the social scale. My mother, dear soul, would speak with something akin to awe of the Tathams, the Broomes, the St. Georges, the Hathorns, the Shepstones, the Pope-Ellises. There was also the fantastic Mrs. P. Davis, who owned or ruled or otherwise held in thrall the *Natal Witness*, Pietermaritzburg's morning daily. She lived in a tremendous house in Alexandra Road, and if I remember rightly, no great work of public mercy could flourish without her patronage. Judges of the Supreme Court, which building stood and stands still at the corner of Church Street and Commercial Road, were members of this local aristocracy, some by the divine right of birth and some by reason of their elevation, which they owed to Queen Victoria or King Edward, and this made them people of great importance.

I do not know what my father earned, but my elder sister thinks it was £40 per month. I think that our home at 19 Pine Street cost £450 or £500. It had five small rooms, sitting room, dining room, my parents' bedroom, and a bedroom for my sisters. I think my brother and I slept in the small enclosed back verandah, but neither they nor I can quite remember. The third bedroom was occupied by my father's mother, who lived with us until she died in 1931 at the age of ninety. She also was not highly educated, but was an extremely intelligent and well-read woman, who kept her clearness of mind until a few days before her death. I do not know if there is such a thing as a Scottish character, but if it is the one that my grandmother had, it is proud and self-reliant, yet with a proper and not servile respect for one's superiors, who were not the rich, but people like governors and judges. Children were no doubt more docile in those days, but be that as it may, we treated her with great respect. Though she was a woman of great force of character, she did not try to manage our home, and she and my mother lived in harmony until the day she died. That of course was my mother's doing as well. She was unselfish and unassertive. She had, however, a very strong will, but unlike many other strong wills, it did not obtrude itself, nor was it aggressive.

My father rented seaside cottages at various times for the school holidays, at Doonside, Winklespruit, Illovo Beach, on the Natal south coast. The first thing that my brother Atholl and I invariably did was to go down to the beach and lie there in our bathing costumes, facing the sky, with no protection from the sun. That was all right for him; he was dark of complexion, and burned himself almost black. But I burned red, and could hardly sleep at night for the pain. All the skin on face, neck, arms, body, and legs would peel off, and then I would go back for another dose, hoping to achieve that mahogany complexion. It was my grandmother, with no previous knowledge of any sun save that of Scotland, who warned and threatened and pleaded with me not to treat my skin in such a way, and told me that I would damage it beyond repair. But I was clever and knew everything and would not listen. It was not until I reached my fifties that I went to see a specialist who told me that my skin was damaged beyond repair, that my top skins did not exist any longer, that the sun was poison to me, and that my only hope was to live in Norway.

This specialist had once looked out of his window at the bare-headed people in the streets below. "There are my patients of the future," he said to his patient of the present. "They'll never get better, but they don't die. It's a lucrative profession."

Our home was frugal and our parents thrifty. On a Sunday night we would each have a piece of cheese, and not a big one. I could have finished it in one or two bites, but I would cut it into twenty pieces. If we had pickles we would get one each, and I would deal with mine in the same way. On one of our coast holidays my father invited Harold Chapman, the cleverest boy in the school, to spend a week with us. One day we had cold meat and pickled onions and Harold emptied nine or ten onto his plate. We watched in fascination but my father said never a word. On another occasion two girls from the Collegiate School came to lunch, and had bread *and* butter *and* jam *and* cheese, all at once. Again we watched fascinated, but never was heard a discouraging word.

I do not remember ever resenting our frugality. Perhaps I did not know we were frugal. My father smoked but hardly ever drank liquor, and if I remember rightly, never drank anything stronger than wine, and that only when he was offered it at someone's house. He certainly did not indulge himself where we could not; he liked to possess books, but could not buy many. His taste was good, but my mother had no time, and I would think no energy, for serious reading except the Bible and Christadelphian books. At the end of the day she was exhausted. In these early years she worked so hard that in old age she could no longer walk upright. She liked the novels of Ethel M. Dell and Ruby Ayres, which were anathema to my father. So she kept them hidden in a cupboard, and would lend them to me provided I kept them out of sight; that was how I made the acquaintance of Jeffrey Farnol and Rafael Sabatini, neither of whom was able to win my father's approval. So my mother and I deceived my father; that was probably the greatest of all her sins.

I regret that I did not superintend the disposal of my father's books. There must have been some which, if I could read them now, would bring back many things from the deepest depths of consciousness. But I still have a book given to me by my paternal grandmother with this inscription:

Awarded
By her teacher
to
Margaret Paton,
who, by the judgement of
the examiners, was found
second
At the Annual Competition
for
The Crow Scholarship.
July 23rd
1857.

Who Margaret Paton was I do not know. The book was *The Northern Coasts of America and the Hudson's Bay Territories*, by Patrick Fraser Tyler, Esq., and was published by T. Nelson and Sons in 1854. I acknowledged the gift by signing my name in it, "Alan S. Paton, 1912" in a hand which appears quite mature for a child of nine. It came back to me today while I was writing these words that it was in this book that I first encountered the word "pemmican," and sure enough it is there, on page 172 and no doubt other pages. For some reason I was fascinated by this word.

My father married my mother on March 31, 1902. She had not yet become a Christadelphian, though my grandmother, my father, and his two sisters Grace and Elizabeth, all were. Grace was a nurse and went to America, where she made an unsuccessful marriage with a Mr. Holmes. Elizabeth followed her brother to South Africa and became a teacher for the Natal Education Department, ending her career in Durban as headmistress of the Umbilo Road School for Coloured Children. She was a good and generous woman. For some reason she did not marry, and she poured out her affection on me, my brother Atholl, and my sisters Eunice and Ailsa. She spent many of her holidays with us, and I do not remember that she ever exchanged a cross word with my mother. What caused her grief was that at least the three eldest children were afraid of their father; they resented his extreme authority, and he came near to destroying their filial affection. I do not think he liked this, but he seemed powerless to change it.

Our home was a deeply religious one. This left an abiding mark on my sisters and myself. My brother became much more a man of the world, not that of high society and the fast life, but a typical Natal world of rugby, Old Boys' associations, the Natal Carbineers, and much drinking of beer. The Christadelphians, brothers of Christ, who address each other always' as "brother" and "sister," were founded by John Thomas in 1848. They believe that Christ was raised from the dead and will come again at the time of the last war of Armageddon, and rule the world for a thousand years. After this millennium God himself will reign and there will be peace forever. All who are judged accountable will be raised from the dead, and those who are worthy will enter the Kingdom. Those who are judged unworthy will enter the state of eternal death. These last Days were foretold by the prophets, notably Ezekiel and Daniel, and again by John of Patmos, in the book of Revelation.

Though Christ was a man, He has been made the Lord, and He is remembered at every "meeting" of the brothers and sisters in the "breaking of bread." The "meeting" is simple; it consists of prayer, reading, the singing of hymns, the breaking of bread, and the preaching of the word. The Christadelphians believe that the truth of the Gospel has become overlaid with the tradition of men. I seem to remember that they also believed that only they knew this truth, but my sister Eunice says this is not so.

The brothers and sisters were simple in life, abstemious in habit, upright in conduct. They kept themselves away from the world, except in such measure as is necessary for keeping themselves alive. They did not gamble, or use strong language, or go to the theatre. Pleasure was not forbidden, but it was most soberly enjoyed. They did not take each other or anyone else to court. They did not marry unbelievers. Their sexual codes were strict. They were faithful in religious observance. They were less prone than many other Christians to interpret the Scriptures to suit their worldly desires. They were real and earnest students of the Bible.

Christadelphians do not suffer from the confusion into which many Christians are thrown by Christ's teaching about the payment of tribute to Caesar, by Peter's teaching about serving God rather than man, and worst of all, of course, St. Paul's teaching that the powers-that-be were ordained of God and that they are a terror only to the evil doer, a belief that is naturally held most strongly by rulers and those who identify their interests with the continuance of their rulers in power. No commandment of God could be set aside by man; therefore because God had forbidden man to kill, and because Jesus had implicitly condemned the use of the sword, no Christadelphian might become a soldier.

Each Sunday we were instructed in what are for me the immortal stories of the Old Testament, most of them being of errant human beings very like ourselves. Although I was young the great utterances of the prophets enthralled me, and their visions of that world where the wolf lies down with the lamb, and they do not hurt or destroy in all that holy mountain. That was also the vision of John on Patmos, of that world where there shall be no more death, neither sorrow, nor crying, neither shall there be any more pain. The visions are ineffable, of a world that will never be seen, but towards which we journey nevertheless. But I do not want to write about that now, because it all pertains to the theme of hope, and at that age I was not much concerned with it.

The stories of the New Testament also enthralled me, of the Last Supper, Gethsemane, the trial, the crucifixion, the resurrection. So did the parables of the Good Samaritan and the Prodigal Son, and the story of the Washing of the Disciples' Feet. The teaching of the parable of the sheep and the goats I took seriously, that in doing something unto the least of men, one did it unto Christ; but I did not like the fate of the goats, which to me almost destroyed the sublimity of the lesson.

For the person of Jesus I conceived a veneration which has never left me, although I cannot claim to have been a faithful servant. I have been called a "distinguished Christian." If that means a Christian who has happened to become distinguished, I accept it. But if it means that I have been distinguished in my discipleship, I could never accept it. All I can say is that there were some things in my faith for which I would have been ready to die. If I had lived under

Hitler, I would certainly have died. I shall explain later why such a choice was never posed to Christians in South Africa, and why therefore the assertion that the South African of the Afrikaner Nationalists is as bad as the Germany of the Nazis is absurd. There are similarities, but the grossest elements of Nazism are absent.

My parents wanted very much to keep their children unspoiled from the world. It can't be done, but that is what they wanted to do. They taught us a great number of moralities that weren't really moralities at all, and a great number that were. Alcohol was almost never seen in our home. My father smoked but not my mother. In fact few women smoked at all; it was somehow considered *wrong* for a woman to smoke. We played card games but never for money. We did not gamble or go to race meetings. We did not dance, and we did not play games on Sunday. We went to the cinema but not to the theatre. Sexual ethics were strict and puritanical. We children were not allowed to go out without supervision, and our friends were chosen by my father.

When the time came for my brother and me to be introduced to the world of girls, my father invited two of them, N. and J., to the seaside cottage he had rented for the month at Doonside. But the experiment—if it was one—was a total failure. The girls either did not wash properly, or suffered from some frightful affliction. My mother and sisters had to endure this for a month.

My sister Eunice, who is nothing if not direct, suggests that N. and J. were invited, not for the education of my brother and myself, but for my father's own pleasure. That could well be so. He was very susceptible to the charms of girls and young women. But I do not know that he ever had a liaison, and I guess that he did not. The conventions of those days were so strict, and our own circle of friends so proper, that one would have had to defy both conventions and friends and face a first-class scandal. My father could not have done it, whether he had wanted to or not.

I shall give one example of his strange kind of philandering. We were very friendly with the F. family, of three boys and four attractive girls. The girls would come to tea, and my father would hold the hand of the eldest daughter under the table. We all knew it and my mother knew it too. It never created any crisis or scandal, and I don't think it ever went any further. I don't remember that I thought it anything except a bit odd. But my sister Eunice told me very recently that my mother resented it deeply though she showed no sign of it.

Many years later I met the three eldest girls on occasions. They talked warmly of the past, of my father and mother and their children, but never referred to the philandering. I think they had regarded it as harmless.

So we were brought up in a mixture of lesser and greater moralities, but the greater were real enough. One did not lie or cheat. If the tram conductor did not come for the fare, you took it to him. One was not contemptuous of people because they were black or poor or illiterate. Justice was something that had to be done, no matter what the consequences. We would have rejected the cynical saying—had we known it, which we did not—that justice is the interest of the stronger. Murder, theft, adultery, were terrible offences, but to be cold and indifferent to the needs of others was the greatest offence of all.

Such was our home. It cannot be compared with the home in which Edmund Gosse grew up so solitary. His mother did not have the warmth of mine, nor did his father the human frailty of mine. He was the only child, but there were four of us, all of us with wills of our own. In Edmund Gosse's home literature was frowned upon, even Shakespeare; in ours books were treasured. He was not allowed to walk on Sundays; we walked over the great hills. His father and mother seldom laughed; our parents laughed often, even though we did not always appreciate my father's jokes.

The thing that I resented bitterly about my home was my father's authoritarianism maintained by the use of physical force. His use of physical force never achieved anything but a useless obedience. But it had two important consequences. One was that my feelings towards him were almost those of hate. The other was that I grew up with an abhorrence of authoritarianism, especially the authoritarianism of the State, and a love of liberty, especially liberty within the State.

Another thing happened too, but I do not know enough to call it a consequence. I grew up to have—eventually, say thirty years later— a will which, though not inflexible or implacable, was in matters of principle unshakeable. Some would call it courage, some would call it inordinate pride. I myself call it stubbornness. I suppose it contains a bit of all three.

Chapter 3

Pietermaritzburg at the beginning of the century was a city of importance. It was the seat of the British Governor, of the Natal Legislative Council, of the Supreme Court of Natal, of the Bishop of Natal, and it was the garrison town of a British regiment. The Governor lived at the top of Pine Street, in a big house which later became the home of the Natal Training College for teachers. He was of course the leader of society; everyone of importance was invited to his great Ball. He drove down Church Street in his carriage to open the new sessions of the Legislative Council, resplendent in uniform. Mr. Peter Carbis, ex-Mayor of Pietermaritzburg, who was a friend of my father, kept in his house a half crown, set in red velvet. This half crown had been given him by the Governor for helping him put on his overcoat.

Of this social world our family knew nothing. Our great day came on the King's birthday, when the regiment in their red coats, and with their brave band playing, marched from Fort Napier down Pine Street to the Polo Ground. They marched past our very house, and a great number of the 30,000 residents of Pietermaritzburg, white, African, Indian, and Coloured, lined the streets to watch them pass.

I remember that the regiments left in 1914, when I was at the most eleven years old. When the soldiers were allowed to march at ease, they winked and nodded at the African girls, who like the rest of us had come out to see the grand sight. The white citizens strongly disapproved. It was something not to be done, and when done in daylight it was even worse. It became worse still because every girl likes a soldier, and the African girls giggled at the attention that was being given to them. I must record that no bolt from heaven ever struck down one of these wicked men.

Such things do not happen today. Openly I mean. We have the Immorality Act of 1927, which forbids carnal intercourse between white and African, and the amended Act, which forbids it between white and any person not white. The great majority of the men who break this law are white. If a white man of any substance, a minister of religion, a professor, a lawyer, a schoolmaster, is found guilty of breaking this law, his life is ruined, even if the court suspends his punishment. At the time I write this, three white men have committed suicide in the last few weeks rather than face trial. More and more white people are beginning to ask themselves which is the greater offence, to commit a sin of the flesh or to destroy the person who commits it.

Of our 30,000 people roughly one-third were white, one-third African, and one-third Indian. A smaller group was the Coloured people, most of them not descendants of white, Malay, and Khoi-khoi as in the Cape, but of early British colonists and African women. We have a legend in South Africa that has become a joke—I think it actually appeared in one of our school history books—that the Cape Coloured people are the descendants of Malay, Khoikhoi, San, and passing soldiers and sailors. Yet our Immorality Act was not made for passing soldiers and sailors, though it catches quite a few. It is one of the meanest traits of white South Africans that they are able to feel such a contempt for the people they themselves have fathered.

In my childhood I had no conception of the complexity of our racial scene, of the political problems it created, and of the richness and tragedy of so much of our history. We knew no African people except our servants. My parents were considerate employers, but they were people of their day and age. My mother was a born Natalian and her mother also. They were upright people, and would never have used violence or abuse; but they would have paid the wages of the time. What they were I do not remember, but I have a vague recollection that you could engage an *umfana*, a boy, for five or ten shillings a month. Most white people spoke a kind of Zulu, which was called by a name unacceptable today, *kitchen kaffir*. My father spoke a Zulu of his own, and when we were out walking he used to embarrass us by talking to every black stranger. His remarks caused tremendous laughter, and I don't think he ever realised that this was not so much because of his wit as because of his Zulu.

He spoke to Indian people too. The man who sold us fruit was Sammy, and the woman Mary, but S. R. Naidoo was Mr. Naidoo. My father did not live to see Mr. Naidoo, in his old and respected age, thrown out of his office in the centre of the town by that evil law known as the Group Areas Act. The words "coolie" and "kaffir" were not used in our home, nor any derogatory racial terms. That is not to say that we had any great ideas about racial politics or race relations. In those days such ideas were limited to prophets and to prophetesses, to people like W. P. and Olive Schreiner, John Tengo Jabavu, Dr. Abdullah Abdurahman, and the Rev. John Dube. The prescience of the Schreiners was remarkable; they could see what was hidden from other white eyes.

Jabavu, Abdurahman, Dube, saw naturally through the eyes of the ruled, but they too could see clearly that white supremacy could not last forever, if only because they knew the powerful aspirations in their own breasts, and knew or guessed that they would come to be cherished by many others.

Of all this we children knew and heard precisely nothing in our home. I should think that my father had vague inklings. He was pro-Boer and was learning Hollands, which was then one of the two official languages of the Union of South Africa. He was a Scot, and was therefore not an unqualified admirer of the English. He had a natural bias in favour of the underdog, and he would guess that the underdog had aspirations. Of all these portents of the future my dear mother had no inkling whatsoever. But one must not judge her harshly. Great people like Paul Kruger, Cecil Rhodes, Lord Milner, Louis Botha, and Jan Christiaan Smuts had no inkling either.

Bishop John William Colenso died twenty years before I was born. He may have antagonised clerics but he antagonised colonists much quicker. He was the champion of the Zulus, he learned their language and gave them a dictionary. His name still lived in Pietermaritzburg because his surviving daughters Harriet and Agnes could be seen in the streets. They were tall women and they wore long black dresses that came down over their shoes. I do not remember them without some small black child in train. Though they were not Christadelphians, my mother thought them holy. It is difficult to imagine that they would have been sent to join the goats, because their lives were devoted to others, and I have no doubt that they believed that in serving these black children they were serving the Lord—a belief that many Natal colonists would have thought decidedly odd. For the middle sister, Fanny, life was tragic. She fell in love with Major William Durnford, a married man separated from his wife. In those days divorce was impossible for a man holding the commission of the Queen. When Durnford was blamed for the British defeat at Isandlwana, it was Fanny who fought fiercely to clear his name. He was killed at Rorke's Drift in 1879, but Fanny continued her fight until her death in 1887.

In our home we were also spared the vulgarity and the hatefulness of anti-Semitism, which was by no means unknown amongst the white people of Natal. Christadelphians took the teachings of the gospel seriously, but more than that, their Lord was a Jew, his father and mother were Jews, his disciples were Jews. Therefore contempt of Jews was an unthinkable and unforgiveable offence. Children learn much more from what their parents are than from what they teach. Anti-Semitism never infected us. And what was more, we were able to grasp the true meaning of Hitler before many other people.

As I grow older I am able to understand my father better. But for years I remembered him with deep resentment. I have written that he was an autocrat at home and diffident outside it. I am sure that is true. I can remember his laughter, which was never rollicking or bawdy or serene, but in a way apologetic. I am sure that his autocracy at home was a compensation for his diffidence abroad. I do not know all the causes of this diffidence, but undoubtedly his lack of professional status was one of them. He moved in the world of the Supreme Court, a world of judges, registrars, advocates, attorneys. They talked a good deal, and his job was not to participate in their conversation but to take it down in shorthand and translate it into type. It is not the kind of job that a man of intelligence, and of gifts too, would wish to do all his life.

He taught us to have a great respect for judges, especially for the Judge-President. The one I remember best was Sir John Dove-Wilson. He lived in a big house at Mountain Rise, and sometimes on our walks we would pass it. That was a long time ago, yet I remember that we did not pass it carelessly but with some kind of respect. I do not think my father would have carried on a Zulu conversation in front of the Judge-President's house.

We were also taught to raise our hats to Sir Michael Gallwey, who after his retirement spent much of his time sitting on the stoep * of his little house in Church Street. We were very well-mannered, though I would think that was more my mother's teaching. We

* American—"stoop."

lifted hats, we walked on the outside of the pavements, we opened doors, we stood when ladies entered. There was only one thing I jibbed at, and that was calling a man "sir" unless he was a schoolmaster. How I could thus resist one of my father's wishes I cannot quite explain, but it may be that he being from the Scottish working class understood my unwillingness. Just why I was unwilling I can't quite explain either. But I agree that when I lifted my hat to Sir Michael Gallwey or Sir John Dove-Wilson, I would say "sir."

I never knew my father to be violent outside our home, but he could be violent in it. Just how continuous or frequent was his use of violence I cannot now remember. It is not easy to remember accurately the frequency of something that one resented intensely. One remembers incidents but not the whole flow of events. I remember once being beaten on the legs with an umbrella, and I remember that the latch of the umbrella cut through my stockings and caused a wound, which distressed my mother greatly. My father believed in the use of the rod, and I have known my grandmother to remonstrate with him. I have also known my Aunt Elizabeth to comfort my brother and me after such an occasion. I believe that what distressed her more than the beating was our adamant unforgivingness.

I shall have in the course of this story to develop the paradox of my docility and my obduracy, my obedience to—even my fear of—authority and my rebelliousness against anything I felt to be unjust. Both the docility and the obduracy, both the fear and the rebelliousness, were in later life—much later life—to disappear, and to give way to or even perhaps to be the progenitors of a certain unshakeableness of will, the very contemplation of which makes me marvel when I think of my childhood. For if in this case the child simply maturing was father of the man, certain qualities were not discernible.

I strongly suspect that my father on occasions used violence towards my mother. There were times when the whole household trembled. It was my father's will that ruled. I remember on one occasion he came into my bed, having clearly quarrelled with my mother. He was in an ugly mood, and I did not dare to move. It was as though an evil humour came on him at times, as it came on King Saul, causing him to try to kill David.

My father's use of corporal punishment had one effect on me. I determined not to use it on my own sons. I lapsed twice, once with my elder son David, once with his brother Jonathan. These lapses I remember, even now, with shame.

Did I hate my father? I think I did then. When I left home to become a schoolmaster, my hatred abated. When I married, it abated still further. Traces of it still remained in my fifties. Now, so far as I know, it has gone. I am not a determinist, and do not believe that we have no responsibility for our actions; at the same time I believe that there are powerful forces that influence our lives and over which our control is nonexistent or minimal. I realise that I have grown up in a strange society where race and its concomitant emotions of fear, hate, tolerance, love, contempt shape our thoughts and actions from cradle to grave. And I give thanks to my home— and to other influences that operated later—that I never became a racialist. I judge my father with much more compassion than I did when I was young.

The Christadelphian meeting disapproved of my father's marriage with an unbeliever. I am not sure whether he withdrew from the meeting or the meeting from him. When my mother later became a Christadelphian, the meeting was ready to forgive but my father was not ready to be forgiven. So it was my mother who took us to the meeting. And faithful she was to the end of her long life. There grew up the odd custom that one of the children must stay at home to keep my father company. My mother bore all this—and I suppose that much of it was childish—with her usual fortitude. I suppose the fact that both my father and my mother were believers helped a great deal, even if he stayed at home. We were spared the kind of home where father and wife, or father and child, cease all communication because one is an unbeliever, where perhaps wife and child are thrown out of the house.

But I must stop now. It is time for me to go to school.

Chapter 4

When I was six I went to school at Berg Street Girls' School, which took small boys in the early classes. I went there with fear and apprehension, though of course that is a common experience of small boys and girls. But I think my fear was extreme. I was in fact a sissy.

I did not go there unlettered. My mother had taught me to read and write and count. She was a good teacher and I was a willing pupil. Like most beginners I was put into Class 1, and after a day or two I was put into Standard I, thus virtually dispensing with what might be called infant education. This happened to me on yet one more occasion, and it meant that I went into high school about three years younger than the average.

This however cannot be compared with the school career of South Africa's wonder child, Jan Hendrik Hofmeyr. He went to school when he was eight, and was put into Standard I in January 1902. In March he was in Standard II. In January 1903 he was in Standard III, in March he was in Standard IV, in August in Standard V. In 1904 he did Standard VI and Form A, and in 1905 Form B and Form C. In 1906 he went into the final class, Form D, and for the first time spent a full year in a class. He went to university in short trousers, a boy amongst men. Whatever else this spectacular career did for him, it made him—in the deepest sense—forever solitary.

I was certainly solitary at Berg Street Girls' School. Whatever my home may have lacked, it was my shelter, the place where I was warm and safe. And when I got into the classroom, I was warm and safe again. The misery of my life was getting from one shelter to the other. The streets and the playground were places of peril. In the playground I stood against the brick walls in the sun, watching the other children play. I would have played if they had asked me to, but no one did.

I did not wish to attract attention, but I did. I wore a pair of shoes that did not lace up, but had a strap that went over the instep and was fastened by a button. These shoes were pronounced by one of the older boys to be girls' shoes, but I denied it, I am sure not hotly and angrily, but no doubt quietly and gently. I had no idea that such a small matter could attract such great attention, but soon there was a crowd of boys around me, and there was general agreement that I was wearing girls' shoes.

After a while they left me, and there I was standing alone, thinking to myself, these shoes look like girls' shoes. I lifted one foot and put it on the other but this of course hid only one of the shoes. So I walked to the big school verandah, and sat down on one of the benches, for there I could put both of my feet under the bench and so hide the shoes. But I had not been sitting there long when a teacher came to me and said, "Sitting, sitting, go and play in the sun." She said, "Aren't you well?" But I had no great experience of lying, so I told her I was well, and she said, "Then go into the sun, it's against the rules to sit here now."

My fear of bigger boys was extreme. It was cowardice that led me into my first offence. We were walking home after school, and a girl of about my age was walking ahead of me. Some of the bigger boys ordered me to push her off the pavement, and I obeyed. I did not think further about it, either to feel shame or regret. It was an act of expediency, designed to save me from further attention. When the shame and regret came later, they had no element of nobility. Next day when I got to school I was ordered to report at the headmistress's office, and there stood the little girl. The headmistress asked if I had pushed a girl off the pavement, and I again, with no experience of lying, said yes. She then lectured me on the contemptibility of such conduct. She looked at the trembling six-year-old boy and passed sentence upon him. He was to eat his lunch on the girls' verandah. I have now lived for seventy years since that punishment, and never again have I pushed a girl off the pavement.

My strongest memory of Berg Street Girls' School is a strange one. I wrote it down more than forty years after it had all happened, because it seemed foolish to feel pain and shame about it any longer. It was a cold day at school and a bitter wind was blowing. We had eaten our sandwich lunches, and were in the playground. It was with dismay that I saw coming up the street towards the gate of the school the black boy who worked as a servant in our house. It was not the sight of him that dismayed me, but the fact that he was carrying a basket, and over the top of the basket was a clean white cloth. I knew at once that it was food, no doubt hot food, that my mother had sent her son because of the bitterness of the day.

I knew that this would attract more attention to me, so I went further along the wall so as not to be seen by the boy. I had not been standing there long when some of the schoolboys came to me and said, your boy's here with a basket. But I, though inexperienced in lying, denied that such a boy could be there. So they brought the boy, and of course it was our boy, and he smiled at me uncertainly because of the strangeness of the place, and I denied all knowledge of him. But he told them he was certainly our boy, and that I was the son of the house, and that my mother had sent me something warm to eat and drink. I denied him the second time.

Then one of the schoolboys took the white cloth off the basket, and there was a jug with a cup in the mouth of it, and another white cloth in which something was wrapped up. He took the cup out of the mouth of the jug and said, cocoa, hot cocoa. He opened the second white cloth and there were the scones that my mother had baked. And I knew that while they were hot she had opened them, not with a knife but with her hands, and had dropped butter into them, to melt and sink yellow and sweet, into their hearts. But I denied her.

One of the schoolboys said to me, "What are you going to do with it?" "It's not mine," I said. He asked, "Can I have it?" " It's not mine," I said. He was so persistent that in the end, although the food was not mine, I said he could have it. So they shared it out. What the black boy thought of it all I don't know. When they had finished he put the jug and the cup back in the basket and covered them with the white cloths. Then he saluted me and went out of the gate, but I did not acknowledge his salute, for why should I salute an unknown boy?

When I wrote this story forty years later, I called it "The Gift," and I ended it with these lines:

As I remember, my mother asked me when I returned if this strange story was true, and I did not lie to her as I had done to the boys at school. I do not remember that she spoke any further. I do not remember that she patted my head or smiled in any special way at me. I do not remember that she ever told the story to my father, but that does not mean that she did not. I do not think she told it to my brother, because he would have plagued me with it. I have no doubt she kept it in her heart.

And so would any mother keep it in her heart. For this is one for whom she fears, going forward and retreating, now confident, now afraid, making his way from her womb into the world.

I finished my Standard I by pleasing my parents, and I am sure myself, by coming top of the class and winning a first prize. It is my big regret that I did not keep any of the books given as prizes. Now that I am old I would like to be able to take them in my hands, and I am sure that if I could read them now, they too would strike resounding chords. It is strange that at twenty a man can destroy a book treasured at six, and at seventy wish that he had not. It may be that at twenty he puts away childish things, but that at seventy he wants to have them back.*

In 1909 the Natal Education Department built a new school called Havelock Road Boys. The school was not far from our house in Pine Street, and its first headmaster was Mr. Harward. Again I went to a new school with fear. The school went to Standard VI so that I now had to deal with big boys, many of whom were decidedly rough. Here I committed my second offence. I wrote the word "fuck" on the wall of the school lavatory.

For this I was taken by one of the older boys to the headmaster. Mr. Harward's sentence was that I should go home and report my offence to my parents, who would deal with it in their own way. I made my way home with much apprehension and told my mother of my wickedness. Then we sat down to wait for my father to return from work. When she told him he called me into one of the rooms and shut the door. He then chastised me, how grievously I cannot remember. That was the last time save one that I wrote on a lavatory wall. Of the meaning of the word I wrote on this first occasion, I had no inkling whatsoever, though I knew well that it was not the kind of word that one would use in front of one's elders and betters.

I must not give the impression that I was totally lacking any spark of individuality. It so happened that I was one day returning home from some errand or another. I was walking up Church Street towards Pine Street, where I would turn right and walk down the

---

* *My sister Eunice questions this account. She says that the books were stored in a trunk and were destroyed by rats, and that I was desolate. I think her account is the correct one.*

hill to our home. I must have been nine or ten years old, or at the most eleven. As I walked up Church Street a soldier from the regiment at Fort Napier was walking down. He had probably had a few drinks, for as I passed he snatched my hat from my head and threw it into the drain that ran at the side of the pavement. In the early days of Pietermaritzburg these drains, in Afrikaans *sluite*, in Natal English *sloots*, carried water from the hills into the town, and citizens drew water from them for their houses and gardens. But I think that at the time of this incident this was no longer done, and the drain water must have been foul.

I rescued my hat and was filled with a burning sense of affront and injustice. Could I let this insult go unpunished? I decided that I could not. Clutching my hat firmly in my hand I went after the soldier. I now exhibited the courage that is born of anger. I launched myself at the soldier and delivered a kick at his back. Whether I reached his bottom is doubtful. But I certainly kicked him in the back of his thigh. With angry curses he turned to grapple with his assailant, but the boy was winging his way home, with un-Christian joy in his heart.

A visit to Durban was a tremendous excitement. The first visit that I remember was to the beach at night, and the sea terrified me. Then there were the ships in the harbour and the zoo at Mitchell Park, and the subtropical richness of the trees and shrubs. There was Musgrave Road, which even at that age I recognised as a residential street of wealth and beauty, of big rich houses in tremendous gardens, many of which ran down unfenced to the road; of these houses hardly one remains today. But for me the great excitement was the tramcars. In Pietermaritzburg there were only two routes, one from the Botanic Gardens to Retief Street, and the other from Howick Road to Scottsville. They intersected at right angles at the Town Hall, and the tramcars met there on the stroke of every quarter. But here in Durban they arrived at the post office every minute, from Toll Gate and Marriott Road, from Stamford Hill and Umgeni, from the Beach and the Point, from Congella and Umbilo. One of our holiday treats was to take the circular route from the post office up Berea Road, then along the whole length of Musgrave Road, and down Florida Road back to the Post Office. It took forty minutes and cost I think threepence for a child. It was like the Sunday piece of cheese, not to be devoured in one or two bites, but to be savoured piece by piece.

These childhood years, which were characterised by an intense response to nature, now witnessed an intense response to words and books, to *Tom Sawyer* and *Huckleberry Finn, Alice in Wonderland* and *Through the Looking-Glass, Water Babies* with some very difficult passages, *Kidnapped* and *Treasure Island, Robinson Crusoe* and *The Swiss Family Robinson.* The word "fell" in *Water Babies* captured my heart.

My father subscribed to *Chums* for us. It came once a week, and its arrival was an event and a weapon to be used by my father. After some time he changed to the *Boys' Own Paper.* Comics were strictly forbidden, so we read them at school; the comics of those days were full of misadventures of amiable simpletons, who walked innocent-eyed into the most diabolical traps. They did not deal with war, sex, violence, and death; why they were thought to be harmful I do not know.

My father was devoted to the novels of Sir Walter Scott, but I do not remember whether I read them then or in my high school days. But I believe I read them all, and I am sure I read them before I started on Charles Dickens, when I was about thirteen. I would not find Scott easy reading today, but I had no difficulty then. Nor did I find the long and descriptive passages tedious. It has been suggested that reading habits have changed drastically with the increased tempo of life and I think this is true. My own have changed considerably. I believe that if you write in chapters they must be short. I find that even when I am reading a good writer it irks me when the chapter goes on too long. If the writer does not use chapters, but divides the work into sections, then I want each section to be separated from the next by a space, and this space should be as much as would be required for three or four lines.

Just what kind of child I appeared to be to my parents I don't know. Perhaps they were glad to have produced one so safe and studious. But I was not prepared to leave the writing of books to Scott and R. L. Stevenson. I cut the few empty pages that I could find in old exercise books into four equal pieces, and made small volumes out of them. My mother stitched the pages together. I then wrote in them, in a style resembling print, stories and other pieces, modelled no doubt on *Chums* and the *Boys' Own Paper.* These, plus some real books, formed the stock of a bookstore of which I was both manager and salesman.

My brother Atholl was on the whole not interested in literature, and certainly not in the childish game of making it and selling it. He was born on 31 January 1904, just a year after me, and was named after the earls and dukes of Atholl. Though he has been dead now for nearly forty years, I remember his birthday every year. But now I had acquired two sisters who were more willing to join in my games. My sister Eunice, named after her mother, was born on 4 December 1907, and my sister Ailsa, named after the famous island rock in the Firth of Clyde, on 6 July 1910. My own names were Alan Stewart, the first with no special significance except that it was Scottish, the second the name of the royal house. My father's love for all things Scottish was very deep, and he imparted it to at least one of his children.

I introduced my sisters to the world of commerce, and we had a little shop which sold jams, meal, salt, and diminutive loaves of bread which my mother made for us. I then entered the building trade, and made bricks; the material came from 17 Pine Street, a vacant plot next to us, and the bricks were made red by having geranium petals stuck to them while they were wet. Atholl was inclined to ridicule these activities, and he corrupted my sisters, who adopted an ambivalent attitude to my work, cooperating at one moment and poking fun at the next.

I can only suppose that it was a happy childhood except for one thing, and that was the authoritarian and often arbitrary rule of my father, which my mother tempered when she was able. But for three things I am grateful—the opportunity to walk the hills of Pietermaritzburg, to know the stories and noble passages of the Bible, and to enter the world of words and books.

When I turned ten I reached the top class at Havelock Road Boys, and was eligible for the Natal Bursary Examination. If I were successful I would win a bursary that would pay for my fees and books at Maritzburg College. If I failed I could try again at eleven, and again at twelve. I was successful and went to Maritzburg College in February 1914, having just turned eleven. I suppose it does not matter now, but I would not wish any of my grandsons to enter a high school at that age.

Chapter 5

The year 1914 was a momentous year for me: I entered as a pupil at Maritzburg College, we moved from the humble home of 19 Pine Street to what we thought the grand house of 551 Bulwer Street, and on August 4 Britain declared war on Germany.

Moving to 551 Bulwer Street was very exciting. It was for us a big house. A wide passage ran through it, with three bedrooms on one side and a sitting room and a dining room on the other. At the top of the wide passage was a small bedroom on the left for my brother and me and a pantry. The small passage itself led into the kitchen. The bathroom had been converted into our bedroom and the bath had been transferred to the kitchen, and remained there until my father built a bathroom on the very spacious verandah that ran round three sides of the house.

We had no water sewage at first. The earth-pit lavatory was a little way from the house, and in the rainy weather it was an unpleasant trip to go there. Our servants, a man and a woman, had no lavatory at all in their quarters, and had to walk several blocks to a communal and unspeakably filthy convenience supplied by the Pietermaritzburg Corporation. This was a common arrangement in those days.

The house was set in about an acre of ground. To us the garden with its drive and trees seemed enormous. But probably the biggest excitement was the orchard. It contained about thirty trees, peaches, pears, plums, quinces, and apples, and one Japanese persimmon. The fruits of the persimmon are astringent when unripe, but when ripe they are soft, luscious, and orange-red. The autumn leaves are very beautiful, in yellow, orange, russet, and red. Against the north and west walls of the house were planted vines which bore splendid grapes, the white and red Hanepoot, the black Barbarossa, the small white currant, and the common Catawba. Both vines and trees bore prodigally.

My father bought our new house for £850. I thought him very clever to have found such a place. To me it was a kind of paradise. One opened the back gate, crossed over East Street, and there a few feet below was the Dorp Spruit. Between that and Mountain Rise, a distance between one and two miles, was unoccupied country. The only house in this expanse belonged to Dr. FitzSimons, who kept snakes, and was as far as I know the first learned student of the snakes of South Africa and the maker of antidotes for the various poisons.

One of my university friends was bitten by a black mamba and lived to tell the tale. Gordon Truscott was staying with another of my university friends in Swaziland, and one hot summer morning went walking in the orchard, which was overgrown with tall grass. There he was electrified to see the head of a black mamba above the grass. He continued warily and then saw the head of another. He decided to return to the house, but as he turned he was struck in the ankle.

The pain came instantly, from two tell-tale red marks. He squeezed the bitten area as hard as he was able, and tied his handkerchief tightly below his knee. In great pain, and with his leg growing rapidly numb, he hobbled back to the house where his friend gave him anti-venom injections in thigh and buttocks. He rushed Truscott to the hospital where he was given an Epsom salts injection, and was covered with many blankets and given hot-water bottles. His thirst was incessant, but he vomited up all liquids. He was given many saline injections and on the second day the miracle occurred. He was not going to die, and nearly every victim of the black mamba dies. That evening he drank some Bovril and his recovery began. It took him five weeks, and then he returned to the school where he taught, still very weak and subject to attacks of vertigo. Though a religious man, he refused to use the word "providential" of his escape, not wishing to set too high a value on his life.

The new house in Bulwer Street meant new duties for my brother and myself. On Saturdays and holidays we had to work in the garden. On these days if the weather was fine, there would be a regular procession of boys on foot and on bicycles on their way to the very deep pool of water in the Ohrtman Road Quarry. The quarry had had to be abandoned because of the water that welled up out of the rocks, and it was the free playground of the boys of my generation. At first my brother and I were not allowed to go there; only later was the ban relaxed. But we certainly did not like having to work in the garden when our friends were swimming, nor did we like their ironic greetings as they passed our house.

I went to Maritzburg College at the beginning of 1914, for a few months from 19 Pine Street but thereafter from Bulwer Street. I realised later that this posed difficult problems for my father. He had never been to a high school himself, and I think he felt it necessary to assert his rights.

The school was a rugby-playing school, and the game of the Scottish working people was soccer. Even in South Africa the class antagonism between rugby and soccer players was strong, and in fact still exists, though it is confined to English-speaking people, and does not apply to Afrikaners, whose devotion to rugby is total. However, when the time came for me to play rugby my father agreed to it. But when my mother and sisters came to watch the rugby, he went to watch soccer in Alexandra Park. I dare say that this arrangement was reached by negotiation, but the separation must have been painful for him—the result of a working-class prejudice, which was no doubt also a working-class hurt, that had been elevated to the status of a principle. I have no doubt that it is this working-class hurt that has amongst other things, one of them the Second World War, done such damage to the economy of Britain.

It was about this time that I committed my only theft. My mother sent me to the little bakery in Retief Street to buy some bread. Mr. Walford the baker told me that the bread was just coming out of the oven, and left me waiting in the shop, face to face with temptation.

On the counter was a glass jar, about nine inches high, with a base about four inches square, rising to a circular mouth. The jar was full of toffees, and they would have been safe if the lid had been on. But it was not, and I took a toffee and put it in my shirt pocket.

I had hardly stolen the toffee when I saw the act in all its enormity. At that moment it was not conscience operating, but fear. I could see clearly the hollow in which the toffee had lain, and I dreaded the possibility that Mr. Walford would see it too, and that he would guess by some shopkeeper's intuition that one of his toffees was in my shirt pocket. However, he did neither, and I left the shop with my guilt and the bread and the toffee.

I avoided Retief Street which was a wide thoroughfare where crime would shout aloud, and turned into Loop Street and then into a lane called Collier Street. In the quiet of the lane I took out the toffee and thrust it into a hedge. I suppose that now both fear and conscience were operating, but conscience was not powerful enough to make me take back the toffee to Mr. Walford. I never stole again.

Another problem was soon to face my father and myself. At the age of thirteen or fourteen I had by law to join the school cadet corps. Now my father as a Christadelphian could not take part in military service. The question now arose as to whether he should allow his son, if not to take part, then at least to prepare for military service. He decided to allow me to join the cadet corps.

Why did he do this? Did he do it for my sake, so that I would not be singled out from the rest of the school community? I must say he had never shown much concern on that score, but I would not be justified in deducing that he was unable to show it. Is it possible that for his own sake he did not wish to make such a stand? The First World War was raging, and there certainly was a kind of war hysteria. In those days conscientious objectors in Britain were held in contempt. The chairman of a tribunal before which objectors were appearing was allowed by this hysteria to make the most insulting remarks about them. Things were however not quite the same in South Africa. In the first place there was no conscription; in the second place there were many Afrikaners who would rather have died than fight for the country which twelve years before had taken away their two republics. They would have gone before a tribunal not with apprehensive courage but with a fierce rejection of the ruling authority. I do not pretend to understand my father's reason.

Now while I was relieved when my father decided to allow me to join the cadets, it was a cowardly kind of relief. For I had already decided—if that is the word—to be a conscientious objector if the war continued until I was of military age, as it showed every sign of doing. This must have been about 1917, and I was fourteen years of age, and I took my decision—if that is the word—with little joy. Maritzburg College was a fiercely patriotic school. Its school badge has the words *"Pro Aris Et Focis."* In its halls were the names of its boys who had given their lives in the wars against Boers and Zulus.

Two of our boys, Pansy Bain and George Weber, ran away from school in 1916 to join up. In October 1916 Frank von der Hyde, who had left school at the end of 1914, was killed in Flanders, and the news cast a gloom over the school, together with a pride that we had produced such a hero. Three of our masters, C. L. Fischer, W.

M. Reid, and D. Morris, were killed in action. In the sixth form there were boys who were waiting impatiently for the matriculation examination, so that they could join the forces fighting against the evil Kaiser Wilhelm, who had invaded Belgium and called his treaty with her "a scrap of paper." Adjoining our property at 551 Bulwer Street was the property of the Baxters, and one of the sons had already gone and the other, Basil, who was a couple of years older than I, was waiting impatiently to finish school and go too.

It must have been the Christadelphian influence that had "decided" me to become a conscientious objector. Yet I think I had at that time more or less made up my mind that I would not become a Christadelphian. This is a further proof to me that I distinguished even at that age between what I called in later life the lesser and the greater moralities. But I did this by no means consistently. I think it would be more truthful to say that what I really rejected was my father's authoritarianism, which so often seemed to me harsh and unjust. Such authoritarianism often turns a child against all religion, but this was not so in my case. I have no doubt that I was strongly influenced by the words of Jesus to one of his followers, "Put up your sword. All who take the sword die by the sword." Although attempts are made today—and particularly in Africa—to prove that Jesus believed in "sanctified violence," and although he drove the money changers out of the temple, it seemed to me that the whole meaning of the gospel was that creative love had a greater power—and a truer and sweeter power—than force. I do not suppose that I reasoned it all out, but I do suppose that the way that I reason it all out now has its roots in my earlier years. I am sure that the forgiving by Jesus of those who reviled Him, the rejection of the third temptation in the wilderness, the Sermon on the Mount, made it difficult for me to contemplate taking up arms. I must in honesty add another factor, and that is that my gentle and at times timid nature made the idea of military service repugnant. Nevertheless as the war dragged on, and was still dragging on when I turned fifteen, I looked forward with apprehension to my eighteenth birthday.

I went to Maritzburg College with fear, just as I had gone to Berg Street and Havelock Road. Although I went to Form IIA, which was not the lowest form, I was the youngest boy in the school. As before, I enjoyed the classroom. As before, I feared the breaks and the playing fields. I was plunged straight into the cricket season, and placed in the bottom pitch. We had fielding practice on the Top Ground, and cricket giants from the First Eleven would come and send back sizzling drives from the balls that we bowled to them. Sometimes the giant would order the big roller to be brought, and he would throw the ball so that it came off the top of the roller at fantastic speeds and in unpredictable directions, aimed unerringly at our fast-beating hearts. Then a silence would fall over the whole field. A god was descending. He came from the high ground of the Victoria Hall to mix with mortals. He was dressed in white shirt and flannels, and wore the blazer of the First Eleven, which in our colours of black, red, and white was a sight to behold. His name was Arthur Clayton, he was eighteen years old, he walked as though he ruled the world. I did not know then that one day he would be the grandfather of two of my own grandchildren. Although he terrified us, he was a quiet, just, and high-principled captain of the school. Fortunately, fielding practice soon ceased to terrify me. I turned out to be a good fielder, though not a good batsman and bowler.

At Havelock Road I had—I hope I am writing the truth—carried off the first prizes in each class without intense application. Now in Form IIA I found myself with bright boys from various schools, and I was by at least two years the youngest. But some change took place in my nature, almost as though I was asserting some kind of right to enjoy myself. I now dropped gracefully into a lower place, perhaps 2nd, more likely 3rd, and do not ever remember being reproached for it at home. Our form master was Mr. F. C. Sutcliffe, who took us for everything except Physical Science and Nederlands. He was a tyrant, and we didn't like him, but he had no peer as a teacher of small boys. He was not one of those evocative teachers who would have a whole class standing on their toes and yelling their heads off. He was a drill sergeant, and I do not remember that he joked much.

Nevertheless he had some kind of humour. I could not remember *portare,* which is "to carry." I was made to go down on all fours, and he piled books on my back and ordered me to take them from one side of the classroom to the other. The Latin sentence for this was *portat asinus libros,* which was "the ass carried the books." Mr. Sutcliffe had a substantial pointer, and would use this to encourage the ass if it showed any signs of rebellion. Thus he illustrated graphically the meanings of Latin words, and it was naturally difficult thereafter to forget them.

One of the reasons why we didn't like him was that he despised "colonials," a word that is no longer in use, and of course we were nearly all born in the colony of Natal. We called him "Sucky" and he came in one day unexpectedly to find written on the board "Sucky is Bucky," which we regarded as the quintessence of wit. Mr. Sutcliffe was extremely angry, but he was unable to discover the author, who preferred to remain anonymous. Our headmaster was Mr. E. W. Barns. He was about five foot four inches in height, and we irreverently called him "Pixie." He had an English degree, and so in those days did most of the masters at Maritzburg College. This gave them great prestige among the "colonials." I shall later write more about our ultra-Britishness, our inordinate pride in the British Navy and our devotion to the Royal Family. These feelings have now, in the intense form, almost gone. My father called Britain "home," and my mother, who had never seen it, did likewise. But their children do not do so anymore, and their children's children have never done it.

Mr. Sutcliffe also despised the Indian people of South Africa, especially the labouring class which had first been brought to Natal in 1860 to work on the sugar plantations. In those days the anti-Indian feeling amongst the white people of Natal was rabid. The Indians were said to live on the smell of an oilrag. They would eventually take all our possessions from us, and this they would do by the use of every kind of deceit and dishonesty. Their language was an unintelligible gabble, and they made the towns stink of curry. Mr. Sutcliffe held all these views and propounded them to us. Eventually the Education Department ordered him to pipe down, after he had conducted himself with loud and vituperative zeal at a public meeting in the Town Hall to protest against the latest Indian infamy.

Maritzburg College was not a bad school for small boys. Bullying was likely to be kept in check by prefects and captains like Arthur Clayton, and in my second year, William Burton, my mother's cousin, another boy with high and unobtrusive principles. He was red-haired and open-faced, and he was another of our cricketing giants. If he greeted me in the passages my heart would be fit to burst with pride.

My first year at school was also eased by the protection given me by Victor Harrison, who still practises as an attorney in Pietermaritzburg. He was fifteen months older than I, and was in the cricket team called the Colts, from which most of the future giants in those magnificent blazers would come. He would not let me hang about timidly in the school grounds, but would include me in his company. He was also a boy, and later a man, of high principles. These principles did not however apply to smoking, and he would come back into class after the small and the lunch breaks, smelling powerfully of tobacco smoke. The smell was made worse by his habit of keeping stompies in his pockets, a stompie being a cigarette not fully smoked, then stubbed out, and stored away for future use. This smoking was usually done in the spacious bicycle sheds, or on the terraces that ran down from the school to College Road. Why Victor was never caught I do not know. I suspect it was because most of the prefects smoked too. But I should have thought that any master would have found him guilty on the smell alone.

By the time my first year ended, 1914, some more assertive strain was appearing in my character and I had developed an enormous pride in the school. But my greatest pride was reserved for the old Main Block and the Victoria Hall. The main block is a long double-storeyed building in red brick with mullioned windows and two splendid gables. While it is dark and gloomy inside, its exterior is impressive, and to my young eyes very beautiful. I am sure it pleased Mr. Sutcliffe, because it was certainly not "colonial," yet at the same time I have not seen a building in Britain which is like it. It has an atmosphere of venerability, and indeed for Natal it is very venerable, having been built in 1863.

When I went back in 1928 as a master, I wrote the following lines about the old buildings:

> *Old walls that echoed to our cries,*
> *Our oaths and prayers and laughter,*
> *And echo now to cries of those*
> *Who follow after,*
>
> *When earth has taken back to earth*
> *Our unremembered bones,*
> *Preserve the echo of our names*
> *About your stones.*

They were printed in the College magazine, and S. E. Lamond, who was a master at the College when I went there in 1914, and who was in matters of emotion very measured and almost prim, said to me, shutting his eyes as he often did for emphasis, that they were sublime. I should not like to go so far as that, but they were sublime for him, for the Maritzburg College, its buildings, its generations of boys and their achievements was for him his life. His memory of Old Boys and old events was phenomenal. An Old Boy would go to Mr. Lamond and ask if he remembered him, and Mr. Lamond would say, "Johnson, James Henry. You entered College in 1911, and you were in Clark's House. Mr. Barns gave you six cuts for going into town without leave. You joined up in 1916, but you didn't get the V.C. And by the way you played for both the First Fifteen and the First Eleven." All those who heard these feats of memory would show their admiration and astonishment, which pleased the performer intensely. A simple man with a single passion. After his retirement the Old Boys raised money and sent him off to New Zealand to see a daughter living there.

When College celebrated its centenary in 1963, it bestowed an honour upon me. I was asked by the Headmaster, Mr. R. E. Fuller, an Old Boy, to give the address and present the prizes at the Centenary Speech Day. I appreciated the honour all the more because in 1963 I was the National President of the Liberal Party of South Africa, which was regarded by the Government as a semicommunistic organisation, and by many white South Africans with hostility. The Headmaster also got me to write the eight lines of verse in wet concrete, and to sign them, and the plaque is to be seen in the southern wall of the gymnasium.

As long as Maritzburg College stands, those lines will be seen on the "old Walls." A humbling thought, but a pleasant one also.

Chapter 6

My brother Atholl later joined me at Maritzburg College. I did not much look forward to his arrival. Though a year younger than I, he was physically bigger, and he liked fighting and I did not. He would settle an argument with his fists, or by wrestling, and being both stronger and more pugnacious than I, he would win. Boys would say to me, "Is it true that your brother can give you a hiding?" This was the kind of question that I shrank from.

Furthermore, our natures were very different. I was a reader, he was not. I was gentle, he was rough. I was an inferior rugby player, he was not. In fact he ended up with one of those resplendent blazers, and what was more, an honours cap, a handsome velvet thing, braided with silver and tasselled. School was for him not a place of learning, but a place for fun and games. His popularity was tremendous. He was some three years behind me in school, and therefore did not arrive until I was near the top of the College.

My father's extreme authority and his arbitrary rules led us both to deceive him. Up till my brother's arrival, I had walked to school every day, a distance of about two miles. The last part of this walk is beautiful; we crossed over the Umsindusi River with its hundreds of willow trees, into the Alexandra Park, one of the most spacious and attractive parks in South Africa. My father now bought us bicycles, and made what was for us a humiliating rule about how to mount them. We were not to put the left leg on the left pedal, and swing the right leg over the saddle. We were to mount by means of the "step," which was a small metal rod which projected from the hub of the rear wheel. We would then be the only two boys at College who mounted by the use of this grotesque method, probably the only two in South Africa. If I remember rightly my father could relate gruesome instances of boys in Scotland who had done themselves severe testicular injury by the pedal method of mounting. I believe also that he argued that the pedal method put strain on the frame of the bicycle.

Our response to this rule was predictable. When we left 551 Bulwer Street in the morning, if my father were at home, we would mount by the step, making sure that no College boy was passing the house on the way to school. When we reached the school we would dismount by the pedal, when we left school we would mount by the pedal, and when we reached home, if my father was there, we would dismount by the step.

It would be strange if my father had not noticed our rebelliousness. Surely he must have known that out of sight we would disobey the rule. I do not remember that he ever asked, "Are you obeying the rule?" to which we would have given a lying answer. There was a second rule that we also disobeyed. Both my brother and I had to wear undervests, perhaps in winter only. Our winters were on the whole mild; I do not remember that we ever had snow in the city, and only occasionally on the surrounding hills. We both thought that the wearing of undervests was only for sissies. In the mornings therefore we would stop at the little thicket in Alexandra Park near the school, and stuff the vests into the bushes. After school we would retrieve the vests and arrive home fully clothed. Luckily for us they were never stolen.

It was about this time, say at about the age of fourteen, that I took a further step into the magic world of the spoken and written word. I should relate that I spent my twelfth year (that is, aged eleven) in Form IIA, and that I was then promoted with the brightest boys of IIA, to Form IVA, this making me more of a child than ever. To make up for this handicap, I had the fortune to encounter another superb teacher, our form master Mr. Herbert Leach, called for some reason "Scratch." In this form one of our set books was Longfellow's "Hiawatha," which I enjoyed, but nothing more. It was in Form V that a door opened to a new world, that of poetry, and it was opened for me by Elaine, the lily maid of Astolat.

I go now to the shelves and I take down *Everyman's Tennyson*, inscribed "Alan S. Paton, 1920." I open it at "Elaine" and I read these lines:

> *Most noble Lord, Sir Lancelot of the Lake,*
> *I, sometimes call'd the maid of Astolat,*
> *Come, for you left me taking no farewell,*
> *Hither, to take my last farewell of you.*
> *I loved you, and my love had no return,*
> *And therefore my true love has been my death.*
> *And therefore to our Lady Guinevere,*
> *And to all other ladies, I make moan.*
> *Pray for my soul, and yield me burial.*
> *Pray for my soul then too, Sir Lancelot,*
> *As thou art a knight peerless.*

And I find that I am weeping a little. And what am I weeping for? Is it for the lily maid of Astolat floating on her funeral barge to Camelot? Or is it for that young boy who first read of her sixty-four years ago? I suspect it is for him and his innocence, and his fearfulness, and his excitement, over trees and hills and rivers and now over words. He had been reading, for ten years probably. But it was rather stories he had been absorbed in. Now suddenly he realises that the words have a beauty of their own.

Nearly forty years later I wrote a poem for him. After thirteen years of living in the high interior I went to live at Anerley on the south coast of Natal. One afternoon I stood on the beach watching the swells come in. They rise and rise, taller and taller, and then become rollers, translucently green, and the white foam blows off the racing crests. Then they curl over, and after a moment of suspense they crash down, filling the air with their roaring. Here is the poem that I wrote for him.

> *The sea roars as ever it did*
> *The great green walls travel landwards*
> *Rearing up with magnificence*
> *Their wind-blown manes.*
>
> *His wonderment I recapture here*
> *I remember his eyes shining*
> *I remember his ears hearing*
> *Unbelievable music.*
>
> *I hear it now, but the high notes*
> *Of excitement are gone*
> *I hear now deeper*
> *More sorrowful notes.*

> *All is the same as ever it was*
> *The river, the reed lagoon*
> *The white birds, the rocks on the shore*
> *Only the child is no more.*

One cannot keep one's innocence, certainly not in boys' high schools. I usually ate my lunch sandwiches with Victor Harrison and his friends, one of whom was my full cousin, Noel Griffin, son of my mother's sister May. We would take our lunches in summer to some place on the terraces or under the trees that border the playing fields. We talked about many things, rugby and cricket of course but not hockey, and the motorcar which was being seen more frequently in the streets of Pietermaritzburg. Mr. Barns had one, but I cannot remember another at school. Most masters and most boys walked or rode bicycles. And of course we talked about our masters too.

I learned about sex and prostitution and brothels. In fact we had a brothel of our own, in prim and quiet Pietermaritzburg, and what is more, it was in Bulwer Street, one or two minutes' walk from our house. The brothel was indeed a strange one; it was in the house owned by an ineffectual man, Mr. B., who had a job at the market, a large blousy wife, two lusty daughters, and a third daughter of about twelve who was clearly being trained for the business. I have no doubt that the mother had been in the trade herself. There was a steady stream of men callers to the house, and it was the scandal of the neighbourhood. Why no police action was taken I don't know, because the newspapers of 1980 are full of the prosecutions of men and women who own and work in brothels. It was the second daughter of Mr. B. who initiated one of our neighbour's sons into the ways of the world. He was a friend of the family and a College boy, and my parents would have been astonished had they known of it. He told me all about it, with a strange mixed look of pride and shame. He had been afraid to go to the house itself, and had met the girl on the banks of the Umsindusi. I think it cost him a pound.

It was about this time that I reached puberty, and discovered the pleasure of masturbation. It gave me feelings of intense guilt, and I fought hard against it, even to the extent of keeping a secret chart of defeats and victories. My parents had never given us any sexual instructions. For most parents of that time it would have been quite impossible. When I was fourteen it was my mother who, quite embarrassed, gave me a book to read entitled *What a Young Boy Ought to Know,* and said to me wistfully, hoping I am sure that I would deny it, "I suppose you know all about it already."

The world is at the moment passing through a sexual revolution, and the new ethic, if there is to be one, has not yet emerged. Some people say we will return to strict conventions. I doubt it. There is surely something to which we should never return, and that is the fear of the body and the flesh. Yet who knows? Michelangelo had no fear of the body, and popes marvelled at his work, yet Catholics have in general been as afraid as Protestant Puritans of the flesh.

I do not find myself competent to lay down rules, except in my own home. I do not find myself able to judge sexual deviations. I recoil from the stories of sexual mutilation, of small boys and girls killed by madmen, of aged women assaulted by boys, yet I follow the modern belief and regard such acts as examples of desperate illness rather than depravity. I do not expect courts of justice to take the same attitude to these acts as I do. Nor am I by any means consistent and I do not regard all offences in this light.

I do not intend in this book to give the complete story of my sexual life, but I shall not omit those things which are relevant to my total life. I am not a saint. I am not afraid of the flesh. I am what could be called a "toucher," but I limit my touching. I am constitutionally incapable of "making a pass." I have great respect for the institution of marriage but I realise that that is an easy thing to have when one is happily married. I have a hatred of divorce and would feel ashamed if I divorced or were divorced. Yet I married a divorced woman and am not only happy with her but I have respect for her integrity and honesty. Sex is a powerful force, and will find expression somehow. If it can be expressed in a loving relationship, the participators are lucky, and I have a strong prejudice that the loving relationship should be a marriage or should culminate in it. I do not judge premarital relationships, but I would not allow them to be practised in my home. I consider myself lucky to have been happy in marriage. If I had not been then I am not sure how I would have behaved. I would find it difficult not to love and be loved by a woman.

I suppose my boyhood was much the same as any boyhood, except perhaps that I was abnormally shy of girls. I learned the facts of life while eating my sandwiches. On one extraordinary occasion I was allowed to go out on Christmas Eve with Victor Harrison and my cousin Noel. They each had girl friends, and they brought one for me. Her name was May Wyatt, and she lived in Boshoff Street. We walked up Church Street to the railway station and went and sat in an empty coach. There was smoking, kissing, and fondling within fairly strict limits. I was a total failure, and I think the girl from Boshoff Street was too. But I can't be sure of that. She may have had views as to who should do what first. My time had not yet come.

It is probable that boys who are abnormally shy of girls enter more easily into homosexual relationships. I entered one such relationship with C., who was in the same class as I but was some two years older. He and I were eating our lunch on the terraces. Just how our conversation proceeded I cannot remember, but it ended up by my feeling his penis, the size and rigidity of which astonished me.

After that I spent the day with him, perhaps two or three times, at his parents' small farm outside the rectangular confines of the city, on which occasions we fondled and masturbated each other. Some two years later, when we were together at the Natal University College, I found a note from him on the notice board. In this letter he expressed his sorrow for what had happened and begged my forgiveness, which I gave freely and briefly by word of mouth.

My other homosexual experience had no element of affection, at least not for me. From an early age I had accompanied my mother to the dentist, Dr. B. He would always compliment her on my beauty, intelligence, and general perfection, which she and I took with some pinches of salt. But the important thing was that as we left, he always gave me a present of a penny or a threepence or a sixpence.

When I grew older I made these visits by myself. If I remember rightly the presents grew bigger. When I was about thirteen their purpose was made suddenly clear. After one visit was over Dr. B. drew me to himself and fondled my penis. I said to him in what for a boy of thirteen were words of extreme clarity and finality: "I don't like that." He gave me the usual present—this time it was half a crown—and said, "That is the reward of virtue."

That was probably the first time in my life that I spoke with such decision. I was conscious of having a will and personality of my own. I did not stop going to Dr. B., but to my regret there were no more rewards for virtue.

There is one question that I find difficult to answer. The sex urge is very powerful, and is part of our nature; then what is the young boy or girl to do with it when it manifests itself in all its strength? This question confronts all parents and teachers. In my case I went through periods when I controlled it, and others when it controlled me. But I never found a final and satisfactory answer to the question.

I have also found difficulty with the words "desire" and "lust." I realise that they can be synonymous, but I would find it impossible to say that I lusted for my wife. I have on occasions been possessed by lust, and I did not like it and I felt polluted by it. When I was a boy I felt polluted because I had committed and wanted to commit a sexual sin, but now that I am older, I see something else. The shame is felt not only because one has done or has wanted to do something which one thought to be wrong. The shame is greater because for those moments the self has lost its sovereignty. It is being ruled by something which is less than itself. That is the greater cause for shame.

This is true of anger also, if we except the case of what we call righteous anger, which is anger for some cause greater or other than oneself. But the more common anger when it subsides leaves me ashamed, again because the self has lost its sovereignty.

Anger and lust, these are volcanic sins. More corrupting of character are envy, jealousy, and resentment. They are not volcanoes, they are smoulderers. They ultimately can do more harm to one's character. It is much easier to repent of lust and anger. But it is difficult to repent of resentment when the cause has not been removed.

Sometimes we tried sexual jokes on the masters. The rugby and cricket lords took pleasure in ragging those masters whom they could bully and deceive. There were some they ragged more cautiously, Mr. Fischer and Mr. Naudé for instance, who were members of the First Fifteen, and mighty and forbidding men. In those days masters could play for the First Fifteen, though not against other schools. If Mr. Naudé thought that things were going too far a vein would start ticking in his temple, and he would suddenly rise to his full height and say in a loud and commanding voice, not to them, but seemingly to the world at large, "Enough, it is enough." And it was enough too. Nor did we rag Mr. William Abbit, who had been senior wrangler of Cambridge. He once made a mistake on the blackboard and I ventured to point it out. He flew into a rage, simulated or not I did not know, and said to me, spluttering as he did when he was angry, "Do you argue with the senior wrangler of Cambridge?" When I assured him that I did not, he was satisfied. But he went at once to the board and rubbed out everything. Then he climbed into the high seat and desk from which he controlled us, with what I suspect was a ghost of a smile on his lips.

The ragging of those masters who were not so frightening often took the form of ambiguous sexual remarks, and the use of words which had both sexual and nonsexual meanings. The big boys knew more about sex than I did, but I knew more about words. I could therefore make more original remarks, and got away from our usual stock in trade. This won for me a half-amused tolerance. This side of my character I do not much like to remember.

We carried this ragging to unpardonable lengths in the case of a gentle woman called Miss Norman, who took us for shorthand. She was the only woman teacher we ever had. We would make these sexually ambiguous remarks, and I never knew whether she understood them or not. Boys would faint during her lessons, and they would be carried out by willing helpers. I do not look back with pride on these exploits. I must record that had I been rebuked for it, I would have stopped at once, as I did when I was punished for pushing the little girl off the pavement.

During the year in which I was thirteen I was in Form V, and Mr. Barns, with the agreement of my father, kept me in Form V for another year. My two strongest subjects were English and mathematics, and when I passed into Form VI, both these subjects were taught by our form master, the senior wrangler of Cambridge. He was another magnificent teacher. He was unmarried and lived in the main block. His nickname was "Fluff" and the stories about him were legion.

One of the best concerned his drinking. That he drank a great deal was well known to us. A short time after school, if he was not on duty, an African rickshaw-puller would arrive at the school, and Mr. Abbit would get into the rickshaw and be conveyed into the city to the exclusive Victoria Club in Longmarket Street. He took no exercise whatsoever and was pasty of countenance and pudgy of flesh. At the club he would eat and drink well, and would arrive back at College after lights-out, so that his return, and his physical condition on return, were seen by few. However, on one occasion he advertised them to the world. When he arrived back in his room he decided it was high time for a fire drill, and he blew the alarm. The boys had then to descend from their dormitories on stout woolly ropes, and parade on the lawns below. The fire drill was very successful, and when it was over, Mr. Abbit blew the alarm again. When he had blown it some six (or nine or eleven) times, only the most cowardly of boys came down the ropes, and the younger masters were full of rebellion. It was at this point that the headmaster, who lived in his own official house not far from the Main Block, arrived on the scene and persuaded Mr. Abbit that the danger of fire had passed, and that boys, whatever their faults, needed sleep. After that peace and silence reigned. But if a real fire had occurred later that night and the alarm had been blown again, the whole population of the Main Block might have been burned to death.

The next day the story was over the whole school. But the culprit mounted his high seat with an air of *noli me tangere,* and not even the most audacious spirits would have dared to make one of their ambiguous remarks, remarks which would have taken the form of "Sir, who invented the fire brigade?" or more daring, "Sir, I was so alarmed last night."

Mr. Abbit was so negligent in his eating and so prodigal in his drinking, and so careless of taking any kind of physical exercise, that he suffered from acidity and would often beat his chest with every appearance of being in extreme agony. Then he would say to me, the youngest, "Boy, quinine, half-and-half" and give me his keys. I would then leave the upper block and descend the steps to the main block, and enter his rooms, which always fascinated me because the walls were lined with many many books. Here I would pour a dose of quinine into a glass, add the same quantity of water, and take it back to him. Still with the look of intense agony on his face he would drink it with every evidence of extreme distaste: he would close his eyes, he would conduct his private struggle with the utmost fortitude, perhaps beat his breast again, open his eyes, survey us with that forbidding air, and return to his teaching. We, although we had seen it all before, watched with absolute fascination. A figure of fun? If so, then not one to be trifled with. His mastery over us, from captains and prefects to small boys like myself, was complete.

I disappointed my parents by not getting a first-class in the matriculation examination. This was put down to my extreme youth, but it was in fact because I had lost much of my earnestness and was beginning to enjoy school and "playing the fool." I won the English prize and a sum of money that enabled me to buy what were for me eight handsomely bound novels of Dickens. Four of them I still have. I also did equally well in mathematics, and well in history and science. I won the history prize, which was J. L. Morley's *Rise of the Dutch Republic* in two volumes. I still hope to read them before I die. I would have been Dux of the school if it had not been for a boy called Julius Goldman. His future seemed bright, but his efforts had been too much for him, and during the following year he was sent to the mental hospital on Town Hill, and did not live many years. His proud and ambitious parents never recovered from this blow.

My father decided that I must go to the Natal University College.

It was then nine years old, and had fewer than two hundred students. If I had been born ten or fifteen years earlier I should probably have gone straight to work, and my life would have been utterly and unimaginably different. I do not care to contemplate the possibility. One could call it providence or one could call it luck. If I had been a Winston Churchill I might be entitled to call it providence. Let us call it luck.

Full of hope, excitement, anticipation, energy, and in my first pair of long trousers, just turned sixteen, I set out for the Natal University College. I did not have to go far, because it was situated in my own city, in the suburb of Scottsville. What I did there I shall soon relate, but I think it is time to say something about the country into which I had been born.

Chapter 7

In the days before writing was known to South Africa, before there were historical records, the majority of the inhabitants were wild animals. The richness of the fauna was fantastic. There were elephant, lion, cheetah, giraffe, rhinoceros, hippopotamus, crocodile, and hundreds of thousands, perhaps millions, of antelope, from the lovely eland to the tiny blue duiker. The bird life was also rich, there being over eight hundred species in the subcontinent. It was not a country of big forests, but it had a wealth of flowers, and that part of the country known as Namaqualand is renowned for its desert ephemerals, which cover the veld for mile after mile after the first spring rain. As in so many countries this wildlife is threatened, but it is preserved in many parks, the most famous and the most spectacular being the Kruger Park, which contains all those animals I have mentioned in an area the size of the principality of Wales.

This earthly paradise was lived in by several peoples of whom I shall name two. One were the San people (once called the Bushmen), people of small stature, magnificent hunters and trackers, superb marksmen with the bow and arrow. They knew all about the herbs and plants of the veld, as food, as medicine, and as the sources of some very virulent poisons with which they tipped their arrows. They worshipped the moon and ascribed supernatural or magical properties to certain creatures such as the praying mantis. But their immortal achievement was their rock painting, in which figured humans, animals, birds, and the pleasures of the chase.

They were not photographic painters; by distortion they gave to their animals a grace and a beauty which excites the admiration of modern artists, and they were great depictors of motion. They were people of no fixed habitation. Occupying the land with them were the Khoikhoi people, of greater physical stature. They were semi-nomadic owners of cattle. Their language shows traces of San influence, the San languages being remarkable for their clicks, most of which are unmanageable by westerners. There were similarities also in their religion.

To these early peoples, who were by no means numerous, belonged this vast and well-favoured country. There was meat and grazing for all. But their ownership—if you can call it that—was to be challenged by two more virile peoples, the one coming from the north, the other coming from Europe and entering the subcontinent from the south.

The people who came from the north were black, African, and tribal in organisation. It is certain that iron-working, Bantu-speaking people were in the northern Transvaal as early as the eleventh century, and that they had reached as far south as the Transkei by the sixteenth century, and probably earlier.* There are records of sailors who were wrecked on the coasts of the Transkei long before the arrival of white settlers, and who were on the whole hospitably treated by the black people already living there.

These facts have come to light only in comparatively recent times. They destroy one of our favourite white myths, namely that the blacks crossed the Limpopo River in the north at the same time the first white settlers landed at the Cape of Good Hope. This myth was created because of the feeling of white guilt caused by the accusation that the white people had dispossessed the true owners of the country. These feelings of guilt are quite useless. Both white and black are responsible for the disappearance, or rather absorption, of the Khoikhoi and the flight of the San to caves in the mountains where they created their unique paintings until they were exterminated or took further flight, finally to the Kalahari Desert, where they adapted themselves to that harsh and forbidding country.

In 1652 the Dutch, under Governor Jan van Riebeeck, established a refreshment station at the Cape of Good Hope. They called their settlement Cape Town, and it is situated under a magnificent mountain called Table Mountain. The Dutch soon made the acquaintance of the Khoikhoi, but the black tribesmen were some four or five

* *Recent archaeological research places these events several centuries earlier.*

hundred miles to the east. Even by this time the San people were on the retreat. They did not keep cattle, but they liked meat, and it was sometimes easier to steal their meat from the Khoikhoi and the African tribesmen. Every man's hand was against them, including now the white burghers, who had become settlers and were moving slowly to the east, establishing farms and keeping cattle. The San were driven into the mountains and into the Kalahari. With their bows and arrows they could not stand up to the spear, far less to the gun.

The Khoikhoi fared better, but many of them were gradually forced away from the fruitful coastal regions into the interior. Those that stayed became the servants of the white people. They, and to some extent the San people, and the Malay slaves that were brought to the Cape towards the end of the seventeenth century, and to a certain extent their masters and employers, created the Cape Coloured people. Once again we had a comforting myth, and that was that the white blood in the Cape Coloured veins came from "passing soldiers and sailors." Some of it did, no doubt, but most of it came from the creators of the myth, the white overlords themselves.

It was not the first intention of the Dutch to found a colony. But the first white burghers, about nine in number, were eventually granted land by the Dutch East India Company. They became farmers on their own account, and began moving away from Cape Town and Table Mountain. That part of South Africa is very beautiful. One is always in sight of mountains, the climate is benign, the rainfall good, the wild flowers magnificent. These Dutch burghers had no desire to return to Holland. Dutch orphan girls were sent out to marry them, and after their narrow and very often unhappy girlhoods, they gave a fierce affection to this free and lovely land and imparted this affection to their children. The Dutch were joined by other Dutch, by Germans, and, most notably, by Huguenot refugees from France who were absorbed by the Dutch and contributed greatly to the growth of the infant wine industry. Although it was not discernible then, already a new race was being born, whose links with Europe became weaker with each generation. They were later to be called the Afrikaners. Another new race was being born too, of Khoikhoi, Malay, and European blood—the Cape Coloured people. These were the servants in the white households and the labourers on the white farms. They spoke the language of their masters in their own way, they brought up the white children, and therefore they powerfully influenced the changes that took place in the Dutch language, until it eventually became the new language,

Afrikaans. Some modern Afrikaners deny this influence, but they are being oversensitive.

I must note that these two races were distinct. The one was the ruler, the other was the ruled. One was superior, the other inferior. The white attitude to the Coloured was a mixture of kindness, paternalism, and in many cases contempt. The Coloured attitude to the white was not necessarily servile, but was certainly docile. That is not true today, but we have not got there yet. It is surely both strange and abhorrent that one should feel contempt for a child that one has oneself created.

The Dutch with their guns more or less had this country to themselves for a hundred years. They could now be called the trekkers or the trek-boers. They were always moving farther east and northeast away from the ease and comfort of Cape Town. They were more and more cut off from European culture. Their language was changing more and more. It was enriched by a host of new words, in an attempt to describe a country which bore almost no physical resemblance to Holland whatsoever. They had almost no books except the Bible, which most families read in daily worship. As they moved farther and farther from Cape Town, the country became more spacious, the distances more vast. In the great expanse known as the Karoo it became more and more like desert. It was almost inevitable that as they moved through this land with their cattle and their sheep, their menservants and their maidservants, they should liken themselves to the children of Israel, they should thank God who had led them to this promised land that seemed to go on forever, and the most fanatical of them should see themselves as a chosen people placed on this continent of Africa for some kind of divine purpose.

It was about 1770 that the trekkers first encountered the African tribesmen. Both were cattle-keeping people. The blacks resisted the advance of the whites. They did not retreat or fade away. Though few had guns they were fierce warriors with spear and shield. The black man would raid white farms, seize cattle, and very often wipe out a white trekker's family. The white farmers would organise a commando, conduct a retaliatory raid, kill black warriors, and seize cattle, some of which were inevitably not their own. With his urge to trek, the white farmer would encroach on what the black man thought to be his land. The Governor at the Cape would try fruitlessly to control the situation; he would forbid further advances and fix new frontiers, all in vain. So grew a bitter enmity between black and white. Practically the only communication between black and white was by means of the gun and the spear. It is fair to say that the black man became part of the white man's mind, just as the white man became part of the black man's mind.

I should like here to make an interpolation. I am not giving my readers an accurate history, but I am giving them what I think to be an accurate interpretation of history. I am selecting the material with one aim only in view, and that is to help readers to understand the strange and to so many people inexplicable situation in which we are today. I would much rather they understood our situation than that they should know all the facts of our history. I need hardly say that what I am giving you is my interpretation of our history, not the interpretation of any other person.

In 1806 by right of conquest, the British, then at war with Napoleon and his ally the Batavian republic of Holland, annexed the Cape of Good Hope and it became the Cape Colony. This was vitally to affect the lives of the Dutch people, and especially the Dutch trek-boer, whom I shall now call, a bit prematurely, the Afrikaner. He had come to regard this land of Africa as his own country. That is why he called himself an Afrikaner. He had never taken kindly to the rule of the Dutch East India Company and he took even less kindly to the rule of the British. The list of his grievances tells us a great deal. They were the use of Hottentot soldiers against white men, the issue of regulations for the registration and treatment of Hottentot servants, the use of white churches for Sunday afternoon services for Hottentots and slaves, the control of reprisals against cattle stealers. Then came the emancipation of the slaves, the manner in which it was done, what the Afrikaner thought to be the Government's weakness in dealing with the incessant frontier troubles, the fiftieth Ordinance of 1828 which gave rights to Hottentot labour, the impartiality of the courts, the Anglicisation of the courts of justice, and the unpopular activities of the foreign missionaries who did not "understand the country."

Many Afrikaner farmers, who were called Boers, decided that they could no longer endure British rule, and so began, from 1835 onward, the great northward migration known as the Great Trek. There were many causes of the Trek, but the prime cause was the desire of the Boers to get away from this new idea of racial equality which to them was abhorrent. To cut a long story short, they conquered one black chiefdom after another, they set aside inadequate lands for those they conquered, and they finally founded the republics of the Transvaal and the Orange Free State. In the Transvaal it was categorically laid down in the constitution that there was to be "no equality in Church or State."

Some of the trekkers turned east and descended the great wall of the Drakensberg into the fertile and well-watered region known as Natal, so called by Vasco da Gama, who passed these shores on Christmas Day 1497 in search of a sea route to India. The trekkers were entering the land of the Zulus, the kingdom created by the great Shaka. The Zulus were now ruled by Dingane, who had assassinated his half-brother Shaka in 1828, and in 1838 slew Pieter Retief, the trekker leader, and a hundred men, who had gone to Dingane's kraal, or village, to ask for land. Dingane then sent armies to the trekker camps in Natal, and killed over 360 of the Boers, men, women, and children, so that the place became known as Weenen, which means "Weeping." This deed was avenged at the battle of Blood River on 16 December 1838, when Andries Pretorius, the new leader, defeated Dingane's army. The Zulus left behind three thousand dead and the Boer casualties were three wounded men. Before the battle the Boers swore a covenant to keep the day holy forever should God give them the victory. It was called Dingane's Day for more than a hundred years, but was then called more appropriately the Day of the Covenant.* It is by law observed as a Sunday, and no cinema or theatre or race meeting or public sports event may be held on that day. For many years it was observed by large throngs of Afrikaners, and though it was a religious holiday it was also a great political occasion. It was in fact the great day of Nationalist Afrikanerdom and of the National Party, an organisation of which I shall tell later. The rest of the South African population, more than ninety percent of them, did not observe the day at all, and it was because of their indifference that the day was finally declared by the ruling National Party to be a solemn holiday. It only remains to add that forty-one years later it was the British who finally destroyed the Zulu kingdom at the Battle of Ulundi, in 1879.

After their victory at Blood River the Boers founded their capital of Pietermaritzburg, the place where I was born. There they laid out their rectangular town and built the Church of the Vow. But their rule was short. The British annexed Natal in 1845 and most of the trekkers returned over the Drakensberg to join their kinsmen in the new republics. But the historical process of change and conquest had by no means run its course.

In 1886 happened one of those events after which things cannot be the same again. Gold was discovered on the Witwatersrand in the Republic of the Transvaal. The city of Johannesburg was founded. Aliens of many races, but particularly the British, streamed into the

* *In 1980 it was renamed the Day of the Vow.*

Transvaal. Between the alien gold seekers and the Afrikaner farmers the incompatibility was almost complete. This incompatibility,
and the fact of the gold itself—the richest reefs in the world—led to
the Anglo-Boer War of 1899, a war which inflicted wounds on
South Africa from which, eighty-one years later, she has not fully
recovered.

Although President Kruger of the Transvaal Republic issued the
ultimatum, the war was the work of Joseph Chamberlain, Alfred
Milner, and Cecil Rhodes. A great deal of nonsense was talked about
the sufferings of the *Uitlanders,* who were for the most part Britishers who worked in the gold mines of Johannesburg. The war was
not fought for them except ostensibly. It was fought for the gold,
and for the conquest of the two Boer republics of the Transvaal and
the Orange Free State. They stood in the way of the expansion of
the British Empire, and of that all-red route from Cape to Cairo,
which was the dream of Rhodes, who told W. T. Stead that he
would annex the planets if he could. Kruger was right when he
burst out to Milner, after endless discussions of grievances, "What
you want is my country!"

There was of course also a noble reason for the war, because the
British—like every nation no doubt—want noble reasons for war.
The noble reason was to "protect the natives." One can only say ha-
ha to that.

Few people realised that the Anglo-Boer War was the beginning
of the decline of British imperialism. The truth is that a substantial
number of British people was ashamed of the war. In 1906 the
British restored self-government to the Transvaal and in 1907 to the
Orange River Colony (that is, the conquered Free State), though
they remained colonies. There were now four self-governing British
colonies, the Cape of Good Hope, Natal, the Transvaal, and the
Orange Free State. I myself was born, not a South African, but a
Natalian. In 1910 the four colonies came together to form the
Union of South Africa, a self-governing dominion. On 31 May 1910,
exactly eight years after the Peace of Vereeniging had ended the
Anglo-Boer War, the Union came into being.

I remember the occasion. The schoolchildren of Pietermaritzburg
were assembled on the Oval in Alexandra Park. We listened to
speeches, but I don't remember them. I remember that we had buns
and ginger beer. Whether the African, Indian, and Coloured children also celebrated I do not know. They certainly did not celebrate
with us. Though this will become clearer as this story goes on, I
shall emphasise now that South Africa was a white man's country,
and that the Anglo-Boer War was a white man's war, that the Union

of South Africa was a white man's Union, that the celebrations in Alexandra Park were celebrations for white children. All this was done in spite of the fact that the white people then constituted one-fifth of the total population. Today they constitute about one-sixth.

Of the four colonies, only one, the Cape of Good Hope, had a franchise open to people of all races who possessed certain qualifications of education and ownership of property. The Cape representatives refused to enter the Union unless they could take their franchise with them. This eventually they were allowed to do, with the provision that the franchise could be amended or abolished by a two-thirds majority of a joint sitting of both houses of the new Union parliament. Thus the Union came into being. Britain had made amends to the Boers, now called Afrikaners, but had placed the black people of South Africa in a position of powerlessness that has lasted until now. The open franchise for African voters was amended in 1936, and abolished in 1960. The open franchise for Coloured voters was amended in 1956 and abolished in 1968.

Thus one of the most generous acts of reparation ever made to a defeated people was deeply and fundamentally flawed. The British won the Anglo-Boer War in 1902, but the victor of 1910 was the Boer policy of "no equality in Church or State." The white people of Natal did not worry about that. It was their policy too, though they never put it into words. Such a statement would not have been British.

Of all this I understood nothing. I believed—because my parents told me so—that our first Prime Minister, General Louis Botha, was a man both brave and noble. And looking back I see that it was so. He had led the Boers throughout the war, and after peace had returned he devoted himself to the reconciliation of the Afrikaners and the British. He died in 1919 but no great life of him has ever been written. Over his grave General Smuts spoke words which should be immortal. He called Botha "the greatest, cleanest, sweetest soul of all the land—of all my days." But who knows if any of our white words will be immortal? History may begin again for South Africa, and the words and acts of people like Botha and Smuts and Hofmeyr and Vorster may be erased from memory. It all depends on how the future comes. If it comes by violence and revenge, none of these names will be remembered. If it comes by wisdom and justice, they will be.

But these thoughts did not trouble my young mind. When Botha died, I was sixteen, and not till many years later did I know that Smuts had spoken such words. Louis Botha was a farmer with very little formal education. Jan Smuts was a product—and a brilliant one—of Stellenbosch and Cambridge universities, yet he was able to call Botha the greatest soul of all his days. Smuts grew up in the Cape district of Malmesbury on his father's farm, tending the horses and cattle. When he was twelve his elder brother Michiel died, and it was decided that the younger son Jan must go to school, which he completed in four years. At the age of sixteen he went to Victoria College, Stellenbosch, and there graduated with honours in both science and literature. He then graduated in law at Cambridge, and in 1948, at the age of seventy-eight, he became the chancellor of that ancient university. At the outbreak of the Anglo-Boer War in 1899 Smuts was State Attorney to Paul Kruger, president of the Transvaal Republic, and he served as a general throughout the war. In 1910, when Botha became the first Prime Minister of the new Union of South Africa, Smuts was his Minister of Defence. During the First World War of 1914–1918, Smuts became the darling of the British people, the defeated Boer general who had become one of the guiding spirits of the British Empire and Commonwealth.

If the British reparation to the Boers was generous, so also was Botha's acceptance of it. Indeed it was far too generous for many of his fellow Afrikaners. The talk of conciliation angered them. There was for them only one thing for Afrikaners to do, and that was to use the franchise and their numerical superiority to the full, to capture parliament, and then to entrench white supremacy and black subordination.

In 1914 the Nationalist Party was founded for that purpose, and it was led by General James Barry Munnik Hertzog, who had broken away from Botha in 1912 because he believed that Botha had too little concern for the renascence of defeated Afrikanerdom. In that same year there came the First World War, and Botha (and Smuts too) assumed that South Africa was automatically at war with Germany. This led to the military rebellion of diehard Afrikaners, and it was Botha who had to quell it. This rebellion, the growing power of the Nationalist Party, and the distrust of so many of his old comrades-in-arms, filled him with weariness. He died on 26 August 1919, and was succeeded by General Smuts. The year following, in the general election, the Nationalist Party won forty-four seats in a house of one hundred and fifty. Smuts won forty-one, and was forced to absorb the English-speaking Unionist Party in order to retain his power.

I entered the Natal University College in March 1919. Of these political events that were happening around me, I knew almost nothing. I did not know that I was watching the first scenes of a drama that was in the end to determine the course of my life. In fact

I was to become an actor myself, in an insignificant part that was of supreme significance to me. It was not only the drama of my country, it was mine too.

The play, like one of Agatha Christie's, is still running. Two things might happen to it. It might be drawing to its end. In that case it will prove—for white people—to have been a tragedy. Or it might continue with a larger and more varied cast. In that case the tragedy will have been averted, by an exercise of wisdom, intelligence, and goodness that have not been conspicuous in the play so far.

Even in those days when I was sixteen I was developing a great love of country. It was in those days not a love of its peoples, of whom I knew almost nothing. It was not a love of party or government or any leader. I am forced to conclude that it was a love of the physical land, of which also I then knew very little. My knowledge was confined to Natal, and not by any means to all of it. My knowledge was of Pietermaritzburg and Durban, the south coast and Oribi Flats, Bulwer, Curry's Post, and New Hanover. It is a very odd thing that one gives this passionate love to a piece of country for the simple reason that one was born there. Later in life one may learn to love other countries, even to love the earth, but this never rivals one's first love.

I must add one more thing. I had also a great love of the mother country I had not seen. In spite of my immature feelings about war, I, and I think my family too, and many other English-speaking families were filled with an almost uncontrollable pride when the great ships of the British Navy came steaming at them out of the cinema screen, or when they saw the King and Queen opening a bridge or visiting a hospital. This feeling, of what I can only call British nationalism, declined in strength as one became more and more of a South African, but burst into new life on such occasions as the declaration of war in 1939, and the speeches of Churchill, and the visit of the Royal Family to South Africa in 1947. It was the coming into being of the Republic of South Africa in 1961, again on the mystical date of May 31, that heralded the end of this deep attachment to another country, an attachment which irritated and even incensed the Afrikaner Nationalist.

Be all that as it may, my attachment to my own bit of country was already intense at the age of sixteen. But after writing seven chapters I am beginning to realise that for better or for worse, my reaction to life was intense.

Chapter 8

Full of hope, excitement, anticipation, energy, I set out for that university college. It had no students' residence so I continued to live at home. I wore socks with clocks, red, blue, green, very smart. In those simple days we wore university ribbons round our hats, university ties, university belts. I felt I had suddenly become a man. But the men said to each other, "We're getting more and more kids." And we *had* men. They had fought in the war, and they were three, four, five, six years older than the rest. It must have been impossible for a man who had seen the mud and death of Flanders to have had anything in common with a sixteen-year-old straight from school.

What was I to study now? I wanted to become a doctor, but my father explained that he just could not do it. It meant going to Johannesburg or Cape Town. My headmaster, Mr. E. W. Barns, thought that my mathematics and science indicated that I should become an engineer, and build bridges and roads and railways all over Africa. But for that I would have had to go to Johannesburg or Cape Town. The real question was the money. The problem was solved by the Natal Education Department, which offered bursaries for student teachers who would staff the new high schools that were going to be built all over Natal. The inducement was paid-up fees and books and eighty pounds a year. The department particularly wanted science and mathematics teachers. It was this that finally decided me to give up the arts.

My wish to become a doctor was quite unmotivated. I decided without regret to become a teacher. In fact I hardly thought about it at all. I was looking forward to those three years at Natal University College. If someone had said, "I'll give you a better bursary to become an actuary," I think I would have taken it. I'm glad that no one did. I became a schoolmaster and discovered that for teaching I had been born. In fact I have been a teacher all my life, and suppose this requires a kind of egoism. So I shall record that I was much more successful in the first half of my teaching than in the second. In the first half I taught boys and girls, in the second half I tried to teach white South African adults the facts of life, but they are a tough proposition.

What was to be done with the eighty pounds a year? If I remember rightly I was to pay my parents five pounds a month for my board and lodging, and I was to have twenty pounds per annum for myself, that is, one pound sixteen shillings and eightpence per month. On this I had to keep myself, and buy my clothes, fares, books. And I did.

In 1919 there were 115 students at the college. I was not the youngest. Eva Grundy, although a year ahead of me, was only fifteen, a first-class matriculant, and reputedly a mathematical genius. She was a pale quiet girl whose gentle exterior concealed a very strong character. She was aloof and virginal, and finally married when she was the headmistress of one of the biggest girls' schools in Natal. I remember her with much affection, which information will no doubt surprise her! Yet I have no doubt it will give her some pleasure.

The University College had only one academic building, a domed block with a central hall two storeys high, surrounded on the ground floor and above by lecture rooms, laboratories, professors' rooms, and rooms for principal, registrar, bursar, and caretaker. The women also had a common room on the ground floor, and the men had a common room in an army hut outside. The only other building was the caretaker's cottage at the gate.

It was in my first year that I met the only human being for whom I ever felt some kind of worship. He was Railton Dent, whom we called Joe. He was about six years older than I, but was also in his first year. This was not because he had been to the war, but because he had felt it his duty *not* to go to the war. He was not a conscientious objector; he was a nongraduate teacher, and he intended to graduate and to devote his life to African education. He was the youthful principal of the Edendale High School for African boys and girls, and he believed that it was his duty to see the school through the war. Now that the war was over he felt free to take his degree.

Dent was the son of a Methodist missionary, and he was a committed Christian. Committed Christians have faults just as commonly as other people, but I could see no fault in him. He was I think the most upright person I ever was to know, and his influence on me was profound. He did not make me into a good man, that would have been too much. But he taught me one thing, the theme of which will run right through this book, with undertones (or overtones, I never know which) of victories, defeats, resolutions, betrayals, that life must be used in the service of a cause greater than oneself. This can be done by a Christian for two reasons: one is obedience to his Lord, the other is purely pragmatic, namely that one is going to miss the meaning of life if one doesn't.

How Railton Dent *taught* me this, I don't quite know. I suppose that my reverence and affection for him was so great that I caught it from him. And I must have caught it thoroughly, because in the course of a life which I have not considered conspicuously good, I have never given up *trying to be obedient*, nor have I ever lost the pragmatic belief that I was going to miss something of the greatest importance if I did not treat my life as not being altogether my own property.

In 1918 a branch of the Students' Christian Association was founded with Eric Pennington as president. In 1919 Pennington went to Oxford to study for the priesthood, and the new president was Railton Dent. It was not long before he approached me to become a member. This was a matter clearly to be discussed with my father, for the association was composed of young men and women who were members of churches which did not "know the truth."

My father had never had the luck to be able to go to a university. As I have written earlier, he had had to go to work when he was fourteen. I have no doubt that it was one of his deep regrets. But he satisfied some part of his hunger by inviting students to our home, where we would talk and sing student songs like "Riding down from Bangor," and Scottish songs like "Ye Banks of Braes o' Bonnie Doon."

This started while I was still a boy at Maritzburg College. A young man called Alan McKenzie left his country home to go to the university and his parents asked mine to have a care for him. And so began the student evenings, with Alan and his friends. In 1918 he was killed in Flanders, not long after he reached there. In 1919 the evenings continued, but now of course I was one of the students myself.

Through him my parents learned to know Douglas Aitken, who died in 1974 after a long and devoted life as a medical missionary at Sibasa in the Transvaal. Another visitor was George Gale, genius, who also devoted his life to medicine and held such high posts as Union Secretary for Health, Dean of the Medical School in Durban, and Director of the World Health Organization in Bangkok. George was regarded as a genius because he passed first-class in everything, and if he didn't pass first-class, he passed first-class, first division, a distinction accorded in those days. In 1919, when I was in my first year he was in his third, and was the only student in short trousers, an unconventionality of the oddness of which he was totally oblivious.* Other visitors were Reg Pearse, later to become the headmaster of Estcourt High School, Cyril Armitage, later to become headmaster of Port Shepstone High School, and Adolf Bayer, later to become Vice-Principal of the University of Natal in Pietermaritzburg. The last visitor I remember well was Railton Dent himself, and it was my mother who sensed at once the extent of my hero worship; although I jib at the word, it was a kind of adoration. Now although Dent was not a Christadelphian, and was a member of a church that did not "know the truth," he was obviously the kind of young man that most parents, and certainly most religious parents, would like to see chosen as the hero of their sixteen-year-old son.

My mother accompanied the songs on these occasions, and also provided us with generous feasts of coffee, scones, crumpets, and cakes. We Paton children were not self-conscious about these evenings. My father presided and we all sang parts. Douglas Aitken was our bass. He was a very mature young man, and had a most piercing gaze, and I felt that he could read my innermost thoughts, which feeling always made me keep my distance. Occasionally we had young women too, but I do not remember this well. In any event in 1919 most of the women students looked upon me as a child.

All of these young men were members of the Students' Christian Association except Adolf Bayer, who was a friendly agnostic. Therefore my request to my father to join the association, after due consideration, was granted. I should imagine that my parents were strongly influenced by the knowledge that these young men all knew what they wanted to do. I do not pretend that the university

---

* He has now corrected me. He wore long trousers except on Sundays. His parents were not rich, and his Sunday suit had short trousers. Therefore he wore them cheerfully.

college of 1919 can be likened to the college of today, nor do I pretend that the small university college of Natal was typical then of colleges all over the English-speaking world. We were powerfully motivated by the desire to find a purpose for life, and it was much easier to find it in 1919 than it is in 1980. It was also much easier to find it in unsophisticated Pietermaritzburg than in sophisticated Oxford and Cambridge. Also there were not Railton Dents at all the colleges in the world, able to win young men for their cause. The phenomenon is by no means unknown, but it was better known then than now, that a devoted young man or a devoted group of devoted young men could exert such a powerful influence on their student generation.

The Scottish element was very strong in our student evenings at home. We sang Scottish songs and my father read Robert Burns. Even at the age of sixteen, I was aware that the puritan and the poet struggled in my father's breast. I read, but not at his invitation, "The Poet's Welcome to his Illegitimate Child," who was "begot upon Elizabeth Paton, in Largieside." I knew well "The Jolly Beggars"; "Holy Willie's Prayer," another dig at the Puritans, like the "Address to the Unco Guid"; "The Cotter's Saturday Night"; and the verses to the "wee, sleekit, cow'rin, timorous beastie," thought by me and by many others before and since to be of unsurpassed beauty. My father, and many other Scottish puritans, had a sneaking liking for, and no doubt, a sneaking envy of, Robbie's rambunctiousness.

My father, and my aunt Elizabeth Paton, instilled in us children a deep love of Scotland. Where were there such names as the Kyle of Lochalsh and Ardnamurchan, Midlothian and the Hebrides? My father was a lowlander, but he was as proud of the highlands as though he had discovered them. At the sound of the bagpipes he would rush out into the street, quite unable to control himself. When he paid his only visit "home" in 1911, he sent us postcards from every place, of lochs and castles and mountains and the heather moors, and we were fascinated by them. He called me Alan Stewart, and if you look up these names you will find that both are noble, and the second became regal. My brother was Atholl for Scotland and Mason for mother's mother. My older sister was Eunice for her mother and Edith for my mother's mother. My younger sister was Ailsa for the island, and Grace for my father's sister.

Our love for England was also deep, but not quite so much a tie of blood. Speaking for myself, I had now read widely, or was soon to read widely, in Dickens and Thackeray, Shakespeare and Milton and Wordsworth, Keats and Shelley, Tennyson and Browning. When I first saw London in 1924, at the age of twenty-one, I knew more about it than I knew about Cape Town or Johannesburg. And then of course there was the patriotic and political emotion, which to my father's chagrin was aroused much more by the mention of England than by that of Scotland. People spoke about the King and Queen of England, and they said that England had declared war on Germany. Although my father disliked war, he disliked this even more.

In the Students' Christian Association I encountered the same lesser and greater moralities that I had met in my own home. With few exceptions the members did not smoke, drink, dance, gamble, or attend the races. The members were just like the Christadelphians, simple in life, abstemious in habit, upright in conduct. Their sexual codes were strict, but in general that was true of the whole college. The greatest of the greater moralities was not chastity or purity, but it could well have been called obedience. It was, if I may repeat, to have a purpose for one's life, and this purpose was the service of others. This included—certainly in Dent's case—the service of black people and of course of black children, but otherwise it was not conspicuously connected with race and race equality or race prejudice and race discrimination.

In fact Dent had one main concern, and it might conceivably be called racial, and that was African education, then called Native Education, and today (fatuously) Bantu education. He, and his parents before him, had encountered great white hostility to missionary activity, and in particular to the missionary schools. This was more a rural than an urban phenomenon. White farmers depended on black labour, and in general they paid low wages, admittedly supplemented by benefits in kind such as simple houses or huts, land to plough, grazing for cattle, free medicine, and the like. But the educated children of black labourers were likely to want to break loose from this (to use a moderate word) circumscription. It was indeed an enlightened farmer who would build a school on his farm or allow the authorities to do so! *

Therefore Dent's main concern for African education was moral rather than political. We may have discussed the politics of race, but not with the idea of reforming politically the South African society. Dent's main concern was to plead for African education,

* *The attitudes of white South Africa to missionary work and African education are dealt with in* Apartheid and the Archbishop, *Alan Paton, Chapter IX, and again in Chapter XXVII.*

and to reply to the charges levelled against it. He was not responsible for my later ventures into unaccustomed territory, but it was he who started me off in that direction. Once you get the idea that your life is not altogether your own property, and once you realise that love isn't much use without justice, you are likely to keep on travelling. It was Dent who first introduced me to Africans who were not servants or labourers, and that was to the teachers at the Edendale school of which he had been the acting headmaster. Here again the thing was *caught.* If you hero-worship someone, you model your behaviour on him. And so I met the first Africans who were introduced as equals, and I called them Mr. and Mrs. and Miss (there was no Ms. in those days), and I shook hands with them. It was not a giant step for mankind, but it certainly was a big step for me.

Our interests were by no means confined to religion and service. Dent gathered round himself, not intentionally I believe but inevitably, a group of boy-men, Reg Pearse from Ladysmith, Cyril Armitage and myself from Pietermaritzburg, and later Neville Nuttall from Durban. This was the beginning of an intense literary education. Pearse was English and Latin, and Nuttall English and French. Dent was Botany and Zoology, Armitage Botany and Chemistry, and myself Mathematics and Physics. But Dent's love for literature was as great as my own. Armitage regarded himself as a camp follower: he did not think he was a literary man, although he had a poem called "A Wintry Soliloquy" published in the college magazine for May 1921. This must have been too much for him, for he never wrote another that I knew of. He wrote it apparently because he belonged to a company that thought poetry was important.

Dent introduced us to Ruskin and Carlyle, and to his own special favourites, Alpha of the Plough, David Grayson of "Adventures in Contentment" and "The Friendly Road," and Michael Fairless of "The Roadmender." But it was with Neville Nuttall that I made endless forays into literature. After an evening at his lodgings or at my home, we would walk back together to the cemetery in Commercial Road, and then would sit in the little arched building among the graves for another hour or more. It was Shakespeare, Milton, Wordsworth, Coleridge, Keats, Shelley, Byron, Tennyson, Browning. Of Yeats we knew nothing, unless it was "The Fiddler of Dooney" and "The Lake Isle of Innisfree," but that is not strange because he did not get into the 1924 edition of *The Golden Treasury* or into *The Way of Poetry,* Drinkwater's anthology of the early 1920s. Nor did we know anything of T. S. Eliot, who also got into neither of these anthologies. We read the war poets, Wilfred Owen,

Wilfred Gibson, Julian Grenfell, and of course Rupert Brooke. We thought Brooke a greater poet than he was. We were devoted to A. E. Housman, especially "Loveliest of trees, the cherry now." Indeed, I cannot remember all that we read.

Meanwhile I was studying mathematics, applied mathematics, and physics. Armitage studied mathematics with me, and E. W. Roseveare was our professor, all of which brings to mind a story of undergraduate humour.

Professor Roseveare went on leave, and his place was taken by Mr. Philip Stein. The lecture room was on the ground floor, and it was possible to step out of one of the windows onto the verandah that ran along the whole of the east wing. We had started our lecture when Armitage stepped out of the window onto the verandah, walked round the building, knocked on the door, apologised to Mr. Stein for being late, and went to his seat. Mr. Stein, who was the very soul of politeness and gentleness, bowed in acknowledgement. Armitage then again stepped out of the window, and again walked round the building, and again knocked on the door, apologising and going to his seat. Mr. Stein acknowledged the apology, with perhaps the faintest sign of a furrow between the eyes. Armitage, lacking in wisdom but not in courage, did this the third time. The result was electrical. Mr. Stein's acknowledgement was to lift the box of chalks above his head and bring it down crashing on the floor, smashing the chalks to pieces. The rest of the lecture proceeded without incident. When it was over Armitage went to apologise to Mr. Stein, but he found difficulty in doing so because Mr. Stein insisted on apologising to him. We never ragged Mr. Stein again. Armitage and I had improved since the days when we were so merciless to Miss Norman.

I soon decided that I must be more of an arithmetician and geometrician than a mathematician. I did not really like this language of symbols that knew nothing of grief, death, or laughter. I was more at home with applied mathematics and physics. Yet I think it was the study of all three of these subjects that taught me exactness of expression, respect for truth, and impatience with the unnecessary. You cannot tell an untruth in these disciplines, at least not for long. You cannot, even mistakenly, say what is untrue for long. I think that all these things have had a powerful effect on my writing, not only in the actual use of words, but also in the act of construction. This is particularly true of the art of constructing articles and essays. The argument must proceed in orderly fashion. If one digresses, one must do so briefly and relevantly. The piece must have form, and it must have beginning and end. That is why, for example, I find Virginia Woolf so difficult to read.

So much for my introduction to the world of the university. Our college was new, small, and remote, but it opened the doors of the world. It is often said of South Africa that its culture and its education are poor and primitive compared with those of the rest of the world. It is true that the members of my circle were not familiar with the literature, the architecture, the art of Greece, Rome, France, Germany, Spain, Italy.* But we lived in a multilingual and multicultural country. I, an English-speaking person, had been born among Indian and African people. I was later to learn to know the Afrikaner, his religion, his language, his history, his literature. I was also later in life to recognise Indian, African, Afrikaner, and Coloured people as my own people, not, I admit, with any encouragement from the powers-that-be. It was a life as rich, though with a different kind of richness, as any life in Europe.

* *I should state that Greek, Latin, and French were taught at the university college.*

Chapter 9

My life at the university college was by no means all religion, high purpose, literature, and study. I joined the Dramatic Society and I suppose that my father must have given permission for this, despite his views about the theatre. I also joined the Rugby, Cricket, and Tennis clubs, and played with much enthusiasm but not so much distinction. Joined by Dent I started running, probably three or four nights a week, and we would run a good two or three miles each night.

I don't know what my parents, and especially my father, thought of all this activity, so different from the sheltered life I had led up till then. They must at times have felt anxiety about the entry of their child into the wider world. There can be no doubt that Railton Dent was their guarantee that I was safe.

Armitage and I began the year 1920 in great style. We borrowed a cart and a donkey from an Indian pedlar, and we dressed as yokels, chewing stalks of grass. We started from the Durban Road and drove up the university drive to the dome. As we approached the main building the student interest was immense, though the veterans of Flanders would not have felt it. Our most fascinated spectators were the new first-year students, who saw before their very eyes the expected excitements and the freedom of a university career.

It was an act of pure exhibitionism, with which I combined an appearance of considerable modesty. But I was saved from becoming an outright poseur by a sense of humour that enabled me to grasp exactly what I was doing. Railton Dent had a story of a man who was telling his shortcomings to his dearest friend, telling of his hypocrisy, his vanity, his general worthlessness. And he said to his friend, "Do you see what I mean?" and the friend said, "Yes, I do," and they did not speak to each other again for a long time after that.

If I made a sally I enjoyed it as much as anyone, not just the making of it but also the reception of it. On one of our debating evenings we had a mock parliament and the speaker of the house was Squibby Aitken, the same one whose piercing eyes penetrated the depths of my soul. In the course of my speech I forgot the proper procedure and referred to the speaker as "Mr. Aitken." Squibby brought down his gavel with a crash. "Mr. Aitken?" he said, "I do not know the gentleman." "Well, Mr. Speaker," I replied, "you haven't missed much." It brought the house down, but it brought Squibby down too, and he was for some moments incapacitated. This kind of triumph filled me with joy, and I made no attempt to hide it.

It was in 1921 at the beginning of my third year that Neville Nuttall came to the university college from Durban High School. My friendship with him was quite different from that with Dent, or with Pearse and Armitage. He was also a member of the Students' Christian Association, but much more a questioner of custom and convention than they. He was a smoker and affected Westminster Magnums, and I did too. Railton Dent said to me, "Smoking? That's a pity." As a result of that I did not smoke in front of him again.

Nuttall came from a strong temperance family, and he questioned the moral importance of abstinence. This led to an experiment. His mother was away on holiday, and he invited me to stay with him at their home in Durban, where we would examine at first hand the condition and experience of being drunk. For this purpose he bought a bottle of port. The experiment was a failure. We did not get drunk at all, and to compensate for our disappointment we went out into the garden and shouted resounding oaths into the Durban air.

Nuttall was also a walker, though not of the hardy breed of Pearse and Armitage. We would take walks in the hills around Pietermaritzburg, and recite apt lines of poetry. His love of nature was also intense but he believed in enjoying it in a moderate fashion. He spent the leisure of his active life as a schoolmaster along the banks of the trout streams of Natal, whereas Pearse spent his leisure conquering the peaks of the Drakensberg Mountains. He became an authority on that great range, and put the knowledge and experience of a lifetime into a splendid book, *Barrier of Spears*.

Pearse, Armitage, and I decided to walk to Dundee using the main road that runs from Durban to Johannesburg, and then I would return by myself. This was because Armitage had fallen in love with May Graham-Gerrie, and while the Natal countryside had its charms, she had charms too, and she lived still further north of Dundee.

Although romance did not strike me down in my college days, it gave me one or two glancing blows. Both Neville and I fell for a vivacious young lady called Dorothy who had blue eyes, and a tipped-up nose, a beautiful figure, and I should think a well-to-do father, if one judged by the way she dressed. I confessed my feelings to her friend M., and I did it with some trepidation, because Dorothy was a year older than I. After a day or so M. told me that Dorothy did not despise my suit, and that she would like to leave some college function early, and that I could escort her home. In those days one did not think of danger in the evening streets of Pietermaritzburg. I am not so sure that that is true today. My escorting was a total failure. Dorothy expected me at least to take her arm and I did not. She told M. that I was still a child. That was the end of the romance. I still see her from time to time, and she has the same figure, the same nose, and the same blue eyes, and I still feel the same affection.

Sex also struck me a glancing blow. She was a student, not at the university, but at the training college for teachers. I went to some function there, and after it was over she walked with me to the gate. A mutual sexual attraction was obviously in the air, and we embraced with some fervour. After that she said, "Now you'll have to marry me." I do not know if she saw me recoil as from a hot coal. But I did. In fact, to continue the metaphor, I dropped her instantly. I just was not yet ready for a romance.

Pearse and Armitage and I became hardy walkers. We planned to walk from Pietermaritzburg to Ladysmith, about 110 miles in those days, in four days, pulling a cart that contained our tent, blanket, and provisions. At the end of the third day the cart broke down, and we put it on the train and decided to continue through the night to Ladysmith. This was a day's march of fifty-two miles, and we dared not sit down to rest because we would not have been able to get up again. We reached Ladysmith at two in the morning, and after a good night's sleep played tennis the next day.

I broke this record of fifty-two miles by later walking from Pietermaritzburg to Durban, which in those days was fifty-four miles. Still later Pearse and I decided to walk from Estcourt to Pietermaritzburg, a sixty-mile journey, but when I reached Howick, a distance of forty-six miles, I had to retire, because a boil on my chest which was not there when we started became too painful for me to continue. Pearse finished the course and has held the record of sixty miles ever since.

On another occasion Pearse and I decided to walk to Natal's Table Mountain, sleep the night on the top, and return to Pietermaritzburg via Umlaas Road. Pearse had catered very parsimoniously and we finished all our food at the evening meal, and were still hungry. It was the month of May, and we did not expect rain, but rain it did. We spent a cold and miserable night.

I was wakened in the hour before the dawn by the crackling of the fire. I opened my eyes to see that Pearse was toasting a crust of bread, our last scrap of food. In my starved and cold condition I jumped to a terrible conclusion, namely that he intended to eat it all. This dastardly act inflamed me, and when Pearse told me that he had intended to wake me and give me half the crust I treated his story with contempt. I was in a thoroughly bad temper, and I put him in one too.

I ate my half-crust full of hatred. We packed, and started on our walk to Umlaas Road. Our first task was to descend from the mountain down a steep and narrow defile. Pearse went first, and I realised that one push from me would send him to grievous injury or death. I played with the idea but did not proceed to the act. One thing however was clear to me, that it would be a proper end for a mean and ignoble life. Only the thought of the death penalty deterred me.

Then the sun came out and we were warm again. What is more, Pearse had two shillings, and bought a calabash of sour milk, half of which he offered to me. When I had finished my share, I realised the contemptibility of my behaviour. I mumbled an apology which Pearse graciously accepted.

Some thirty years later Pearse invited me to present the prizes at Estcourt High School, and I told the story of Table Mountain. I thought it was funny, and the boys and girls thought it was funny, I think the staff thought it was funny, but I don't think the headmaster thought it was funny. Funny or not, it was the true story of an episode in our long friendship, which has now lasted over sixty years.

At the end of 1921 I retired from the secretaryship of the Students' Representative Council, and received a handsome tribute in the magazine, which mentioned among other things "an energy which was indefatigable." Whatever else is true, the bit about the energy is correct. But it was not wisely and properly used. In my degree examination I passed in mathematics, of which I was afraid, and failed in physics, of which I was not. It was a desolate time for me when the results came out. It was the first examination in which I had failed. I remember my own desolation rather than any reproof from my parents. In order to get some money I took a post teaching mathematics at the Epworth High School for girls, which was then in a little lane called Gutridge Street. My success was minimal for the girls had not had a real teacher for years.

At the end of 1922 I made amends for my failure by passing again in mathematics and gaining a first-class in physics. Yet to this very day I dream, two or three times a year, that I am going into the examination hall knowing nothing of the subject I am going to be examined in. When I wake I lie for a short while in trouble of mind, till I say to myself, "Don't be silly. You don't have to write examinations anymore."

After graduating I entered the final eighteen months required for the Higher Diploma of Education. I thus forsook the safe world of mathematics and physics, and entered the unsure, uncertain, undogmatic, questioning, inexact world of psychology, philosophy, and contesting theories none of which could be proved. For a while I was lost. I wanted to know which was right, but my professor, G. W. Ferguson, would explain to me gently, for he was a very gentle man, that no one would ever know. He led me into a new world in which I am today at home, but I have never regretted having lived for a while in the world of the sciences, not because they are exact, but because they make it difficult to lie, to deceive oneself, to pretend that one had a solution when one had not. Now I was to learn about a new kind of truth, the kind which one would never find, but for which one would never stop searching.

I also believe that a training in the more exact sciences has a great influence on one's literary style, not to make it more exact, but to make it more simple and more clear. Such a training teaches the writer to avoid overembellishment and extravagance. Its only danger is that it may influence his writing to become too spare.

Chapter 10

Our course for the Higher Diploma of Education was divided into two distinct parts. At the university college we were to study education academically, some psychology, some philosophy, and the methods and theories of some famous educators. At the Natal Teachers' Training College we were to study the art of teaching. There was a course called "the principles of education," in which we learned how to plan a lesson and a course of lessons, and we taught one period a week at one of the Pietermaritzburg schools under the joint surveillance of Professor Ferguson and a lecturer from the Training College. In addition to this we had instruction at the Training College in the Use of the Blackboard, Elocution, Art, and Woodwork.

Our attitude to the Training College was frankly snobbish. The staff, except for the Principal, Sandy Reid, and lecturer E. H. Allsopp, were nervous of us. Mr. L. Thompson, in charge of art, was outraged when Adolf Bayer, asked to design a coat of arms, produced one which featured a bleeding lump of beef in one quarter, an old boot in another, and two now forgotten objects in the others. Bayer sought to justify his design by interpreting the meaning of each, but our lecturer was not appeased.

We also had to attend woodwork classes at the Maritzburg College. The instructor didn't want snobs, and the snobs didn't want instruction. In any case one cannot, unless one is especially gifted, learn a craft in weekly sessions spread over nine months. We were more tolerant of instruction in elocution and the use of the black-board, but we were snobbish about that also, and went round saying to each other, "how now, brown cow?"

The more academic study under Professor Ferguson was more to our taste. It was of course puzzling to me to study McDougall and instincts, Kohler and Gestalt, and Watson and behaviourism, and to find that one could not know which one was right. I had to learn that I was there not to discover the truth, but to study the work of those who had tried to find some way of describing and accounting for human behaviour.

The first weakness of the course was that it was held in two centres, bringing about what everyone knows should be avoided, the divorce of thinking from doing. Its second weakness was that the teaching practice was never integrated with the rest of the course. One never discussed what had happened in a lesson with one's teachers, except extremely briefly. The criticising lecturer would write a few words at the end of one's Notes of Lessons.

One cannot always expect a student to know in his first year what he is hoping to do with his life. But for those who know what they want to teach I would start practical teaching as soon as possible. The school classroom, and not the university lecture room, would be the heart of the business. And some of the lessons at least would be taught in front of some of one's fellow students, and would later be discussed by them, oneself, and the professor.

I have one last and weighty criticism to make. We had no apti-tude test whatever. I can think of three of our fellow students who should never have been allowed to become teachers. We knew it then. I would not say that a sense of humour is indispensable for a teacher, but it is a golden asset. Not one of those had a sense of humour. Their careers were sad; one was tragic. Two of them were demoted when they had reached the rank of headmaster or assistant headmaster. The third, also a headmaster, after a departmental and public enquiry, pressed for by parents, was pensioned years before the normal age for retirement. Whether he ever smiled or laughed again, I do not know, but he withdrew from the world into a dark house made darker by trees. It would not be strange if he thought of his fate every day for the rest of his life.

In 1923 I was elected President of the Students' Representative Council (SRC). We now had 223 students, so that the president of the SRC was known to them all. It was as president that I took disciplinary steps of which today I would disapprove.

A men's hockey team undertook a tour of the towns to the north of Pietermaritzburg, and one of the places visited was Harrismith. A dance was held for them, and some of them shocked citizens of the town by becoming drunk and uproarious. Reports reached Pietermaritzburg, and one of these was made to a leading Methodist minister who took it to Railton Dent, who in turn brought it to me. I took it to our Principal, Dr. Bews, who told me that the Senate would rather not intervene, but would leave the matter in the hands of the SRC.

The feeling in our small college was very strong against the hockey team. At a crowded student meeting their behaviour was condemned, and a Vigilance Committee was established to ensure that such an incident would not be repeated.

When it was all over a troubled student, Lawrence McGuire, a war veteran, came to see me. He put his case clearly and moderately, that we had established a kind of police force on the campus, that we had divided the student body into two, and that although our intention was to do the college good we would in fact do it harm. I called another meeting, the Vigilance Committee was abolished, and the hockey team gave an unsolicited assurance that it would exercise its own vigilance. The student rift was healed, and my year as president was thereafter untroubled.

I learned a lesson that was to serve me well, and especially when I became head of a reformatory. My staff was half white and half black, and most of them believed that a good society, and therefore a good reformatory, could be maintained and strengthened only by force. They believed that the morality of a society could be maintained only by the punishment of offenders and offences. They believed that there was some kind of sovereign virtue and potency in punishment. They admired severity, firmness, consistency, and were inclined to be contemptuous of compassion, mercy, and forgiveness. They treated concepts such as love and justice with suspicion. By the time that I reached the reformatory—twelve years later—I had come to believe that the value and importance of punishment in the educational process was limited. I never came to believe with A. S. Neill that punishment should never be used at all, and by punishment I don't mean just the infliction of physical pain, but also checking, rebuking, reprimanding, depriving.

I must note that my father now begins to fade from memory. I must write about this carefully. He was now, in 1923, about fifty years of age. He was much troubled by headaches, but worse, he was beginning to be afflicted by forgetfulness. My mother told me that he had been sent for by the Judge-President—who had spoken to him about mistakes in his work. The effect of this was to aggravate the diffidence which accompanied the authoritarian side of his character. More and more I am convinced that he looked back on his life as a failure. Three of his four children had grown away from him. I had become the leading student of the university college, and it was clear by now that I would never become a Christadelphian. My brother Atholl, who was now nineteen, had gone to work in the Electricity Department of the muncipality; he was one of the most popular young men in the city, and it was clear that he too would not become a Christadelphian. My sister Eunice, now sixteen, was in high school, but she had already developed a strength of character which was to serve her well in a life that was of necessity devoted overwhelmingly to duties and very little pleasure. Perhaps she inherited the stubbornness of my mother, to whom she was deeply attached, and under whose guidance she became a faithful Christadelphian. My younger sister Ailsa, now thirteen, perhaps because of her youth, perhaps because my father was mellowing, perhaps because he did not dare to lose the last of his children, was far less critical of him than the rest of us. She too was deeply attached to my mother, and she too became a faithful Christadelphian. I have not written much about her because during her girlhood years I was no longer at home. She also had a gift of personality. I heard her teach only once, and recognised immediately the gifts of the teacher, the clarity of explanation, the patience with slowness, but above all the vital response to children, and the ability to evoke enthusiasm in the most unlikely. This outpouring of vitality is a natural expression of the personality of such people and is abated only by sickness or some pressing anxiety, and even in these circumstances it can often succeed in manifesting itself. There is hardly a child who can resist it.

Was my decision not to become a Christadelphian due to a rejection of Christadelphian doctrines? Or a rejection of my father? Or an attraction to the less exclusive beliefs of my friends of the Students' Christian Association? To all three, no doubt.

It was also due to the possession of an ecumenical temperament, a desire to make common cause with those who cherished the same ideals. Membership of the Students' Christian Association made differences between Anglicans and Methodists seem unimportant. It was this same temperament which later made me reject the enforcement of racial separation by law, and to seek cooperation with any person who shared my ideals. But it never in any circumstances impelled me to seek cooperation with any person whose ideas were

incompatible with my own. I never sought to make common cause
with anyone who believed in the doctrines of racial separation, later
called apartheid. That is the reason why I was never to join the
worldwide Fellowship of Reconciliation.

I shall have to write later about the difficulty of accepting dogmas, and the still greater difficulty of whether one can reject dogma
without rejecting faith. In the meanwhile I decided that although
my friends could not accept "the truth" of the Christadelphians,
they were just as upright in their lives, and that was good enough
for me. I hurt my mother by saying to her that it did not matter to
me so much what a person believed as what kind of person he was.
With all her loving heart she wanted me to believe as she did; or
would it be more just to say, she wanted me to believe what she
believed to be the truth? She would look at me with eyes full of care.
It was not quite enough that I should accept Christ as Lord. She
wanted me also to believe certain expositions of certain prophecies
of the end of the world, and to believe that Daniel and John of
Patmos had been given some kind of *knowledge* of the end of the
world. She wanted me to be baptised by total immersion. She
wanted me to pass the test on "Judgement Day." What joy it would
have given her if her son, who was President of the SRC and
speaker in the debates, could have expounded the truth to the brothers and sisters at the meeting, for the Christadelphians encouraged
their young men (but not their young women) to expound: Alas it
was not to be.

At the same time my mother accepted my brother Atholl's world-
liness with a kind of equanimity, and when he was at his most
outrageous, with a kind of reluctant pride. He called her Eunice,
but more than that, he called our revered grandmother Bessie, and
our adoring aunt Lizzie. He was irreverent, he went in and out
much as he pleased, he was a humourist and a bit of a wit, and was
a great favourite with the Old Boys and with the rugby players of
the city. As I look back on it, he seemed to have thrown over altogether the discipline of his father.

And I suppose I had too. Yet in view of the fact that I do not
remember any declaration of independence, any act of defiance, I
again conclude that it was he himself who had withdrawn. He was
certainly no Hatter of Hatter's Castle. As I have written earlier, I
look back on him now with an understanding and a pity that I could
not have felt for him when I was twenty.

In this year 1923 I suffered much religious doubt, and it was
caused by the writing and thinking of J. B. Watson, founder of the

psychology school known as Behaviourists. It challenged my notions of the self, of the possibility of its sovereignty, and therefore of the whole concept of using one's life, by conscious resolve, for the service of God and man. I did not hold any extreme dogma of free will, but I felt that I, and I alone, was responsible for my actions. If I felt that I had done wrong, I would not have blamed my parents or my home or my school or my country, even though I would have acknowledged that all these agents had helped to make the self that is I. It was this conviction of my responsibility that finally made me reject the dogma of behaviourism. *I do not regard this as a scientific refutation of behaviourism; I regard it as an act of choice on my part,* that I did not choose to lead my life believing that I was nothing more than the product of a hundred external forces over which I had no control, and that the concepts of purpose, morality, responsibility were unnecessary to the understanding of life and behaviour.

I also had no doubt that an acceptance of the dogmas of behaviourism would lead some people who had hitherto believed in purpose and striving to attempt them no more, and to deteriorate in conduct and character. I believed that this would happen to me. *Therefore I chose to reject the extreme dogmas of determinism.*

I did not dispute the view that the self had come into being largely without the aid of the I. But now the self and the I were the same. It was my self, within the limits set by nature, that was going to run my life. If this was arrogance, it nevertheless contained a strong element of responsibility. Thus I rejected both determinism and indeterminism, and chose to believe in self-determination.

Chapter 11

Railton Dent left the Natal University College in the middle of 1923, and was appointed a school inspector in the African sub-department of the Natal Education Department. He was to serve his whole life there, and was finally to become head of the subde-partment.

He had exercised a powerful influence over me. He was a man and I was a boy, and he gave direction to my life. No one later exercised a comparable influence over me, but of course as one grows older one is less inclined to have heroes. What would have happened to me if I had not known him in those eager and impres-sionable years? I would have had the same gifts, such as they are, but would I have taken their possession so seriously? And quite apart from his influence, what would my life have been like if I had never gone to Natal University College? I almost tremble at the thought of it, but I suppose the questions are foolish.

I must record with pain that we drew apart in later life. When *Cry, the Beloved Country* was published, I sent him a copy. It was the gift to him of a book that owed something important to those early days. But he was not enthusiastic about it. This was a blow, not only to my pride, but also to my affection.

I must record with pain that we drifted still further apart when I helped to found the Liberal Party of South Africa in 1953. In that year Dr. Verwoerd's National Party Government passed the Bantu Education Act, which not only drastically decreased the missionary

influence in African education but also took it away from the provincial education departments and placed it under a national department of Bantu education. Dr. Verwoerd was determined to
diminish the missionary role in schools for he contended that missionary schools gave black children a false idea of the life that lay
ahead of them.

The Liberal Party opposed the Act uncompromisingly, and contended that the standard of black education would fall. Dent was
not prepared to pass such a judgement. We condemned the Act
whereas he had the duty to make it work. He was a public servant,
and public servants do not criticise governments. He thought us
extreme, and we thought him cautious. The modern young radical
would have classed us both as reactionaries.

It is both painful and ironical to reflect that though our paths
diverged, it was in great measure due to his early influence that I
later took a path about which he was not enthusiastic.

After I had gained my higher diploma I still had six months of
bursary to run, the first six months of 1924. I would have liked to
begin the Master of Education, but Professor Ferguson regretfully
declined, not because he did not want to take me, but because he
was running a one-man department. Therefore I took mathematics,
my costudent being Harry Lundie, who later became Deputy-Direc-
tor of the Natal Education Department. I joined the staff, briefly,
when Professor Mesham went on leave and I ran the physics department. I was not paid much, but I took over the professor's room,
made tea, and felt very important.

At the end of my six months my fellow students did me a great
honour. They decided to send me to England to represent the Natal
University College at the first Imperial Conference of Students. The
SRC voted twenty-five pounds I think and collected another twenty-
five. I seem to remember that my grandfather Thomas James gave
me five or ten pounds, and expressed the wish that I would visit
relatives in Bristol. I think that altogether I had about one hundred
pounds. Here is one of the events of my life that I do not like to
remember. I bought a two-stroke motorcycle in London, and after
the conference did a grand tour of England and Scotland, including
the West Country. But I did not go to Bristol. When I returned my
grandfather asked if I had gone there, and I said I had not. I do not
remember and I do not like to remember. It was a thoughtless,
careless, selfish act of omission.

Now I saw for myself the London of which I had read so much,
Fleet Street, the Strand, St. Paul's, Westminster Abbey, the Houses

of Parliament, the Tower, Buckingham Palace. Also Piccadilly and Leicester Square, which we knew from the song "It's a Long Way To Tipperary." I had read that Park Lane was one of the finest residential streets in the world, and I went there hoping to see something even more beautiful than Musgrave Road, but that long line of solid masonry disillusioned me. I also took a bus to Swiss Cottage and was disappointed to find no such building there.

My official hosts were Mr. and Mrs. Allen of 13 Queen's Gate Gardens, South Kensington. It was a grand place then. The style of living overawed me, the housekeeper, the butler, the footmen, the maids, the chauffeur. The Allens could not have been kinder, but I was conscious of being a "colonial." Mr. Allen was a Liberal M.P., Mrs. Allen was a devoted worker in the slums, the elder daughter worked for the Civil Liberties Union, and the younger was active in student affairs and later became a nun and went to India. They made no attempt to overawe me, I did it myself. I knocked over the morning tea tray, and broke what to me seemed priceless china. I confessed my colonial clumsiness to Mrs. Allen and asked to be allowed to replace the set, but she would not hear of it. That was just as well because it would have meant the end of my holiday. After a while my exuberant self asserted itself and I became part of the family.

It interested me that this sense of inferiority did not seem to affect the Canadians. I became friendly with one of them, E. A. Beecroft of Toronto. He wore the kind of cap that one wears only on the moors. Six of us were received at the Palace of St. James's by Edward, Prince of Wales, later Edward the Eighth, later still the Duke of Windsor. We had to leave all hats, sticks, and umbrellas below, and after the interview, Beecroft's umbrella had gone. I would have lost six umbrellas and not said a word, but Beecroft stood on his democratic rights and made a big fuss. They took down his name and address, and he told them what he thought of their organisation. I don't know if he ever got his umbrella. He may have acquired this boldness in Toronto, but some of it may have been due to the fact that his host was the Governor of the British Museum, and that Beecroft was saluted by policemen every time he went in and out of the place.

It was a new world to me. Lunches and dinners were given by the Government, the Lord Mayor, and the Worshipful Company of Carpenters, teas at Ranelagh and on the terrace of the House of Commons. Then we adjourned to Trinity College, Cambridge, where we lived in the Great Court, but not before my exuberant spirits had again been brought low. After the Government dinner at Lancaster House I retrieved my raincoat and was putting it on as I walked out. But at the door a very imposing person stopped me and said, "One does not leave Lancaster House improperly dressed."

After Cambridge I returned to London and went to see the slums in which Mrs. Allen worked. They were in what was called the East End, and it was certainly a different world from Kensington. It was the world of the Cockneys, and they spoke a version of English sometimes difficult to comprehend. They belonged to what were known in those days as "the lower classes," and their poverty was manifest. In places like Limehouse a great many of them were Chinese, but the number of black people in the East End, or in the whole of London in 1924, was not considerable. The Cockneys were renowned for their fierce love of England and their courage as soldiers. Some of them may have thought that England had given them a poor deal, but if England was at war, they were at war too.

Mrs. Allen had a strong sense of guilt about the poverty of the East End, but it was accompanied by a strong sense of duty. The kind of work that she and other women did was called "slumming," and she was inclined to poke fun at herself but not for long; she might disparage herself, but her code did not allow her to disparage her duty. Her daughters belonged to a new generation that believed it was the task of government to wipe out poverty; their father was a Liberal, but they were the new socialists. They poked fun at their mother too, but with affection. The Allens were in fact a shining example of the upper middle class at its best.

I did not see any signs of the class hatred which later so divided the British people but I was not then an observer of society. Yet it was quite clear that the world in which I was moving, of Kensington and Ranelagh and Lancaster House and Cambridge, was far removed from the world of the East End. One of the great contrasts was in the style and standard of living. Another was in the kind of English that was spoken. The Allens did not speak that affected kind of English which has been so often lampooned, but they spoke the kind that would be heard at Eton and Harrow and Oxford and Cambridge. In 1924 it would have been almost impossible for a Cockney to get into any of these places. I must say that I admired the kind of English spoken by the Allens, but I never made any attempt to speak it. In 1924 only the most percipient would have foretold the decline of Britain and her Empire, or the independence of Ireland, the emancipation of India, the declaration by South Africa of a Republic outside the Commonwealth, and the achievement of nationhood by the British colonies of Africa. The Imperial Conference which I was attending was a sign of the vigour of the Empire. In those days the Union of South Africa was one of the most honoured nations of the Empire, and this was largely due to the immense regard which the British felt for the defeated Boer War generals Botha and Smuts, who had forgiven the hurts of the Anglo-Boer War, and had brought South Africa into the First World War on the side of her one-time conqueror.

It was time to say a temporary good-bye to the Allens. I bought a Douglas, a two-stroke motorcycle, and so did Herbert Maunsell, son of a Pinetown doctor. He had travelled with me from Durban on the S.S. *Beltana,* return fare to London, twenty-nine pounds. We set out to explore the English countryside. I shall say no more than that I was enthralled by a beauty of a kind unknown to me. It is a local beauty of tree, hill, field, and river, and of village, country house, and cathedral, while ours is in large measure one of sky and space and distant mountains. The more countries one visits, the less inclined is one to say that one is more beautiful than another.

The cathedrals overwhelmed me, Salisbury, Exeter, Wells, Durham, York. We went to Stratford for Shakespeare, Tintern Abbey for Wordsworth, Ludlow for Housman. Herbert had no literary pretensions, and humbly left all the planning to me. The beauty of Scotland is more grand than that of England, but softer than that of South Africa. The Scottish mountains manage to look very majestic though they are not very high. I lost Maunsell in Scotland. He went too fast down a hill and broke his leg. I left him in good hands and went to Bankfoot in Perthshire, to the Allens and their grouse moor, where I wore plus fours and would not shoot. Then to Edinburgh to see Princes Street, Abbotsford for Walter Scott, Durham for the cathedral.

I had an urgent letter from Herbert Maunsell, who had now returned to London. I must come back at once to see a fortune-teller who had given him the most fantastic account of his character and gifts and the most glowing prophecies of his future. He sent me her analysis and I do not wonder that he thought it fantastic. After five years of physics, mathematics, and education, I decided not to hurry back to the fortune-teller. When I got to London I went to see Sybil Thorndike and Lewis Casson in Shaw's *Saint Joan* instead. Also I ventured foolishly into the bookshop of J. & S. Bumpus in Oxford Street, and spent almost all that I had. I then set sail with my books on the S.S. *Ballarat,* arriving at the Cape in October. The sight of Table Mountain rising from the sea overwhelmed me. I doubt if I put my thoughts into words, but it was clear that at the age of twenty-one I had, for better for worse, for richer for poorer, given myself to this strange country, to love and to cherish till death us did part.

I had to go to a friend of my father, John Leask, manager of the Standard Bank in Cape Town, and borrow money to get home. After the long journey through the Karoo and the Orange Free State, hot and dry and rainless, I came suddenly to the wetness and greenness of Nottingham Road and the midlands of Natal. I was filled with joy and pride. I was still more of a Natalian than I was a South African.

Chapter 12

It was now October 1924, and it was near the end of the school year, which in those days closed on or about December 14. The Natal Education Department sent me for those last few weeks to Newcastle High School, where I was to be the class teacher of Standard IV. Newcastle was then a town of about five or six thousand people, but today it has almost a hundred thousand and is still growing fast, having been chosen as the site of the second plant of the Iron & Steel Corporation.

The high school was for white boys and girls. All schools were then racially segregated, and indeed they still are, except for certain private white schools which are slowly admitting children of other races. In 1924 Newcastle had two white State schools, the high school and a new junior school. The language of instruction was English, although there was quite a large minority of Afrikaans-speaking children. Today English and Afrikaner children are also segregated from each other, and this has intensified the cultural and political differences between the two races.

Newcastle High School was an old-fashioned building with wide verandahs, iron pillars, and an iron roof. Its pupils were the children of public servants, professional people, workers on the railway and the coal mines and in the iron and steel works, and farmers of the district. But the children of parents with social pretensions went to the select schools of Pietermaritzburg and its environs.

My headmaster was Lancelot Hodges, a fair-haired bachelor with very blue eyes and a very attractive personality. He was immune to feminine charms, but the small girls would wait for him every morning so that two of them could have the privilege of holding hands with him on the way to school. This endeared him to the entire population and he ruled the school effortlessly. He had a troublesome heart, and had finally to give up his headmastership and become a form master at Maritzburg College. There he died suddenly in the classroom. His gifts as a teacher were immense but not conventional. Not only did he hold the little girls' hands, but if he were walking past a classroom and a child looked in his direction he would put out his tongue at it. He said to me, "I always do that, don't you?" I had to admit I didn't.

My Standard IV boys and girls were eleven- and twelve-year-olds. Although I didn't put my tongue out at them, I fell in love with them. Unremembered were the days when I might have become a doctor or an engineer or an actuary. My time with them was all too short. Hodges was disgusted when he received an official letter saying that I must report to the Ixopo High School at the beginning of the school year of 1925. He tried to have it changed but the department said that they could not have a teacher with a higher diploma teaching Standard IV.

On the last day of school I received a cheque for two months' work, sixty pounds minus the usual reductions. This money I hid beneath the clothes in one of the drawers in my room at Mrs. Adendorff's boardinghouse. The following day I went for a farewell picnic at the Incandu Falls, given to me by the senior boys. I returned tired and hungry, but there was no food at Mrs. Adendorff's boardinghouse. The cook had disappeared. When I went to my room I knew why. He had gone off with my sixty pounds. I had planned to spend it all on Christmas gifts for my family, and was desolated. I had to go to another friend of my father, John Nelson Crook, a most respected lawyer in Newcastle, and borrow money to get home. I caught the night train to Pietermaritzburg, and in spite of my loss I stood on the open platform at the end of the coach, feeling the exhilaration of the wind. I was full of excitement. I did not think of the world as my oyster; it was rather my flower and it was opening out.

I had realised that I could not stay at Newcastle, and I was now eager to go to Ixopo, a village about fifty miles southeast of Pietermaritzburg, known for the beauty of its countryside, for the productivity of its farms, and for its rolling hills of grass and bracken. To reach it one either travelled direct by road from Pietermaritzburg, or one had to take a most devious route, by train to Donnybrook, and then by narrow-gauge to Ixopo, past wayside halts with names like Eastwolds, Mabedlane, Lufafa Road, and Loch Buighe. I must record again the intensity of my response to this magic country. It is possible that I invested it with a beauty beyond its merits, a common occurrence that is recognised by the saying that beauty lies in the eye of the beholder. Yet of course it is not quite true, because there are certain kinds of beauty that are recognised by too many eyes to be considered as wholly subjective. The Ixopo countryside laid me under a kind of spell, and this was enhanced by the prevalence in summer of the mists that would descend on the village and hide it from the world. The only two lights in the main street were the two bright lights of the Offsaddle and the Plough hotels, and they would be haloed by the mist.

Ixopo was the centre of a strong white farming community, and it was the farmers that kept it alive. They grew a great deal of maize and bred some of the champion cattle of South Africa. The rainfall was good, and the rain fell mainly in the summer months, keeping the hills green and beautiful.

Each white farm had its black labourers, living in huts some distance from the farmhouse. These labourers were poor, but were given the use of land on which they grew maize, pumpkins, and potatoes. Very few farmers cared whether the black children went to school, and the degree of illiteracy was high. One could only have regarded the black labourers as a depressed group, but at the age of twenty-two I was not concerned about such matters. Communication between white and black was essentially that between superior and inferior.

There was also a substantial Coloured community, originally the offspring of black and white, but now a group on its own. Some of its members were fiercely independent, some docile, some subservient, but all were dependent on the white community for work. There was more communication between white and Coloured people, partly because the latter spoke English and were professing Christians. All the Coloured people had English surnames which indicated clearly their origins, and their names were sometimes the subject of white jokes, mostly good-humoured, but sometimes acid.

Finally there were the Indian shopkeepers, to be found in every Natal town and village. Although Ixopo High School, like the school in Newcastle, was for white children only, Indian children had gone to the school in the earlier years of the century.

The white farming population was overwhelmingly English-speaking, just as in the Transvaal and the Orange Free State, and indeed in northern Natal, it was overwhelmingly Afrikaans-speaking. However, there was a substantial minority of Afrikaners in the village, mostly court officials, policemen, railwaymen, stock inspectors, and a couple of teachers at the high school. Afrikaans-speaking children came to the school and were taught in English.

All these communities led their own lives and made their own pleasures. History, conquest, and prejudice had separated each from the others. The African, Coloured, and Indian people would have come together with whites only in the most special circumstances, such as the celebration of the enthronement of a British king or queen, or the mourning of a royal death. Yet it must be recorded that all these communities lived together in what can only be described as a kind of peace.

Whether beauty be in the eye of the beholder or out there in the world of nature, we shall not further explore but the sad fact is that much of the beauty of the Ixopo countryside has gone, because the grass and bracken and the rolling hills and the rich farms have in large part given way to the endless plantations of gum and wattle and pine, and the titihoya does not cry there anymore. Many of the farmers have gone, and their farmsteads are now the homes and offices of timber managers, and the lowing of cattle has given way to the whining of sawmills.

In 1924 Ixopo High School started with Class One and Class Two for infants, and ended with Standard IX, one year short of matriculation. Now in 1925 Standard X was added, and this would be the first matriculation year. I became the form master of Standards IX and X, which had three and four pupils, respectively, and I taught mathematics to Standards VII, VIII, IX, and X, physical science to Standards VI, VII, VIII, IX, and X, and English composition to Standard I. My most obstreperous pupil was Pat Kippen in Standard I, age about nine or ten. If I asked a question he would leave his desk at the back and come advancing up the aisle, with contorted face and flicking fingers, consumed by zeal and exhibitionism. I would shout at him, "Kippen, if you leave your seat again, you will suffer the extreme penalty," whereupon he would retire scowling to his seat. But not for long; when I asked the next question he would be up there again, snapping his fingers under my very nose. I remember well the business letter he wrote to the stationmaster which was supposed to have been about a parcel that had not arrived, or some other railway matter.

> *Dear Mr. Chapman,*
> *Your cow has eaten my lorn. If you don't pay*
> *up I shall put it in the pound.*
> *Yours sincerely*
> *Pat Kippen*

Eventually we agreed that he would answer only alternate questions, otherwise no one else would have had a chance. His bright young life came to an end in the Second World War.

Except for the city schools, Ixopo High School was the biggest boarding school in Natal. It had one big hostel for girls and small boys, and one small hostel for big boys. The pupils came from High-flats, Umzinto, Umzimkulu, Creighton, Himeville, Underberg, Bulwer, Donnybrook, and Lufafa Road, mainly from the farms of this rich countryside. I was in charge of the small boys and three matrons were in charge of the girls. It was at this hostel that I had my first experience of making an enemy.

One afternoon when I returned to the hostel from school I found that the senior matron, Miss Shimmon, a most aristocratic and needy Irish gentlewoman of about fifty, had shut two small girls in a cupboard for some offence. In my anger I told her that such a punishment was disgraceful, after which she would not speak to me. The atmosphere in the common dining room became very unpleasant, and when the second matron advised me to apologise, I did so. But Miss Shimmon would not accept my apology, and for two long years we ate meals at the same table and never exchanged a word. In fact we became enemies, and in the end I became totally indifferent as to whether she spoke or not. Therefore when I am asked to interpret the commandment "love your enemies," I do not know how to do it. I did not hate Miss Shimmon, but I certainly did not love her. If Jesus *loved* the Pharisees and the hypocrites, then He loved them in some sense of the word *love* that I do not understand. My failure to understand one of the commandments has from time to time troubled me.

Whether it was because of this incident, or because of the easy-going nature of my colleague Piet Barnard, who was in charge of the boys' hostel, I do not know, but Mr. Buss made us change places. Was it the days in which we lived? Or was it the simplicity of the countryside? Whatever it was, the boys were obedient to a degree, some would say to a fault. But in a way I was like an elder brother to them, and on a free weekend would often walk with one or more of them to their homes, over those hills where I heard the titihoya crying.

I was four years older than the eldest boy in the school, and five years older than a few others, and six or seven years older than quite a number. I have met some of them after not having met them for forty or fifty years. It is a strange experience to be stopped in the street by a man or woman of about sixty-five, and to be asked, "Do you remember me?" I look into their faces and try to remember the boy or girl of fifty years ago, but I cannot. Then they tell me their names and more often than not I can then remember. One of my strangest encounters was when a little old man approached me in the main street of Durban with the question, "Do you remember me?" And when I told him I did not, he told me his name, Douglas Eva, and at once I remembered. Then he said to me, "My you are *madala*," *madala* being a corrupted Zulu word for "old." He was puzzled that I thought his remark so amusing, but I did not describe to him just how he looked to me.

But in those days there was no thought of age. The world was young, the boys and girls were young, even the teachers were young, and the countryside was beautiful. It was an unsophisticated world, and most of the people of village and farm looked up to teachers and thought they must be very clever. They were unforgettable days, and they were made still more so because something out of the ordinary happened to me. I fell in love. (I have come to a halt here. The reason is that I have already told this story in *KONTAKION for You Departed* (published in America as *For You Departed*), but I realise that part of it must be told again, because *For You Departed* was written after Dorrie's death, under the influence of deep emotions that I do not feel now. Therefore I can hardly lift long passages from it. It must be in a way written anew, and that won't be easy. I am writing this parenthetical note in the hope that the mere writing will remove the difficulties—of literary craft rather than emotion—in the way of retelling the story.)

The odd thing is that I fell in love with a married woman. Her name was Dorrie Lusted and she was the wife of Bernard Lusted, owner of the Ixopo Garage and Service Station. He had come from Street, Somerset, to South Africa in the hope that the southern climate would arrest the advanced tuberculosis from which he suffered. Dorrie, who was the daughter of G. E. Francis, one of the three Ixopo solicitors, fell in love with him and he with her.

Dorrie's mother was strongly opposed to such a marriage. She had nothing against Lusted, but she did not want her vivacious young daughter to marry a dying man. Her daughter was equally determined, and it was soon obvious that she would not marry anyone else. She was not self-willed, but her strength of character was considerable. She married Lusted not many months before I arrived in Ixopo.

I think I first met her in February 1925, on the tennis courts in Ixopo, where we were both members of the Ixopo club. There was something in her of the urchin. She was full of mischief and zest and repartee, and played with all her heart. We played a great deal, both together and against one another. I was full of mischief and zest too, and our conversation was full of banter and teasing.

I remember one incident well from those days. Two nuns from the Hospital of Christ the King came to the school hostel where I was living, asking for donations for their work. I gave them half a crown, or perhaps five shillings, and signed my name on their list. That evening I went to Morningview, the Francis home, and there Dorrie and her sister Rad, full of triumph, produced the subscription list and handed back my donation. They had played the same trick on their father, and they gave him back his donation also.

Dorrie's father was a strange man. He would wander from house to office, and from office to the main village street, and from village street to house, and house to office. He would infuriate his wife—or she would pretend to be infuriated—by going into the kitchen and throwing pinches of curry and spices and herbs into the pots on the stove. He appeared to be in a chronic bad temper, and would grunt and mumble and even bellow on occasion. He wore a bad-tempered mask, but when his daughters returned him his donation, the mask broke suddenly into an unwilling smile that transformed his face. Either Dorrie had said to Rad, or Rad to Dorrie, "Alan (or Mr. Paton) is too cocky, and we'll take him down a peg or two." I had not been very bright, because it happened to be All Fools Day. But who would have suspected two nuns of such a dirty trick?

It gave me much pleasure to have been thought worthy of such an elaborate deception, especially as the two deceivers were so proud of themselves. It was sex, and it wasn't. It confirmed me in my attraction.

Dorrie was twenty-seven then, and her sister Rad a year or so younger. Dorrie was worried because her sister had not married, and I think she would have liked us to fall in love. She asked us both to dinner at her house. When we had gone, her husband said to her, "That youngster's in love with you."

It was true too. And it was of course very foolish, especially for one who had studied mathematics, physics, and education. Men did fall in love with married women, but if one was sensible one did not do so with a woman who had, after much opposition, married a man whom she intended with all her heart and will to care for in sickness and in health, and almost certainly there was to be more sickness than health. What was more, I was not born, so to speak, into a tradition of falling in love with married women, and certainly not into a tradition of having a liaison with one, still less of enticing one away from her husband. In those days, and in Ixopo such a thing would have been unspeakably scandalous. The memory was still green of the time when an Ixopo shopkeeper ran away with a farmer's wife, and indeed while I was there, the wife of a business-man was to run away with a foolish young lodger who was some twelve years younger than herself, a boy in fact, of about the same age as myself, who could not distinguish between a woman's re-bellious boredom and the grand passion. These things were scan-dalous, but they were exciting too, and even Dorrie's mother Agnes Francis would recall them with a look on her face compounded of matriarchal rectitude and scarcely suppressed glee, and I suspected that the contemplation of human frailty and of male discomfiture was not wholly without appeal for her.

My love was pure, not only in this conventional sense, but in one more real, for it did not desire to possess the loved object. I do not remember that I ever thought of touching Dorrie Lusted. No one *knew* what I knew, although Bernard Lusted had divined it. The whole thing must be regarded as a phenomenon decidedly odd.

But I did not go mooning about, because I had a second love and that was my work. I loved the school and teaching, and the boys and girls, including that irrepressible Pat Kippen. To be loved by a fair proportion of two hundred boys and girls is quite an experience, though naturally the girls were more demonstrative than the boys. Indeed a young schoolmaster has to be careful of girls when they are blossoming; and not always just the young schoolmaster either. One blossoming thirteen-year-old had all the nature of a kitten, and one had to be very careful of going too close to her. I was saved from temptation by the fact that I was already in love, and also because her father was an irascible farmer who had the reputation of shoot-ing trespassers on sight.

On May 24, which was then called Empire Day and was a public holiday, I went home to Pietermaritzburg for the weekend. On May 25 there happened an event in Ixopo which in great measure deter-mined my life. Bernard Lusted died. I suppose I must have heard it when I returned from the weekend. What I thought I cannot now remember. I cannot even remember if I thought that I would like to marry Dorrie. I cannot remember what I said to her when I saw her again. Strangest of all, I cannot even remember whether I called her by her Christian name.

But I remember the grim black clothes. In those days it was still a prevailing custom. Dorrie had gone back to her childhood home, Morningview. Her father, mother, and her sister Rad were in England, and Dorrie, her young sister Ruth, and her still younger brother Garry were being looked after by a Mrs. Cox. Dorrie walked past the school every day on her way to work, and Marjorie Mc-Laren, who was one of my fellow teachers and who had been with me at the university college, said to me, "Why does Dorrie wear those terrible clothes?" I was so filled with pity for her that I did not think the clothes were terrible.

I seem to remember that Dorrie went away, and that when she returned I had gone away for the holiday month of July. We naturally did not meet on the tennis court, not in those days, when mourning was so strictly observed. I did not see her again until I returned to school in August. By that time the constraint caused by her bereavement had died away, although she still wore the grim black clothes, and did so for three months, after which the conventions allowed her to mix white with the black. It was probably after a period of six months that she began to wear colours.

Her vivacious and mischievous nature soon asserted itself. Of all the younger men in the village, I was probably the one with whom she felt most at home. For one thing she and her sister had a lively interest in literature, and literature was far from being a major concern in that countryside. Dorrie was devoted to plays, acting, and the theatre, and we planned to produce James Barrie's *Quality Street* as soon as her mourning was over. She had been sent by her mother to London to Beerbohm Tree's School of Acting, in the hope that her love of the theatre would oust her love of the man from Street, but it did not work. She and her sister came back to Durban, and Dorrie took a commercial course at the Technical College, in preparation for the work that she had determined to do in the office of the Ixopo Garage and Service Station.

She and her sister Rad were very close, as close as any two sisters I have ever known. The third sister, Ruth, was ten years younger than Rad, but she too was going to be drawn into this close and affectionate association. There was a fourth sister, Beryl, the daughter of G. E. Francis by his first marriage, who was married to an up-and-coming sugar farmer, George Coates. Both Beryl and he inspired something akin to awe in the younger sisters, perhaps because they were older, perhaps because George was a member of what might be called a well-known family, the Coateses, makers of inks. He himself was a handsome, confident, successful man, held in respect and affection by his three sisters-in-law.

Dorrie and Rad were also, in the decorous manner of those days, pioneers of women's liberation. They decided to take a bold public stand on a controversial issue, namely smoking by women. Their boldness was to have fatal results for them both, painful to endure and painful to watch, the terrible disease known as emphysema, the dying of the lungs. That danger was not known then. Their mother's strong opposition to their smoking was based on conventional grounds, tinged with a kind of morality that irrationally believed that smoking was right for men and wrong for women. Matriarch though she was, Mrs. Francis eventually gave in, and her two daughters, by joining the ranks of women smokers, probably doubled their numbers in that conventional countryside. Apart from this rebellion they were both conventional young women, but this was not in any docile fashion, for they were both strong-willed and had very clear ideas on what was right and what was wrong; and these ideas were in accord with what I have earlier called the greater rather than the lesser moralities.

When I returned to Ixopo High School in August 1925, Dorrie asked me to coach her sister Ruth in mathematics. Ruth was sixteen and very shy, and Dorrie used to tease her about me, which embarrassed her extremely. I found that I was spending more and more of my free time at Morningview. This suited me for more than one reason, but one of them was that after my row with Miss Shimmon I found the atmosphere of the hostel dining table very unpleasant. One evening in the little room where I coached Ruth, Dorrie decided to read my hands. She announced that my character was strong, but I cannot remember anything else, only that my hands were in hers. She knew that but she did not know that my heart was there also.

Yet perhaps she did know. Perhaps she knew what was happening, and she wanted it to happen. She was lonely, and the desire to live was returning to her. She had much in common with me. She liked the verbal sparring. Surely she must have known that I was in love with her. I can only suppose that the desire to love and be loved was stronger than the desire to remember and the conventional obligation to mourn. She was not yet three months a widow. She had loved and I had not. She was five years older than I. Did she know fully what she was doing? Fifty years as I look back on it, I come to the conclusion—not painful or condemnatory—that she did not.

Chapter 13

On September 19, 1925, I had dinner at Morningview. After Ruth, Garry, and Mrs. Cox had gone to bed, Dorrie and I sat on by the fire. Dorrie left her chair and sat on the floor. She complained that she was uncomfortable. With incredible courage I suggested that she should rest her back against my knees, and she did so. Then I with incredible cowardice did nothing. Then she, impatient perhaps with this poltroonery, put her hand up to adjust her collar, and our hands met, and my arms were about her, and she turned up her face to be kissed, and I said "I love you," and she said "I love you too." Eventually, at about two in the morning, I thought I should return to my duties at the hostel, and she walked along the verandah, and kissed me goodnight, pressing herself against me as no one had ever done before. And I, knowing well that she was a chaste woman, knew what it was to be loved. In the midst of this emotional welter, reason reared its sober head, and we agreed that things must be kept a secret for some time, out of respect for the decencies of those days.

I wrote in *For You Departed* that I walked home like a man to whom a door has opened so that he may look into heaven. This certainly seems like unbridled language, but it will have to stand, for it happens to be true. In those days love was no doubt over-romanticised. Sighing lovers would marvel at the million-to-one chance that had brought them together in the love affair of the century, if not of all history. It could be nothing else but Destiny. I never went as far as that, but I could not help thinking that in my case one man's death was another man's luck.

So I entered a period of bliss. This was no doubt made more intense by the fact that I had not experienced this powerful emotion before. I had never before entered an intimate relationship with another human being. The sense of release was immense. One was now expressing oneself in a way not permitted before, and in a way that accorded with convention. Mrs. Cox watched it all, and with approval I should think. I now finally gave up having dinner at the hostel, and went every evening to Morningview.

This blissful course did not continue uninterrupted. There were two reasons. One was my immaturity, which permitted a jealousy of the past, of a man who was dead, and a complementary over-possessiveness. The other was Dorrie's sense of guilt in loving so soon after her husband's death. I cannot remember what brought it to a head, but I do remember—even if not exactly—her saying to me, both of us standing in front of the Morningview fireplace, "There is one thing you must understand clearly and that is that I shall never love you as I loved my husband."

I do not remember that I replied. I let myself out onto that same verandah, and walked down the dark road to the boys' hostel. The boys were all asleep, and I let myself into my room and went to bed with my misery. I had suddenly seen a woman I had not known before. The one I had known was tender and loving and teasing and warm, and this one was a woman speaking to a boy who had presumed too much.

I do not remember that I was filled with anger. In fact I am sure I was not. Yet I resolved that I would never go to Morningview again. Then the door of the room was opened, and Dorrie was there at the side of the bed, weeping, and asking to be forgiven. So we were reconciled, neither of us having acknowledged or confronted the two causes of it all.

We also had to be sensible. There, at a late hour, was a woman in my room. If she had been found there, I would have been dismissed from the service and she would have been disgraced. It was lucky for us that the boys were all sound asleep. I let Dorrie out and stayed in my room for a minute. Then I followed her, and together we walked up the dark road to Morningview. That night had one consequence. We never spoke of Dorrie's husband again, until forty-one years later our younger son Jonathan asked why we should have two table napkin rings, one marked "D" and the other "B." His mother would not—or did not—answer him. It was I who said, "That is the initial of your mother's first husband." Jonathan was astonished, and said, "You're not serious? Are you joking?" I said, "He died, and three years later I married your mother." Dorrie said nothing, but later she said to Jonathan's wife Margaret, "There was nothing scandalous about it."

In November of that year 1925, Dorrie's father and mother and her sister Rad returned, and I was accepted as a suitable acquisition. Dorrie's mother was delighted, not so much about the acquisition, but for her daughter's sake. As far as I remember this was Ruth's first official intimation. She was very shy, and Dorrie said to her, "Kiss him, go on, kiss him." Garry, who was eleven and a kind of Huckleberry Finn, mumbled something that I couldn't hear. Our respective families were let into the secret. That Dorrie's father was told I doubt, because he did not say a word to me until some months later when in the fashion of those days, I asked permission to marry his daughter. He grunted and mumbled, but what it was I cannot remember. He probably said, "Have you asked Mother?" It was she who was the head of the family, except in matters of money. The whole family, including Mrs. Francis, were afraid of him about money. If money were wanted, it was she who had to ask him for it, and he would grunt and grumble, or if the request was outrageous, he would bellow like a bull that had been wounded.

As for my own family, my father said never a word that I remember. My mother was full of unselfish love, and so were my sisters and my brother in his offhand fashion.

I am sure the whole thing was not long a secret. Dorrie and I played a great deal of tennis together and I was every day at Morningview. When her six-months mourning period was over, we began to rehearse Barrie's *Quality Street*. However, we decided to keep the "secret" until September 20, 1926, the anniversary of that evening by the fire.

In the meantime I had made a decision to make myself proficient in the use of Afrikaans, the other official language of the Union of South Africa. At Maritzburg College I had learned Nederlands, the language of Holland, taught to me by those giants Naudé and Fischer. Afrikaans is overwhelmingly the child of Nederlands, and in another sense it is overwhelmingly the child of South Africa. It is idiomatically rich, and a great deal of this richness is indigenous.

I had two reasons for doing this. The first was because of my sympathy for the renascence of Afrikanerdom after its defeat in the Anglo-Boer War of 1899–1902. I have already related my father's attempts to learn Nederlands, which at that time was the other official language. When Hertzog came to power in 1924, one of his first acts was to make Afrikaans an official language, and in the course of time it was to displace Nederlands altogether.

My second reason for learning Afrikaans was that a working knowledge of it entitled a teacher to an extra annual increment of salary, and if he was adjudged proficient to teach through the medium of Afrikaans, he was given a double increment.

The striking difference between Nederlands and Afrikaans is in the extreme simplicity of the new language. The involved tenses of future perfect and past perfect are seldom used. Stories are related by the use of the narrative present. It is a convention and one gets used to it very quickly. The spelling is also radically simplified, and becomes almost entirely phonetic. The two definite articles *de* and *het* have been replaced by *die*, which is an enormous boon for non-Afrikaners learning the language. Another striking change was the elimination of "I am, you are, he is, we are, you are, they are" and the substitution of "I is, you is, he is, we is, you is, they is." Purists found all this very painful, but what was happening was that the language of Holland was being shorn of its rigidity and solemnity, and was being made into a supple and vigorous instrument, one of the simplest languages in the world.

Many Afrikaners are far too sensitive about the way in which this metamorphosis took place. Some like to think it was brought about by some incorporeal something known as the "genius of language." And of course it was, but the genius of language used many corporeal agencies, and they must have been the Germans, the Huguenot refugees, the Malay slaves, and the Khoikhoi (Hottentot) aborigines. Some sensitive people like to think that the Malays and the Khoikhois merely introduced a few new words like *piesang* ("banana") and *donga* ("gully caused by erosion"). But the influence of servants and slaves on the speech of the Dutch children of the Cape must have been immense. One can well imagine the indignation of the mythical first Dutch parent who heard with horror the mythical first Dutch child say *ek is* instead of *ik ben*. But the evolutionary process was irresistible. In any event, how did the Spanish produce Spanish and the French produce French?

I tried to speak Afrikaans regularly to Piet Barnard, our Afrikaans master. He was my age, and an extraordinary young man. He was a rugby football fanatic, and the rugby idol of the district, more fond of play than of work. He was also a charmer of young women, and a lover of young people. He was not a buffoon, but he liked to play the part, and did it often. He had a degree but no teaching certificate, and he had just taken a teachers' examination. He was teaching Standards VII and VIII when a telegram arrived. He opened it and his face fell. He then said to his class: "This telegram says I have failed in all subjects; and woe to any of you who follow my example." When I asked him later if this were true, tears came to his eyes and he said to me, "Patie, it's true."

I remember another occasion on which tears came to his eyes. Rugby football matches in the Ixopo countryside were almost invariably played on Sundays. Now Piet Barnard had been brought up in the biggest of the three Dutch Reformed churches, the Nederduits Gereformeerde Kerke, and all three of these churches regarded with extreme displeasure the playing of any game on Sunday.

Therefore Piet was being unfaithful to the teaching of his church by playing rugby football on Sundays. Luckily for him there was no local predikant and no local church building, and he did not attend the occasional services held by a visiting predikant.

I was with him one Sunday evening at evensong in St. John's, the Ixopo Anglican church. We were singing a hymn with the verse

> *If any erring child of thine*
> *Should this day spurn the yoke divine . . .*

Piet had been singing with great gusto until we reached this verse, and then he stopped. I looked at him and saw that he was weeping, and he did not recover for some time. He later said to me, "Patie, you saw me weeping, eh?" I said, "Yes I did." He said, "Patie, I know I am doing wrong." He then became very dramatic, "Patie, my old father and mother would die if they could see me here. . . . and I would die if I had to give it up." He was near to weeping again but the buffoon came to the rescue. "And if I gave it up, Patie, the rugby boys would kill me."

Although he was an Afrikaner, he was one of the most popular young men in this English-speaking countryside, the people of which in those days, if not contemptuous, were at least certain of their racial superiority. Even in those far-off days, twenty-three years after the close of the Anglo-Boer War and fifteen years after the establishment of the Union of South Africa, English-speaking people were learning to express, if not their contempt, then their racial superiority, in private and amongst themselves. These feelings of superiority were strengthened by the fact that the Afrikaners of Ixopo were railway men, policemen, and civil servants, and with exceptions they were not welcome and were not made welcome by the farmers of the countryside. Most of the Afrikaners spoke faulty English, and the fact that the English-speaking people spoke no

Afrikaans at all did not prevent them from feeling superior to those who spoke English badly. Dorrie's young brother, Garry, the one I called the Huckleberry Finn of the village, distinguished himself by writing a brief Afrikaans essay on a dogfight. The Afrikaner word for "dog" is *hond* and the essay went as follows:

Een hond met another hond. Een hond attacked the other hond, and sparks flew. Een hond was killed.

My resolve to learn Afrikaans was my first attempt to move away from any exclusive race feeling. I had also learned from my father to feel sympathy for Afrikaner aspirations. It took me fifteen years to discover that Afrikaner exclusivism would accept me on one condition and one only, namely that I became an Afrikaner. That I could never have done. I took up the study of the Afrikaans language and its literature not to enter a racial exclusivism but to escape from my own.

But my interest in politics did not go very deep. Those were the halcyon days. I was young, I was in love, the countryside was green. The pleasure of teaching did not abate. Our first four candidates for matriculation wrote their end-of-year examinations. After these were over we essayed the impossible. We marked all the papers from memory. The wish prevailed. We got all our candidates through, but not by much. By dint of the most exhaustive marking and remarking of these papers recalled by memory, we teachers were able to correct a failure score of thirty-ninepercent to a pass score of forty-one percent.

Alas reality was different. All four failed. Mrs. Francis took Ruth away and sent her to the Collegiate School in Pietermaritzburg. The postmaster took his daughter away and sent her to a German school in northern Natal. The parents of Johannes van den Berg sent him to Maritzburg College. The fourth candidate was Martin Buss, who being the son of the headmaster, had to stay and try again.

At the end of this disastrous school year I went home to Pietermaritzburg for Christmas. That was when I received my first love letters. They were addressed to "My Dearest One." It gave me a very strange sensation to be called this. These letters were very loving, but they concealed the fact that Dorrie was in a state of great doubt. That may well be why we did not see each other for the whole six weeks of the holiday, though our homes were only fifty miles apart. If we did decide together not to see each other for six weeks, then it was certainly Dorrie who made the decision, and I who fell in with it. Throughout those six weeks I looked forward to our reunion. Then the great day came and I, now the proud owner of a powerful Indian motorcycle, set out for Ixopo. Unlike Lysander, I had never heard by tale or history that the course of true love never did run smooth.

When I got to Morningview on my powerful Indian motorcycle, Mrs. Francis and Rad and Ruth all came out to meet me. But not Dorrie. She was in the bath. We sat in the drawing room and talked, for a long long time. Mrs. Francis was skilled in the art of small conversation, and it was a good thing that she was, for I had nothing more to say. After a while Mrs. Francis went out, and when she came back she said, "She won't be long now." How long I had sat there I do not know, but it was a long time, much longer than one would expect to be kept waiting by a woman who was to be reunited with her dearest one.

Why had I not already walked out of the house before Dorrie came out of that interminable bath? Why had I not said to Mrs. Francis, using cold words, "If I am wanted, if any person should happen to want me, I can be found at the boys' hostel"? But I could not. I had had no experience of speaking cold words. I was in love, I was twenty-three. If I had been thirty-three, I might have walked out and never come back. But I did not, because I was in love.

Well, eventually it all came out. Dorrie had gone to Mrs. H., a widow herself, thought by Dorrie to be a woman of great understanding of the ways of love and the world. She had gone there because she had begun to doubt the wisdom of her actions. Mrs. H. had told her that she had been caught on the rebound, and that her love must be suspect because she had been lonely and had wanted to be loved again. But who was there in Ixopo, of her age or older? Therefore in her loneliness she had turned to a young eager boy, who like herself was keen on tennis and banter and amateur dramatics.

The upshot of it was that either Dorrie now asked me if I did not think I should marry a younger woman, or told me that she thought that is what I should do. And I said to her, in spite of my pain, "I don't want to marry some other woman."

I wrote all this down more than forty years later, after Dorrie had died. With the permission of Malcolm Muggeridge I quote these lines, written when his wife Kitty was very ill:

The thought that she might die filled me with desolation. All our quarrels and jealousies and harsh sayings and infidelities dissolved away. . . .

I now record that after thirty-nine years of marriage which must have been very like that of the Muggeridges, I could still feel the pain of that long-gone time. I quote these lines with my own permission:

I would be nobler, wouldn't I, if I didn't feel it? But then I would not be myself, nor would I be writing what I am. For I am writing a story of love that began with joy and pain, and ended in steadfastness.

I, who could not speak cold words, was angry with Dorrie for the first time, that she should take our affairs to a woman who was almost a stranger to me, who had a worldly wisdom no doubt, but no spiritual understanding that I had ever discerned.

I asked her some hard questions. Who had asked me so often to her parents' house? Who had arranged for me to coach her sister Ruth? Who suggested my hands be read? Could she not see that I was in love? Why did she not go to Mrs. H. then, and tell her what was happening, not only to me but to her too? Why did she not ask then for advice from this wonder-woman who knew all the secrets of the human heart? Why raise me up to this great height, and then take her arms away?

After that we all sat down to dinner, G. E. oblivious of the world's burdens, Mrs. Francis keeping the conversation going, Rad and Googie and Garry, Dorrie, and me. What did we talk about? What did I say? What do you talk about at dinner when your lover has just told you that perhaps you should find another?

After dinner Dorrie and I went into the garden with a rug and cushions. I told her again that I did not want to marry some other person, I wanted to marry her. In her turn she told me that she had not stopped loving me, but that she had decided that either she did not or could not care as much for me as I deserved. In any event we decided not to part, and she hoped that the day would come when she would love me as much as I deserved.

At the age of twenty-three I could hardly comprehend the situation. She was suffering from a twofold sense of guilt, first because she had loved so soon after her husband's death, second because she had encouraged to love her a boy six years younger than herself, to whom she could not give the raptures of first love.

Much more was made of first love in those days than is now. It was a romantic tradition, and no one remembered that Juliet was not Romeo's first love. I would not say that the tradition exists no longer, but its hold is weaker than it once was.

The irony of the whole affair was that I would never have

thought Dorrie's love defective if she had not told me that it was. The problem was not only her sense of guilt, the problem was my demandingness.

But it must not be thought that I lived in pain. Dorrie was not the only love in my life. There was my work. Quite apart from my enjoyment of it, I had ambition and wanted to rise to the top of my profession. I was in love with that countryside and its bracken and its mists. To this day the sight of bracken on a hillside gives me pleasure. Like the taste of good bread and new potatoes, and the smell of mint and the rose, it is a sensual delight that never seems to pall. When I am dying, it would give me pleasure to have a sprig of bracken put into my hands. That may be the influence of Stevenson's lines to S. R. Crockett.

It was not long after this that our love affair took a turn that made our marriage a certainty. My university degree was in physics and mathematics, and I had not taken chemistry beyond the high school. Nevertheless I was teaching physical science, a subject which was half physics, half chemistry. I should have told my headmaster Wilfred Buss that I was not qualified to teach physical science. Perhaps I did, perhaps I did not. Perhaps I did not because I did not want to leave Ixopo. I do not know.

One of the experiments which a chemistry teacher has to perform is to demonstrate that the element sodium has the power to break up water into its constituent elements, hydrogen and oxygen, and to form caustic soda and hydrogen. Sodium is kept in paraffin to prevent it from oxidising, that is, taking oxygen from the atmosphere. But our small piece of sodium in the Ixopo High School refused to perform. I cut piece after piece from it, but it refused to react with water. Where it came from I do not know, but apparently its external surfaces were heavily oxidised. Finally in desperation I took it and the physical science class into the recreation ground of the school. I made them stand back and then with a pipette I dropped water on the remaining piece of sodium. Suddenly it went off with a tremendous explosion, blinding and searing me, presumably the caustic soda and the burning hydrogen together. Wilfred Buss rushed me in his car to the district surgeon, who applied some soothing ointment to my eyes, and ordered that I be taken to Pietermaritzburg at once, in the hope of saving my sight.

The news was all over the village in a few minutes. I, blinded and bandaged and now free of the unendurable pain, waited passively for whatever might be done for me. Who came to Pietermaritzburg besides Wilfred Buss I do not remember, except for one, and that was Dorrie herself, who came and sat by me, and held me protectively and lovingly, and whispered to me, "I haven't any doubts anymore." So the great "secret" went up in the explosion too.

I did not lose my sight after all. The final damage was a defective tear duct in the right eye, but Dr. Ingle in Pietermaritzburg, after saying a prayer at the operating table, made me a new one which has served me well for over fifty years.

So the halcyon days returned. Playing tennis for the Ixopo second team, with Dorrie as partner, at Highflats, Umzimkulu, Lufafa Road, Eastwolds. Buying a motorcar together, a Chevrolet, second-hand for £175, the price depending on the model. Acting in plays, making school gardens, walking the hills with an energy that seemed to be limitless.

Our second matriculation results were not spectacular, three entrants, two third-classes, and one failure. I might have thought that I was not fitted for teaching, but the junior certificate results were excellent, including one first-class. In fact the results were so good that parents from other parts began to send their sons and daughters to Ixopo, and plans were made for the building of a new hostel.

Dorrie's mother said to her, "Alan is going to make a mark in the world." This pleased me, especially as Mrs. Francis did not pay compliments easily. She was a formidable woman, with high and strict standards of conduct, and a tremendous will. I never came into conflict with her will; I think both she and I knew that it would have been a disaster for us all, and would have faced Dorrie with an almost impossible choice.

I once played a joke on her. The Francises were the proud possessors of a new Buick, which was the most luxurious car in the district. Working for Mr. Francis in his lawyer's office was a young clerk, Laurie F., whom I had taught at school, a quiet, serious young lad of about eighteen. For some reason Mrs. Francis took a strong dislike to him.

Imagine the scene when just before dinner, when the whole family was together, she received this note:

> Dear Mrs. Francis
> I have to go home this week-end and would
> like to borrow the Buick.
>
> Yours sincerely
> Laurie F.

The result was electrical. Mrs. Francis opened the letter and read it with a look of shocked incredulity. Her hands shook as she held it

out. "The impudence of it," she said, "the little upstart, the Buick!"
The letter was handed round and all read it, while Mrs. Francis
poured down imprecations on Laurie's head. Then Dorrie and Rad
joined in, "What impudence! What unbelievable cheek!" Mrs.
Francis said, "I'll Buick him!" She herself realised that this was
funny, and for a moment amusement struggled with anger on her
face. Then the anger returned. She was clearly about to do something and I thought it was time to tell her that it was not Laurie
who had written the letter, but myself. The family was convulsed
with laughter, and when she was able she laughed too, saying to me,
"Alan, you wretch!"

On September 20, 1926, Dorrie and I became officially engaged. It
was exactly one year since that evening by the fireside, when she
had found it uncomfortable sitting in the chair and had sat on the
floor in front of the fire. I shall record one more event of that year.
On May 25, 1926, it was the anniversary of Bernard Lusted's death.
That day I was not to see Dorrie or touch her or speak to her. I was
sick at heart, and consumed with jealousy of a man who was dead.
After eight months of loving and being loved, for one day I had to
cease to be. I did not see the sense of it, I did not understand it at
all. I went to have my evening meal at the hostel, and they must
have looked at me with astonishment and speculation, for I had not
eaten dinner there for almost a year. I record this event for one
reason only that I know of. That is the way it was. So here it is
written down.

It was in 1928 that I first heard of the British movement known
as Toc H. In November 1915 a young chaplain called Philip Clayton
was sent to work in the Ypres salient under Neville Talbot, son of
the Bishop of Winchester, and Senior Chaplain to the Sixth Division. Talbot and Clayton discovered a great empty house in Poperinghe, which they decided to use as a club for the troops. They
called it Talbot House after Gilbert, the youngest son of the same
bishop, a young man of great promise who had been killed in July
1915. In December the house was opened. It acquired almost in-
stant fame. Philip Clayton, soon to be known to the world as Tubby,
was undoubtedly a genius. He decided that Talbot House would be
"a place of light and joy and brotherhood and peace." And that is
what it became.

He was at that time thirty years old. His influence over men, his
gift for giving them a meaning for life and for confirming a meaning already held, in a house a few miles behind the carnage of the
trenches, was immense.

So was his sense of humor. His notices became legendary:

IF YOU ARE IN THE HABIT OF

SPITTING ON THE CARPET AT HOME,

PLEASE SPIT HERE.

Over the chaplain's room he put the notice

ALL RANK ABANDON YE WHO ENTER HERE.

The loft of the house became a chapel, and Tubby found an old carpenter's bench to serve as altar. Tens of thousands of soldiers made their communion there, many for the first time and some for the last. This was Talbot House, the initials of which, T. H., became in the signaller's alphabet, Toc H. *

And Toc H became the name of the movement that was to recapture the spirit of Talbot House, of worship, fellowship, and service to one another. Its aim was nothing less than to achieve a new spirit between man and man. It began to spread throughout Great Britain. It attracted the great and the not so great, the rich and the not so rich, the professional man and the worker in the factory. It was a religious movement without dogma, it was Christian but not closed to any man who could subscribe to its principles. Its aim was to spread the Gospel without preaching it.

The Toc H Compass had four points, To Love Widely, To Build Bravely, To Think Fairly, To Witness Humbly. The lamp became its symbol; it was to be one of the lights of the world. Tubby composed the Toc H prayer, beginning, "O God who hast so wonderfully made Toc H." The administration of the new movement was taken over by an eminent civil servant, Peter Monie, freeing Tubby to become Founder Padre and the Vicar of All Hallows-by-the-Tower. In 1922 Toc H was a national movement of great spiritual power. It began to spread into the whole of the English-speaking world.

Toc H came to South Africa in 1926, where a group was started by Bert Oldfield, a lay worker at St. Matthew's Mission, in a small nearby village called Keiskammahoek, in that region known as the Eastern Province. In 1927 it came to Pietermaritzburg, where it exercised a profound influence over what one would call very earthy men. It grew so quickly in my hometown that the group had to be broken into two. Two of the most important members of the

---

* See *Clayton of Toc H, by Tresham Lever. (London, England: John Murray, 1972.)* I find it impossible to read Chapters 4 and 5 without experiencing deep emotion.

group were the padre and the jobmaster. The function of the first was to articulate those things about which these earthy men felt deeply and spoke seldom. The function of the second was to distribute the "jobs," the visits to the sick, the crippled, the aged, the arrangement of outings. One of the corporate jobs in Pietermaritzburg was to start raising the money to establish a Toc H boys' hostel, which would offer a reasonably inexpensive home for working boys who came from the country to the city to take jobs or attend schools or technical colleges. Toc H in Pietermaritzburg, and in many other places too, changed the lives of many men, turning their attention to the needs of their fellows and their communities. And of course it attracted many whose attention was already there.

It was not long before Toc H realised that there was need for a women's organisation too, especially for those women who had become "Toc H widows." When this organisation arrived, it was given a typically man-made name, the League of Women Helpers. I must record that in those days of the 1920s it never occurred (to my knowledge) to any member of Toc H to consider opening the organisation, whose supreme aim was to create a new spirit between man and man, to any person who was not the possessor of a white skin.

There was, however, considerable talk of the reconciliation of English-speaking and Afrikaans-speaking white South Africans. This came virtually to nothing for several reasons. One was that Toc H was essentially a British organisation, born out of a war in which many Afrikaners refused to take part; the very name, Toc H, was alien. The second reason was that Afrikanerdom was in the process of creating its own organisations, all with their own Afrikaans names, parallel to (and therefore never or seldom meeting) the Red Cross, the Boy Scouts and the Girl Guides, the Rotary Clubs and the Lions Clubs, even the Chamber of Commerce. The third reason was that the number of Toc H members enthusiastic about such reconciliation was decidedly small.

I was tremendously attracted to Toc H, partly because of its emphasis on service, partly because of its relative unconcern with religious dogma, partly because I felt it would give some purpose to the aimless lives of so many of the young men of the village of Ixopo. I went to Pietermaritzburg and asked Toc H if they would help to establish a group in our village. It was easy to get twenty Ixopo men, most of them young like myself, to come to a meeting which we held in the Memorial Library.

I must here relate one of those incidents that is embarrassing to remember. Some things in one's life one recalls with shame, regret, contrition, and some with embarrassment. On this occasion I invited half a dozen men from Pietermaritzburg to come fifty miles at night to our village to address a meeting to found a group of Toc H, to go fifty miles home again, and I completely neglected to do anything about their sustenance. It was left to Frank Smith, who worked in the blacksmith's shop, to ask me if I had made any arrangements, and I had to say I had not. It was Frank who went to the Plough Hotel, and returned with flasks of tea, bread, pickles, cold meat, and cheese. I might have said that man does not live by bread alone, but I did not have the necessary impudence.

So Toc H was launched in Ixopo in 1926, and it continues till this day. To it I devoted a great part of my life for twenty-five years, in Pietermaritzburg and then in Johannesburg, especially during the war years 1939–1945, when I became the National Chairman of the YMCA–Toc H War Work Council of South Africa. In 1949 I was appointed by Toc H, Britain, as Honorary Commissioner for Toc H in southern Africa. In due course I shall relate how this relationship also came virtually to an end, and how my offer to resign as commissioner was accepted by the Southern African Council in 1954. I tendered this resignation for two reasons. The first was that I knew that a very large number of Toc H members objected to the identification of the commissioner with the newly formed nonracial Liberal Party of South Africa. The second was that I no longer wished to be associated with an organisation that maintained a colour bar, and that refused to give it up, on the grounds that "the time was not yet ripe." This painful experience I shall later relate. It was made doubly painful by the knowledge that Mr. J. H. Hofmeyr, our previous Honorary Commissioner, had been fully acceptable to Toc H Southern Africa although he had been one of the leaders of the United Party. It was not the political identification that Toc H objected to; it was the nature of the politics.

My intimate connection with Toc H, Ixopo, lasted a very short time. Dorrie and I had decided to get married in July 1928, and the headmaster had failed to get the Education Department to appoint an extra man, who would be single and take my place at the Boys' Hostel. At the same time Maritzburg College had decided to introduce physics as a matriculation subject, and the department appointed me to the new post. On June 30, 1928, I taught my last day at Ixopo and said farewell. Ambition was tinged with regret, regret was overwhelmed by ambition.

Chapter 14

We were married on July 2, 1928, in St. John's Anglican Church, Ixopo. During my years in Ixopo I had been a faithful worshipper at the Methodist Church, but I did not join it, although I taught in the Sunday school. For those three and a half years I had refused to play games on Sundays and had once been commended for it in this same St. John's Church, in the course of a sermon delivered by the vicar. I don't think the commendation was so much for the Sunday observance as it was for the willingness to stand for a principle, and one that had very few supporters in the Ixopo countryside. Even the number of Methodists who observed it was very small.

The reason why I attended the Methodist church rather than the Anglican was that the Students' Christian Association had been strongly nonconformist. Yet already I was inclining towards Anglicanism. Perhaps most of all it was the language of the Book of Common Prayer that attracted me strongly. I did not make my final choice then, largely because it would have caused pain to the Methodist community, and especially to the Allen family, whose father was the minister, and whose daughter Ruth was one of my most shy and earnest pupils.

For the wedding I bought my first tailor-made suits, one to be married in, and one to "go away" in, according to the custom of those days. They each cost six pounds (twelve rands). My father and mother and sisters came from Pietermaritzburg for the ceremony.

The wedding reception was held at Morningview, and there I

drank an alcoholic drink for the second time in my life. It was a deliberate decision on my part to break with the teetotalism of my upbringing. It was also—may bishops forgive me—another step in the direction of Anglicanism. It was also a tribute to Dorrie, to the wholesomeness of her life, to a morality concerned with affirmations, not prohibitions.

At the reception we were congratulated by a long line of guests, and there was a great deal of kissing. Emboldened for some reason— not by the champagne, which we had not yet drunk—I offered to kiss the wife of the vicar, who drew herself up and said, "No man kisses me except my husband." Apart from this rebuff, everything went off well.

Dorrie and I had decided to go in our £175 car to the Victoria Falls for our honeymoon. This was still a brave venture in those days, though not so brave as the honeymoon journey of Reg and Edith Pearse to Uganda; yet neither of these could compare with the journey of Peter Stayt of Underberg and her blind anthropologist husband Hugh, accompanied by an African codriver, who in 1936 drove from Tangier to Pietermaritzburg via the Sahara Desert. To cross the desert at that time was a bold and dangerous deed.

We spent our first night at Howick, and it was then that I first noticed that Dorrie had moved her first wedding ring to her right hand. I asked her, "Are you still going to wear your first wedding ring?" To which she replied, "Yes."

In 1969, in *For You Departed*, I said that I was writing "of this pain" for the last time, and this would have been true if I had not decided to write this autobiography. Dorrie finally gave up wearing the ring seven years later in circumstances that I shall tell of. When she died I searched the house for it. What she did with it I do not know, but if I had found it I would have treasured it. It is no doubt a strange story but that's the way it was. And I am trying—with certain qualifications—to write of things as they were.

At the end of July 1928, after having spent five days at the Victoria Falls, and having made the long journey back to Ixopo, we set up our new home in Pietermaritzburg, where I assumed my duties as the form master of IIIA, and the introducer of physics to the boys of Maritzburg College.

My headmaster was Septimus Pape, of St. Bees School and Oxford, a classical scholar who at morning assembly floored the boys by calling a cinema a *kīnēma*, and floored more than one of the masters by referring to the "*in*clemency of the weather." He was a teacher of great vigour, and his voice would at times echo round the hollow square building where all the classrooms were situated. On one of these occasions Charles Carpenter, form master of IVA, vice-principal of the school, who had been a fellow master of Pape at Durban High School, sent his headmaster this note: "Dear Pape, I'm afraid my class didn't quite catch your last sentence. Would you mind repeating it?" No one else would have risked it.

Pape was a strong headmaster, strongly opinionated, and overbearing at times. His weakness was that he bore down hard on those who were afraid of him. He once reprimanded me in front of my class for an offence which I had not committed. After school I went to his office and pointed out to him that his judgement had been arrived at too hastily. From that day on I never looked back. He formed a high opinion of my ability and I was regarded by some of my colleagues—though not nastily—as the headmaster's favourite.

On the staff were three men who had been masters when I was a boy at the school from 1914 to 1918. Cyril Armitage called them Leach, Lamond, and Goldstone, but I never omitted the handle "Mister," nor did they ever invite me to do so, an invitation that I would probably have not accepted.

There were over four hundred boys at college. There were five fourth forms and five thirds. Carpenter's IVA and my IIIA were composed of boys of high intelligence, the forms being arranged in that pattern. To teach such boys demanded no drudgery, but it was not easy work, because one had to keep wide awake to stay ahead of them. Indeed, if they had not been kept fully extended, they would have behaved badly, and they did so towards those masters whose mental equipment was inferior to their own.

As far as I can see, the problem of the exceptional child has not been solved. Are the brilliant ones to be grouped together, or should 150 pupils be put into five classes by the casting of lots, or in alphabetical order, or by subject choices? When Carpenter retired, I became form master of IVA, but I took IVE in arithmetic. It was exhausting work, and was made yet more disheartening by the total apathy, and sometimes total unwillingness, of a large percentage of the class. Most of them should have been learning and doing something in which they could have scored some success, which would have helped to decrease their sense of failure and inferiority. The only ones who escaped this were those who excelled in sport. Even in IVA one would encounter a brilliant pupil who was incapable of learning mathematics, and if one persisted with him, the rest of the class would become inattentive.

Once in New York I spoke to a girls' junior school where every pupil had an intelligence rating of 130 and over. My subject was "South Africa," of which country and its problems most New York children knew nothing, but after I had finished I had to answer the most searching questions from girls of eleven, twelve, thirteen, fourteen years of age. When the lecture was over, I had an hour with the principal of the school, who told me that the segregation of brilliant children solved many problems and raised many others.

Controversy still rages as to the advisability of separating brilliant children from their fellow pupils. In Britain, where today the drive towards equalisation in every field is very strong, it is argued that the harm caused to brilliant children by separation is greater than the advantage of it. I listened to these arguments but did not take sides, as it was forty years since I had been a teacher. Yet I could not help noting the heat of the debate. The passions that were aroused were not purely academic; they were also political.

In the magazine *Encounter* of July 1973, John Wain, professor of poetry at Oxford, wrote an article "Swing High, Swing Low," which dealt with the problem created in society by the simple fact that not all children are equally gifted. After an evening spent with cheerful young people who were keen on making music and listening to Wain's readings, he and some friends went for refreshment to the cafeteria of the town's motel. While they were there another kind of young people arrived, the motorcyclists in metal-studded leather jackets, boots, and helmets. They were aimless and bored, appearing to be of low intelligence, their highest entertainment the slot machine and the soccer game, and the slashing of train seats when their teams lost.

For generations it was class origin that determined the future of a child. But in modern Britain the poor child can move "upwards" if he or she is clever and ambitious. But what of the child who is not clever and not ambitious? Wain writes: "In all those vacuous faces there was something closed, secret, unreachable: the self in its shell of resentment." And these children are resentful, not because they are poor, but because they are not clever. They are the ones who must tend the machines, dig the coal, load the ships, wash the floors. They are the ones without whom the employers would starve. The new class warfare is even more terrible than the old.

My Form IVE did not present a problem as fierce as that. After all, they were white, and they would fill the lesser managerial and supervisory jobs. The machines would be tended, the ships loaded, the coal dug, by black hands. But the dead weight of their indifference troubled me.

From what one reads and hears it seems to be the People's Republic of China that has achieved the greatest success in giving a sense of social significance to every member of its society. The hospital doctor takes his turn at sweeping the floor. The teacher shares with the pupils the menial tasks of the school. In some magic way the people devote themselves to China, and not to the search for material comfort and possessions. One does not feel that about the Britain of today. One certainly does not feel it about the South Africa of today, where love of country is inextricably bound up in the case of white people with a determination to hold on to their material possessions, and in the case of black people a determination to have more of them. There is another difference; people are denied social significance in South Africa not because of their low intelligence but because of their colour.

To teach my Form IIIA was arduous not because one had to keep pushing them from behind but because one had to keep running in front. In Carpenter's IVA—and he was a superb teacher—silence reigned. In Paton's IIIA a great deal of laughter and noise; this was an indication, I think, of the temperaments of the teachers. It was Carpenter who supervised the morning assembly until the headmaster and staff entered formally; four hundred boys, and all silent. Lucien Biebuyck, our senior Afrikaans master, called my class the Tickey Bazaar. Once in the course of conversation I said that I liked my class to like me, whereupon Biebuyck said, "I do not care whether they like me or not, so long as they do what I tell them." He was also a superb teacher, and became finally the Director of Education for Natal. He was that rare creature, perfectly bilingual in Afrikaans and English, which means that he spoke these languages with a complete mastery of both grammar and idiom.

I did not really much concern myself with the burdens laid on society by the intelligence quotient. But for better or worse that entity called "society" was getting hold of me. I realise that the high school boys and girls of today, the earnest ones, can discuss "society" and its problems with considerable maturity, but that was not the case with me.

It was Toc H, which I had joined in Pietermaritzburg, that made me feel *responsible for society*. The motives were I suppose religion, morality, vanity, and ambition. Society is a big pond in which to swim and display one's aptitudes. The society for which I was beginning to feel responsible was a *white* society. I have no doubt that I *knew* there were other societies, but I felt no responsibility for them. The realisation that all these societies were interdependent was hidden from me. Least of all did I accept the belief which was later to become the driving force of my life, that all these societies were in fact *one* society. I use the word *accept*, because this particular belief has to be accepted by an act of will. It is possible also to reject it by an act of will, and indeed a large number of Afrikaners do so, believing that it is unthinkable that these societies should become *one*. For these Afrikaners the integrity, the separateness, the self-renewal of all these societies are great values that must be preserved in all their purity; only by remaining separate do they preserve their beauty. It is perhaps unnecessary for me to say that this dogma is incapable of intellectual proof, and its acceptance depends on many irrational factors, such as, for example, racial fear and racial pride. But that does not prevent its upholders from spending a great deal of time on the intellectual proof of the doctrine that these various societies can retain their health and beauty only by remaining separate.

At that time I had no foreknowledge that I would come to hold the ideal of one common society, nor did Toc H have foreknowledge that it would for many years resist it. Toc H was there to concern itself with the problems of a *white* society; it was in fact itself a *white* society. In 1928 it was far from clear to Toc H or to myself that in fact the existence of a colour bar in Toc H was quite incompatible with the high ideals that had brought it into existence.

I had not long been in Pietermaritzburg before a white social problem began to weigh on the conscience of the city. In 1929 disaster hit Wall Street. In September 1930 Hitler's Brown Shirts appeared in the streets. In September 1931 Great Britain went off gold. The prices of South African diamonds and wool slumped heavily. The world was in the grip of the Great Depression. One-half clung to the gold standard, the other half to sterling. The Hertzog Government decided to adhere to the gold standard; Mr. Havenga, Minister of Finance, gave pragmatic reasons, but these were underlaid by a powerful psychological motive, namely the desire of the Government to assert its independence of Great Britain, and therefore to resist the temptation to follow sterling. This temptation was considerable, because the gold mines were contending with rising taxes and rising costs, while the price of gold remained static. As a consequence some of the poorer mines had to close down. These mines, though poor, were employers of many workers and purchasers of many goods. Their closure in turn hit commerce, industry, and agriculture, and unemployment became a serious social problem.

Pietermaritzburg, though not a great industrial centre, also had its unemployment problems. These affected, in those days, men rather than women, and boys rather than girls. It was the municipality that concerned itself with the problem of unemployed men, but no one was concerned about the large number of boys, mostly from the primary schools, who left school and could find nothing to do. It was a matter written about in the newspapers, but no one did anything about it.

It began to weigh on my conscience. Why this should have been so I am not quite sure. No doubt the duty to be one's brother's keeper had something to do with it. But there must have been at least two other motives, the feeling of embarrassment and guilt that I myself and Toc H, the servant of society, were doing nothing about it, and the desire to stand well in my own eyes and those of the community. Whatever it was, I persuaded the two branches of Toc H in Pietermaritzburg to start a relief operation for unemployed boys.

The municipality decided to create a very big wild garden in the spacious Alexandra Park, and unemployed men could find a job there. This was the origin of one of the most beautiful parts of any park in South Africa, and it is doubtful if it would ever have come into being had it not been for the Depression.

I persuaded Toc H to collect the money which would enable us to pay any boy two shillings a day if he was prepared to do this kind of work. Subscription lists were printed, and it was hoped to get regular donors who would give a small amount each month. My fellow members enrolled subscribers and the first batch of boys went to work in the Alexandra Park. This was not a success. Friction developed between the boys and the supervisors, and we had to move the scheme to the Botanic Gardens, where the friction disappeared. The scheme was also a boon for the Botanic Gardens, which were perennially poor.

Some of the boys then asked for a club, and this we called the 18–30 club, and it had a girls' section run by Mrs. Barnett Potter. We found unused premises in a side street, and opened the club two nights a week. I cannot say it was a great success. I for one had no knowledge of how to get money, nor did I know many people in the business world. So the club equipment was poor. The task of collecting small sums each month became burdensome, and it was difficult to get enough helpers to run a club with several activities. Some of my associates in Toc H were of the opinion that we were expending too much energy for too little result. Certainly the employment scheme and the club took an undue amount of my leisure time, and I was glad when in December 1932, South Africa went off gold. Money became plentiful; the poorer mines reopened; industry, commerce, and agriculture recovered fast; unemployment disappeared, and the need for unemployment schemes with it. The boys went to work and began to earn good money; support for the club melted away, and we closed it down.

Both the scheme and the club gave me a reintroduction to the class distinctions of Pietermaritzburg. Though many of the boys came from those same parts of the city where I had grown up, I had, by virtue of my education and my profession, moved into another class, though not into the local aristocracy of which my dear mother spoke with respect. The Maritzburg College itself, though not as expensive and exclusive as schools like Michaelhouse and Hilton College, was a school of class. There we played rugby, while the boys of the club played soccer. The boys of Maritzburg College would become farmers, bank clerks, civil servants, magistrates and judges, lawyers, doctors, accountants. The boys of the club would become plumbers, electricians, bricklayers, barbers, bakers. These distinctions were by no means absolute, but they were real enough. One of the reasons why the class difference was nothing like so great or so divisive, as for example in Britain, was that the real working class in South Africa was black.

Yet for all that it was there. When unemployment had declined, and the club had shut down, I took a job at the Technical Institute for two nights a week teaching a kind of practical mathematics, designed to help white apprentices to the various trades to cope with problems of weight and measurement. I think I earned a pound a night, say eight or nine pounds a month. In those days it was quite a sum of money, and a welcome addition to my income.

The job was enough to break one's heart. Ninety percent of the boys resented deeply the law that compelled them to attend apprenticeship classes. The ten percent that wanted to learn had to do so in the face of the contempt of the others. I was told by other instructors that teaching the apprentices in their second and subsequent years was a pleasure, but it was a pleasure denied to me.

Several members of my class were also resentful when I forbade smoking during lectures. They would lounge in their desks, and make no attempt to listen to me. A ten-minute smoking break in the two-hour period did not appease them. They would not use strong language to me, but would do so to each other in my presence. When the period was over I fled for home, and looked forward to the morrow when I would meet my IIIA, the Tickey Bazaar, all eager and bright.

I had one particularly unpleasant student in my class. Let us call him Smith. He too would lounge in his desk, and look at me with what one could hardly call a veiled contempt. I would at the close of each evening set an exercise for the next, but if I remember rightly, I was told that the law demanded the physical presence of the apprentices for so many hours a week, but that one could not demand of them anything else whatever.

When I asked Smith for his work he said to me, "I didn't do it, see," and when I asked why, he said, "I didn't feel like it, see." When I asked him if he did not wish to learn, he would look at his friends and say, "Oh yes, we all want to learn, see?" I had to swallow my rage, but shortly after that when one of the willing students was coming to the board, Smith put out his foot and brought him crashing down. I said to him, "You're a lousy specimen of mankind. Please leave the lecture," which he promptly did.

On the following day I went to see Mr. Seymour Hosley, the principal of this heartbreaking place. We had never liked each other, but today less than usual.

"Mr. Hosley," I said, "I have come to speak to you about a student in my practical maths class."

"Yes," said the principal. "His name is Smith, and you called him a lousy specimen of mankind."

"That is so," I said, "and I have come to tell you why I did so."

"There is no need for that," said the principal. "I take a serious view of any instructor who calls one of my students a lousy specimen of mankind."

"Is that so?" I said. "In that case . . ."

"There is no need for you to resign," he said. "You are fired."

"That suits me," I said. "And let me say at parting that I wouldn't be the principal of a soulless place like this."

"It takes certain qualities of character," he said, "which no doubt you do not have."

So I left the Pietermaritzburg Technical Institute, glad to be out of it. I could have fallen into despair over the state of the apprenticeship system, but I didn't. I had come into contact with a class of young men who had no desire to learn anything. What they were like at their places of employment I never learned, nor whether they treated the trade instructors in the way they treated their lecturers. It seemed to me that they resented not only the law which took away two of their nights per week, but the very fact of having to work at all. And they resented me, not just because I had to teach them, but because I came from a superior class, the members of which wore white collars and didn't dirty their hands.

I did not try part-time teaching again.

Chapter 15

At the end of 1928 I decided to take a further step in learning to speak and write Afrikaans. Piet Barnard had left the Ixopo High School in 1927, having been invited to teach Afrikaans at the exclusive and expensive boys' school, Michaelhouse, which is situated in the heart of the Natal Midlands, also a beautiful countryside of rolling hills and grass and bracken. This invitation added very greatly to Piet's reputation, but in fact he was invited for his rugby, not his teaching.

He was succeeded by Frikkie Burger, also a Stellenbosch University graduate, and also a very good rugby player. There the likeness ended, for Frikkie was earnest, methodical, strict, and a first-class teacher. He and I became firm friends, and in the school holidays of December 1928 I took the big train to Cape Town, and a smaller one to Porterville, a small town in that part of the Cape province known as the Boland, which means "the Land Above," so called because it lies north of the Mother City. I was met at Porterville by Frikkie Burger with trap and horses, and I had my first experience of the sound of wheels grinding on the gritty gravel of the Boland. These are the great wheatlands of South Africa. One year a field is sown with wheat, the next year with rye, the third year it lies fallow, a barren expanse of yellow earth and stone which looks as though it could produce nothing.

Frikkie's father and mother knew no English. They belonged to a generation that has gone. They wore the clothes of the previous century, they worked hard, they had no luxuries. They were devout and I am sure without guile; family prayers were held, if not twice, then at least once a day—I do not remember. Their *volk*, that is, their labourers, who were all members of the group called the "Cape Coloured," lived in small dark houses built of stone. They had no lavatories, but used the bushes, which was a part of the farm to avoid; abundant space, air, and sunshine prevented any outbreak of disease. Their wages were low, as indeed farm wages tend to be all over South Africa, though they have risen slowly because of competition from the factories of a country that is one of the most highly industrialised outside North America, Europe, and the Soviet Union. Part of the remuneration of the farm workers is the "sopie," the draught of sour inferior wine that is given them three or four times a day. The Cape Coloured people have a higher degree of alcoholism than any other racial group in South Africa and how far this is due to the sopie and how far to the fact that they are a depressed people no one can decide. The sopie has been condemned by generation after generation of social workers, teachers, and ministers of religion. These reformers have tried to get Parliament to legislate against the practice, but the wine industry is very powerful and the practice of the sopie enables it to sell to farmers millions of litres of wine that would otherwise be unsaleable.

I have described the Cape Coloured people as a depressed group. This generalisation must be qualified, in that they have produced teachers, doctors, poets, and singers who can rank with any. But they are a rejected people. In 1852, when the Cape Colony was given representative government, the franchise was open to all who could claim certain qualifications. In 1910, when the Cape Colony entered the Union of South Africa, the other three provinces agreed to the retention of the Cape franchise within the borders of the colony, with one fatal provision, namely that it could be abolished or amended by a two-thirds majority of both houses of Parliament sitting together. This two-thirds majority was obtained by Prime Minister Strijdom in 1956, and he did it by greatly enlarging the Senate and filling it with his supporters. He used this majority to remove all Coloured voters to a separate roll. In 1968 Prime Minister Vorster abolished the franchise altogether. These actions have disturbed the peaceful relations that have existed between the white and the Coloured groups for more than three centuries. The Coloured people regard themselves, and rightly so, as rejected, rejected by the very people who created them.

In 1928 such ideas had not entered my head, nor had they entered the heads of my friend, and his father and mother. To me they were hospitable, kind, courteous. They were not rich, and one of our regular dishes was Cape snoek, which is caught in great numbers on the Atlantic coast, and is salted away in barrels. Snoek appeared to be the staple food of the household, and of the labourers as well.

I stayed with the Burgers for four weeks, and spoke no English. The first week was a terror. I toiled and struggled, sweating and groaning, making no progress. I thought I would give it up. Then suddenly I was on the plateau, beginning to move at great speed. At the end of a month I was virtually bilingual, though never to be in the same class as Lucien Biebuyck. My speed of progress was not so much due to my own ability as to the fact that the vocabulary of Afrikaans is easily recognisable as the simplified vocabulary of Nederlands.

Although my companions, who were the young farmers of Porterville and Piketberg, were unilingual, they could swear in English as well as anybody. They used words the equivalents of which they would never have dreamt of using in Afrikaans. Although I was not a prude, the continual coarseness of their language at least provoked me to retaliation in Afrikaans with the oath "thunder and lightning." They were absolutely aghast, there is no other way to describe it. They beseeched me not to use such words, and agreed to omit the coarsest English expressions. By the time I left them I could read the leading Afrikaans newspaper, *Die Burger,* with ease if not always with approval. This fact astonished them, for some of them found its Afrikaans at times incomprehensible. They were simple, artless fellows, and decided that the English were not so bad as they had thought. One of them was a comedian, and for my benefit he would mount the table and act the part of an auctioneer. He would cry out, "Ladies and Gentlemen, last chance, last chance, fine oxes from Natal, ten pond per kop." This wit had his simple companions rolling in the aisle.

In 1928 my sympathy with the aspirations of the Afrikaner people was very strong. I had by this time reached the judgement that the Anglo-Boer War was a scandal and that although it had been declared by President Kruger, it was really the work of Chamberlain, Milner, Rhodes, and Jameson. This sympathy for what one might call Afrikaner nationalism lasted ten years, and in due course I shall explain why it came to what was almost a sudden end.

It was about this time, 1929 or 1930, that a man called Loudon Hamilton was invited by our branch of Toc H to talk about the movement known then as the Oxford Group. The group was a

Christian movement, aimed largely at the reconversion of Christians who had lapsed or drifted or become lazy or even been seduced by the world. Its aim was utopian, nothing less than the salvation of the human race. For this reason it selected key men and women for its targets, for if they were reconverted, their countries would turn to the ways of righteousness and peace. In this regard it made exaggerated claims of converting or deeply influencing South African and other statesmen. It claimed some credit for the coming together of General Hertzog and General Smuts in 1933, and the cessation—for some time at least—of our bitter political strife. But if their aim was justified, the morality of the achievement was dubious, for the coming together of Hertzog and Smuts had one consequence that made for neither righteousness nor peace. It gave Hertzog the two-thirds majority that he needed for the removal of the African voters of the Cape to a separate roll.

The Oxford Group demanded absolute purity and absolute honesty. Its converts would, before large groups of people, confess sexual infidelities and financial dishonesties. The effect of such honesty on the hearers was tremendous. It moved many others to make similar confessions, and to make a new Christian beginning. Every convert was expected to become a converter, an evangelist, a fisher of souls. Thus would the whole world be changed. "Change" became the key word. How could one change the world if one was not changed oneself? Converts began to use expressions such as "the day I changed" and "since my change."

The influence of the Oxford Group was very considerable. Dominees and ministers and priests, professors, teachers, workmen, boys and girls admitted their hypocrisies and dishonesties, and began a new life. Edgar Brookes, whom many thought to be a pillar of righteousness, admitted his worthlessness and began again. Another notable convert was George Daneel, whose conversion appeared all the more remarkable because he was a Springbok, a rugby player who had represented South Africa. Another was Bremer Hofmeyr, cousin of Jan Hofmeyr, who became Minister of Education in 1933. Bremer married Agnes Leakey, the cousin of the famous Kenyan paleontologist who had made such world-shaking discoveries in the Olduvai Gorge in Tanzania. Her father and stepmother were murdered by the Mau Mau, but this deterred neither her nor her husband from their attempts to bridge the racial gulf between black and white in Kenya and many other parts of Africa.

The Oxford Group claimed to have played a great part in Britain in lessening class antagonisms. They claimed to have created a better understanding between capital and labour, between employer and employee, and between the classes. That these antagonisms were very real is shown by the fact that Toc H in its Royal Charter of Incorporation formulated the fourth of its four objectives in these words:

To mitigate by habit of mind and word the evils of class-consciousness, and to endeavour to create a body of public opinion free of all social antagonism.

In 1980 this particular claim of the group is seen to have been an exaggeration.

The group claimed to have played a similar part in South Africa in the field of race relations and race antagonisms, but in 1976 the claim was again seen to have been exaggerated.

It is, however, true that many South Africans, under the pitiless searchlights of absolute purity and absolute honesty, now saw themselves as they were. Afrikaners with bitterly hostile feelings towards the British and all those South Africans of British descent, English-speaking people with contemptuous feelings for Afrikaners, white people and black people who feared and perhaps hated one another repented in public of their hostility, their contempt, their fears, and their hates.

Nevertheless the influence of the Oxford Group, while immense in individual cases, failed to convert the nation, and converted very few of its political leaders. In fact many political leaders, particularly among the Afrikaner Nationalists, distrusted it, because it was exalting love and brotherhood above national solidarity, on which the Nationalists relied for their sustenance and continuance. Afrikaner Nationalists, being devoted to both nationalism and religion and determined to keep them both, reconciled these two elements in the compound known as Christian-Nationalism, and because they could hardly profess a belief in anything higher than the gospel, they identified Christian-Nationalism with the gospel. This identification disturbed a number of Afrikaner Christians, but it was a brave man who would actually put his religion above his nation. And was it really necessary to do so, when they were really one and the same?

Loudon Hamilton's visit to Toc H made a deep impression on some. Others were afraid of his uncompromising religion, and yet others regarded it as too extreme for the ordinary man, and thought that Toc H was a much better and more human way of practising one's religion. I myself was strongly attracted to Hamilton, and de-

cided to go to a second meeting with him. I was willing to take my
religion more seriously, but three things finally deterred me from
joining the group.

The first was the relentlessness of the Groupers. Together as a
team they possessed what I can describe only as an inexorable intensity of purpose. Can an intensity of purpose be called palpable? Was
the palpability there, or did it exist only in the consciousness of
those who were being hunted, who knew of their infidelities and
dishonesties, and who dreaded the possibility that they might be
revealed? Do we not clutch to ourselves the false reputation for
righteousness that we have earned from the world, and do we not
prize it above the joy of liberation, seen already in others, that they
experience after they have confessed that it is all a lie?

I attended yet a third meeting of the group, a house party held at
the Riviera Hotel on the Durban Esplanade. The purpose of these
house parties was not primarily fellowship. Their primary purpose
was to hunt and capture souls. One could see on the faces of some
that they were being hunted, that they were praying with St. Au-
gustine, "Give me chastity and continency, but do not give it yet." I
did not know that prayer then, but I knew, from my days with
Railton Dent and Neville Nuttall, those words of Francis Thompson:

> Fear wist not to evade as Love wist to pursue
>> Still with unhurrying pace,
> Deliberate speed, majestic instancy,
>> Came on the following Feet,
>> And a Voice above their beat—
> "Naught shelters thee, who wilt not shelter Me."

He wrote also

>> I said to dawn, Be sudden; to eve, Be soon;
> With the young skiey blossoms heap me over
>> From this tremendous Lover!

It was not only the chastity and the continency. It was the yield-
ing of the sovereignty of the self, to that Power to which alone it
may be safely yielded. I have never been to the island of Sark, but I
know it in imagination, because that is where Loudon Hamilton
went to make up his mind whether he was willing or not to yield the
sovereignty of his self to the Holy Spirit. That was nearly fifty years
ago, but I still remember clearly his telling of it.

He yielded himself and I did not. It was more than ten years after that I yielded the sovereignty of my self, and it was not through the consideration of chastity and continency. It was because I decided to live by the belief that all men are created equal. I already *held* the belief. Now I decided to *live* by it.

The inexorability of purpose of the group repelled me. I knew that if the hunters caught me they would love me. I knew that if they did not catch me they would love me but not much. I did not blame them for that because they had no time to spend on those who would not be caught. They had given up their jobs, their careers, their material security, their luxuries in order to save the world.

I have in only one other sphere of life encountered a relentlessness equal to that of the Groupers, and that is the relentlessness of the South African Security Police. They have the same inexorability of purpose, the same intensity of gaze. They are hunting too, but if they catch you it will not be to love you. Yet in both of them it was the relentlessness that repelled me.

My second reason for not becoming a member of the group was that I knew I could not live on this plane of dedication, that I could not live for saving the world every minute of the day. My will to serve the world was rather like a trusty weapon that you bring out of the armoury when you want to shoot, but you do not go about shooting with it all day. In 1928 or 1929, I had not learned to distrust utopianism, not because one does not long for the world where the wolf will lie down with the lamb, but because one distrusts the means that will be used to build it. I had not yet learned— though I am not sure about that—that the world cannot be made anew, that the battle between good and evil is perennial, that the purpose of the good life is not to win the battle, but to wage it unceasingly.

My third reason was simple. Dorrie, who was beginning to take her Anglicanism seriously, was repelled by the group and its intensity. On December 4, 1930, she bore a child, David Francis Paton. I decided that it was time for me to become an Anglican.

It was in this year of 1930 that a tragic event overtook our family. My father's powers of memory and concentration were failing, and the department approved an early pension. He had always been a great walker, and he would now set out from home once or twice a week with his stick, a rucksack containing sandwiches, and a flask of tea or milk.

On Thursday, the first day of May, he set out for the Town Bush

Valley, and that evening did not return. It was speculated that he was suffering from loss of memory. Dorrie and I had gone to Ixopo for the weekend, but my mother telephoned and asked me to return as soon as possible.

On Tuesday of the following week, the sixth day of May, a hundred scouts combed the countryside from Claridge to Town Bush Valley without avail. There were reports aplenty, from Howick, Mooi River, even as far north as Ladysmith. Atholl and I and friends followed all these trails but found no clues whatsoever.

On Thursday the eighth day of May, and on Sunday the eleventh, and again on Sunday the eighteenth, scouts, ramblers, Old Collegians, Natal Carbineers, members of Toc H, and many others searched the great hills that lay to the north of Pietermaritzburg. These hills were covered with plantations of gum, pine, and wattle, and this made searching very difficult.

On Wednesday the twenty-first of May, my mother and her four children expressed thanks to all those who had helped us, in the columns of the *Natal Witness*. My mother now accepted that my father was dead, and that one day his body would be found. She had borne the long ordeal with fortitude. So also had my grandmother, my father's mother, who did not long survive her only son and died at the age of ninety-one. On the thirty-first of May my mother expressed her final thanks.

On Tuesday the seventeenth of June, my father's body was found "lying half immersed" in a pool of a stream in the Town Bush Valley. It was stripped of all possessions and was identified by Atholl and myself, a task that I have never forgotten. The police searched the whole terrain, including all African huts, but found nothing. After the postmortem, the police declared that they were satisfied that my father had not been murdered. It was suggested that he may have bathed in the stream and suffered a heart attack. But in fact to this day the manner of his death is a mystery.

The pond in which my father's body was found was passed by many searchers, including my brother, but it was hidden from them by an overhanging bank.

So my father's life came to a tragic end. For all his jokes and jollity, his life had in some way been solitary, and he made it more so by alienating the affection of his children. Now of course I think of him with nothing but pity.

Chapter 16

Harry Skelton was an Anglican priest and the vicar of the Church of St. Peter. He was a big burly man and was widely regarded as a saint. He was also the padre of our Toc H branch, and it was to him that I first revealed my desire to become an Anglican. But I told him that I would have difficulties with the Thirty-nine Articles.

He told me not to worry about the Thirty-nine Articles, nor about dogmas that I just could not believe. If I could accept the Christian faith as set out in the Apostles' Creed, and if I could "purpose to keep" God's will and commandments, I would be halfway there. All that remained was to renounce the world, the flesh, and the devil! I would rather have promised to try to resist unseemly temptations of the flesh and the seductions of the world; and I didn't believe in the devil. But in the end I did all three. I was confirmed by Leonard Fisher, Bishop of Natal, in his own chapel of Bishop's House, and if I remember rightly, Harry Skelton was the only other person present. I have used all my life the confirmation prayer: "Defend, O Lord, this Your child with Your heavenly grace, that I may continue Yours for ever; and daily increase in your Holy Spirit more and more, until I come into your everlasting kingdom." Just how far I have increased in the Holy Spirit is a question I would not like to go into too deeply.

Dorrie had taken our baby son David to the family home at Morningview, and I wrote to tell her of my confirmation. She was much moved, and I must say she was astonished also. I must have been very secretive about it. I had a second reason besides the attraction that Anglicanism had for me, with its affirmation of the good rather than its condemnation of the bad, and its aversion to emotionalism. This reason was that I did not want our children to grow up in a divided home.

In 1924 I had wanted to read for the degree of Master of Education, but Professor Ferguson had felt unable to take me. Now in 1930 the University College of Natal decided to enlarge his department and to offer courses for the M. Ed., and I enlisted. The course included a study of McDougall's *Abnormal Psychology*, not now well regarded. There was John Dewey on *Democracy and Education;* Sigmund Freud on the interpretation of dreams, sexuality, the unconscious; Giovanni Gentile on education; the educational theories of Comenius, Pestalozzi, Rousseau, A. S. Neill, Froebel, and Montessori; more Watson and Kohler; and a history of education in Natal, our lecturers being Professor Allsopp and the redoubtable Dr. C. T. Loram, then Superintendent of Education for Natal, and later Professor of Education at Yale University. And then a book that was to change the direction of my life—Cyril Burt's *The Young Delinquent.*

The M. Ed. examination was in two parts—a written examination, to be followed by a thesis. I never wrote the thesis, although my thirteen years at Diepkloof Reformatory offered me an unparalleled opportunity. I shall try to offer excuses for this later. Though I was teaching all day, I worked hard for the written examination, often until after midnight. One could say that I mastered, not Dewey and Freud, but their two books, by the simple though exacting method of rewriting them both in my own language. Off went the papers to the external examiner, not to be heard of again for more than thirty years. That was not because they got lost, but because I never completed the thesis. However, in 1966 the University of South Africa decided to award a degree of bachelor of education for the written examination, and my ancient papers were brought to light. Obviously the filing system of the university was exceptionally good.

Those years with Professor Ferguson gave me a further introduction to the world of great thought. The professor was the same as ever, gentle, diffident, apologetically witty, and a superb teacher. When he delivered a judgement his nose would suffer a small twitch or spasm. He had a great respect for Dewey, regarded Freud with a certain Scottish scepticism, and thought Rousseau odd. I actually wrote "decidedly odd," but changed it, because the professor in general abstained from expressing decided opinions. He was sceptical about all dogma. He questioned me once about my religion, and when I told him that I had become an Anglican, and felt at home in the Anglican worship, he shook his head gently and said almost apologetically, "I did not."

When the examinations were over, he said he would like to give me a gift of books, and he hinted that I should not ask for too small a gift. So I asked him for three books which had been reviewed by the *Times Literary Supplement* and had received high praise. They were by Alfred Garvie, the Scottish theologian, *The Christian Belief in God, The Christian Doctrine of the Godhead, The Christian Ideal for Human Society.* Ferguson inscribed them all

A. S. Paton
d.d. June 1934
G. W. Ferguson.

They are still part of my library, and even now I refer to them, though theology has much changed.

I parted from Professor Ferguson with great regret, and I think he with me. When he sent my examination papers to Pretoria, he said to me, his nose suffering the small spasm because he was delivering a judgement, "They are good, I think." But he did not tell me that he had rated them *summa cum laude*.

I have written that *The Young Delinquent* changed the direction of my life. For the first time I considered giving up ordinary school teaching, but it was by no means a serious consideration, because I had begun to cherish the ambition of becoming headmaster of the Maritzburg College. Some extra compulsion was required, and it was provided by a minute creature with the name of *Salmonella typhosa*.

In the month of April 1934, Vic Evans, one of the leading members of Toc H Natal, and I paid a weekend visit to the branch of Toc H at Melmoth in Zululand. On the way home we stopped at a river ford, many rivers and streams being still unbridged in those days. It was a warm day and I cupped my hands and drank from the river. Whether it was there that I encountered *Salmonella* cannot be proved, but the meeting took place almost certainly during this weekend.

It was not until at least eight days later that I received the first warning that something was wrong. Dorrie's sister Ruth, who had now married, was staying with her husband Dick Tatham as our guests, and the four of us and three-year-old David went to the Valley of the Dargle for a picnic. We decided to have lunch in an old wattle plantation, with a few big trees and an abundance of firewood. I took on the task of making a fire. I gathered some sticks and chose two stones between which to lay the wood. Then I sat on the ground and looked at the sticks and the stones for a long long time. I knew that something was wrong, but I did not know what it was. After a while Dorrie realised it, when she saw me sitting looking at the unlaid fire, doing nothing. In the end it was Dick who made the fire. After lunch they decided to go home and put me to bed.

After a troubled night *Salmonella* engaged in a bitter struggle with my conscience. My conscience told me to go to school and *Salmonella* told me to stay in bed. Conscience won. I was in charge of the rugby football fixtures for the first four fifteens and the Senior and Junior Colts. If this work were not done, the world would fall to pieces. So I went to school. My colleagues told me I was a fool, and that not even I was indispensable. They made me go to see the headmaster, who told me to go home, and the school would stagger along without me. The next morning *Salmonella* won. She did this by giving me a temperature of well over 100° F.

Dr. Hugh Croudace came to see me that morning, diagnosed malaria, and told me to stay in bed. I sent messages to the headmaster, and he sent messages to Dorrie, telling her that the rugby fixtures were in capable hands. The next day I was worse, and the doctor diagnosed typhoid, or as it was called, enteric fever. He ordered me to hospital, and the municipal ambulance came to fetch me. I decided to complain to the town clerk about the attendant who carried the head end of the stretcher, because his hands reeked of cigarettes.

They took me to St. Anne's, the Roman Catholic hospital, called the Sanitorium. It stood on the high ground above the Umsindusi River, on the other side of which was the Maritzburg College, which was staggering on without my assistance. As for me, I was being very ill, for the first, and up till today, the only time in my life. After a few days my temperature went up to 105° F, and I talked a great deal in my delirium. Dr. Croudace told Dorrie that my condition was grave. He said to her, "I wish he would stop thinking."

In the early 1930s the treatment for enteric fever was starvation. The only food allowed was milk, and the only drinks were diluted barley water and orange juice. The flesh falls away, partly because of the starvation and partly because of the nature of the disease. I was not conscious of this because of the temperature, which after climbing to the 104s and 105s oscillated there for about a week. When it began to fall I was aware of my tremendous hunger, and when I first saw my body I was filled with pity, for it and for myself. The calves of my legs—of which I had been very proud—had disappeared, and so had the muscles of my arms. I asked for a mirror so that I could look at my face, but the doctor would not allow it. I was now given food such as mashed potatoes, and liquids such as beef tea, but the hunger continued unabated.

I was now allowed visitors besides Dorrie, who had visited me faithfully twice a day. They were on the whole subdued rather than joyful, as though in the presence of one who had returned from a celestial country. Septimus Pape had told the assembled school that they would not be allowed to visit, but the head prefect and one of his colleagues came to congratulate me on my return to the terrestrial world. In my fourth week I began to eat substantial meals, though after each one I was still ravenous. My night nurse was a lay sister, and I remember her name, Sister Liversedge. She had her dinner at midnight and never failed to bring me some of it. I began to read and to laugh, and I longed with all my heart to go home. And at last the great day came, and Dorrie came to fetch me. I was bathed and dressed, and as a last precaution they took my temperature. Back I went to bed again, and a tearful wife went home.

I do not think that I again had the same fierce temperature. But back I went to the milk and the barley water. Still more flesh fell away. My weight had dropped from 150 pounds to 90 odd. I was that thing called skin and bone. So again we went through the whole process and in the eighth week I began to read and to laugh, and to have midnight supper provided by Sister Liversedge. Sister Mary, who had nursed me all those weeks, brought me Willa Cather's novel *Death Comes for the Archbishop*. It put me in thrall. I thought it the most beautiful book I had ever read, but I do not think it was a proper judgement, because I could hardly be said to have been in the frame of mind that befits the critic, even when deeply moved. I did not read it again until some twenty years later; I again found it beautiful, but not as compelling a work of art. I intend to read it again soon, perhaps for the last time.

So back I went to reading and laughing, and longing with all my heart to go home, to enjoy all the love and the solicitude that would be showered on me, and the feasts too. The great day came, and Dorrie came to fetch me home. I was bathed and dressed, and as a last precaution they took my temperature. Back I went to bed again.

This time it was I who wept. Indeed I think I broke down and cried. In my pitiful state I fully believed that I would never leave St. Anne's alive. It seemed as though I had contracted an incurable disease. Doctor and nurses and even wife were all conspiring to keep the truth from me.

I don't think I wasted any more. There was nothing left to waste. At last I rebelled against the milk. The very sight of the glass made me ill, and I was then allowed milky drinks, probably of the nature of Ovaltine.

It was while I was in this feeble state that I experienced five minutes of uncontrollable panic. I accidentally swallowed a glucose sweet. I could actually feel the sweet perforating all those vital tissues that if perforated would cause me to die. That is what Dr. Croudace had so feared in the first two weeks of the illness, and he told me so not knowing that I would have to go through those two weeks again. I rang the bell continuously because I was afraid to die. Nurses came running, Sister Mary among them. To her I told the terrible news that all these weeks of devoted nursing had come to nothing because I had swallowed a glucose sweet and would surely die. Between tears and laughter she told me that the sweet would have become liquid long before it reached those places which if perforated would cause me to die. I believe I actually laughed myself.

During these abnormal days I conceived the idea of going round the world. Only such a trip could compensate one for this ghastly "salmonellic" joke. I made poor Dorrie go to the travel agents and bring me the mouth-watering brochures of Hawaii, Fiji, the Seychelles, the Norwegian fjords, and the Italian Dolomites. I read these brochures avidly, and made tremendous plans. Dorrie wanted to tell me that we had no money, that it would take us years to pay the hospital and the doctor, but she was afraid to do so. She probably feared yet another relapse.

Seventy-seven days. The great day has come again. I have been helped to the third valedictory bath. I have to be helped because there is almost nothing to walk with. My legs are hardly more than the bones which form them. In all these eleven weeks of devoted nursing there was only one thing lacking. The hospital made no attempt to teach me to walk again. I shuffled round on flat feet and the arches dropped. I might have become permanently flat-footed except that I practised walking about on the balls of my feet. It was very painful but I persevered with it, and it took me some years to recover some of the muscles.

So there I sit, bathed and dressed, waiting for Dorrie to come to fetch me home. The terrible moment comes. As a last precaution they take my temperature again. If it has gone up again, my spirit will break. Sister Mary looks at it and holds it up with a cry of joy. It is 98.4°F. She embraces me, and I embrace her. The nursing nuns do not embrace me, but they smile at me all chaste and demure, which is pretty good of them, because I grossly insulted one of them in my delirium. I shuffle along the passages and into the lift, and I shuffle into the waiting car. I cannot believe it. I am going home. *Salmonella* and I have parted company, and if Dr. Croudace is right, we shall never meet again.

A period of bliss. Apart from the joy of being home again with Dorrie and our son, of being visited by many friends, there were the physical pleasures of being waited upon, of sitting in the winter sun which in these southern latitudes is generously warm, the return of physical desire to the emaciated frame.

Yet greater than all these was the sheer pleasure of eating, of being almost continuously hungry, and of knowing that there was no danger that the hunger would not be satisfied. How long this lasted I do not remember, but it must have been between one and two weeks.

Now that the danger of relapse was past, Dorrie told me that I must give up these phantasies of Hawaii and the Dolomites. The hospital bill was almost £150, the equivalent of three months' salary. I cannot remember the amount of Dr. Croudace's bill, but he treated us very generously considering that he had visited me almost daily for seventy-seven days. It took us almost four years to pay these two amounts.

Dr. Croudace advised me to take a further three months of sick leave. If I had been teaching for ten years I would have been given the whole six months on full pay. However, I had been teaching for only nine years and nine months, and therefore would have to take these extra months on half-pay.

I was still somewhat light-headed and I regarded this as an injustice of the grossest kind. I wrote a letter to the Education Department, and in my opinion it was a masterpiece. The most brilliant part of this masterpiece was a passage in which I compared the sick-leave regulation to a game of snakes and ladders. Any letter written by a teacher in those days had to be sent through the principal of the school. Whether the principal was entitled to read it, I don't know, but Septimus Pape read mine, and after consulting with Dorrie decided not to send it. Thus Dr. C. T. Loram, our renowned

Superintendent, was robbed of the chance of reading as fine a piece
of controlled invective as has ever been produced by an impover-
ished schoolmaster. By the time I learned of the fate of the letter,
my crusading passion had died down. My reason had reasserted
itself, and I was able to see that a regulation was a regulation, and if
it said ten years it could not be manipulated to mean nine and three-
quarter years.

So instead of going to Hawaii we went to Park Rynie, a seaside
resort about forty miles south of Durban. There we stayed for three
perfect months, in Grandfather Thomas James's holiday cottage.
David was now three and half years old, and I taught him to read
and write. Despite our poverty we ordered a case of assorted wines
from the Stellenbosch Farmers' Winery. We bathed in the sea every
day, and walked in the afternoon. Slowly the flesh returned to the
emaciated frame. The only trouble was that I never wanted to work
again.

At the end of September we locked up the cottage and returned to
Pietermaritzburg. On the first day of the fourth term I crept, like a
snail, unwillingly to school.

Chapter 17

Well, not exactly like a snail, and not exactly unwillingly. I was greeted enthusiastically on all sides, not least by my Form IVA, who for six months had been without my care, and after another two months would have to sit for their junior certificate examinations, in which I hoped that most of them would pass in the first class.

I remember my first Saturday morning walk up and down Church Street, ostensibly to go shopping. Pietermaritzburg was still a small town, and one knew at least half of the people whom one passed. I was stopped by Mr. Arthur English, a leading nurseryman of the town, whose son I taught.

"What are you going to do now?" he asked.

"I'm back at school," I said.

"You won't stay there," he said. "You can't stay in the same place after an illness like that."

Where he had acquired this prophetic wisdom I don't know, but he was right.

In 1934 South Africa took a great step forward in the treatment of young offenders. In that year parliament transferred all reformatory institutions for juveniles from the Department of Prisons to the Union Education Department. Up till now I had been a servant of the Natal Education Department, one of the four provincial departments (the others being the Cape, Transvaal, and Orange Free State) which controlled what might be called the ordinary conventional schools. All special education was controlled by the Union

Education Department, all schools for the blind and deaf and dumb, all industrial schools to which were sent children in need of care and also mild delinquents, and all technical schools and colleges; also the Union Department had the oversight of the universities and the university colleges.

The word "reformatory" in South Africa in 1934 was used only by state institutions charged with the duty of accepting and keeping in safe custody and "reforming" all juveniles committed to them by a court of law. It was not used as it is in several countries, of an institution concerned with adult offenders. In law a child could commit an offence at the age of seven years. Any offender between the years of eighteen and twenty-one could be sent either to a reformatory or to a prison. At twenty-one he went to prison.

The fact that the word "reformatory" was used at all was an acknowledgement that the institution had an educational as well as a custodial function. In the reformatories for white boys there was a programme of instruction in the "trades," such as building, carpentry and cabinet-making, metalwork, and painting; in the reformatory for Coloured boys, there was also some trade instruction, but a great many of them worked on the lands of the historical estate of Tokai, on the periphery of Cape Town. In the reformatory for African boys, all of them worked on the lands of the beautiful farm known as Diepkloof, just outside Johannesburg. There was a theory—not unknown in other countries—that the land exercised some mystical therapeutic influence on juvenile offenders. This theory could be carried to absurd lengths, and continued to be held even when more than ninety percent of juvenile offenders placed on the land ran away from it to get back to the lights and the sounds of the cities.

The Union Department of Education naturally decided to appoint as principals of its new institutions men and women from the world of education. Four posts for men were advertised, two for the white reformatories at Tokai and Houtpoort, one for the Coloured reformatory at Tokai, and one for the African reformatory at Diepkloof, on the outskirts of Johannesburg. I wrote a private letter to Mr. J. H. Hofmeyr, Minister of Education, and told him that I would like to get a post at a reformatory.

Why did I decide to take such a step? One reason was undoubtedly the restlessness caused in me by my long illness and my long absence from school. Another was undoubtedly ambition. But a third reason was that I was attracted by the idea of working with young offenders.

Cyril Burt's book *The Young Delinquent* had quickened my interest, and this was increased by the books of Sheldon and Eleanor Glueck, and by reading of the work of the George Junior Republic and Homer Lane.

I first met Jan Hendrik Hofmeyr in 1927, at a boys' camp held by the Students' Christian Association (SCA) at Umgababa on the south coast of Natal, on a flat piece of ground at the foot of the railway bridge.

It was Reg Pearse, Cyril Armitage, and myself who launched the boys' camps in Natal. We had the powerful aid of Oswin Bull, an Englishman who had come to South Africa in the early 1900s as a travelling secretary for the SCA. He was a tall and handsome man, with a commanding presence and a powerful carrying voice, which he used to quell riots and insurrections. He may be said to have had a hunger for souls, because that is why he was in this job at a salary that permitted no luxuries. The aim of the camps was to win boys to an allegiance, or confirm them in an allegiance already held, to Christ as the Lord of life, and to Christian principles in life and in society. Bull's appeal was to the will rather than to the emotions, and his influence on Pearse, Armitage, and myself, and indeed on many other young men including Neville Nuttall, was very considerable. Three men exerted this kind of influence on me during this first half of my life. Dent was one, and Bull was another. I was now to meet the third.

Hofmeyr came to our second and last camp at Umgababa, and then year after year to the new campsite on the Idomba River at Anerley, which site he helped the association to buy and develop. He was then thirty-three years of age, and was the Administrator of the province of the Transvaal, a very high post indeed. After an academic career which led him to the degree of bachelor of arts in the classics at the age of fifteen, bachelor of arts in the sciences at sixteen, master of arts at seventeen, and a further degree at Balliol at the age of twenty-one, he was at the age of twenty-four appointed principal of the Johannesburg School of Mines, which under his principalship was to become the University of the Witwatersrand. In 1924 at the age of twenty-nine he was appointed by General Smuts, the Prime Minister, to the Administratorship. He was unmarried, and lived his life under the watchful and possessive eye of his mother. Many years later I was to spend four years—spread over eleven years in time—writing his life, and of course, hers.

Hofmeyr was a camper of the first water. He wore an ancient canvas hat, a khaki shirt and shorts, and discoloured sandshoes, known as tackies. He played every camp game. To oppose him at rugby football was a profound physical experience. This was one of the few activities for which he took off his thick-lensed spectacles, without which he could see nothing but night and day. If he got the ball, he would charge for the goal line, two hundred pounds of concentrated material. If one were of slighter build, there was only one thing to do, and that was to get out of his way. If some extra-heavy camper decided to try conclusions with him, the air would be full of cries, of agony from the one and of uncontrollable giggling from the other. It was strange that one who almost certainly in the whole of his life had never struck a living thing in anger should revel in this gross physical contact.

It was often said that Hofmeyr lacked gifts of personality. It is truer to say that not every environment could bring them out. He often felt constrained with people, and indeed his extraordinary intellectual gifts had made him a child among boys at school, and a boy among men at university. Then at last at Balliol in 1913 he had the chance to be a young man amongst young men, but before he entered his second year the First World War broke out, and he, with his thick-lensed spectacles and an inclination—not very decided—towards pacifism, was, in the words of an Oxford poet, left at a "Balliol bare of all save mild Hindus."

However, with boys he felt no constraint, and as a consequence he was for them the most important, the most zestful, the most loved personality in the camps. Everybody, from Commandant Bull to the youngest boy, called him "Hoffie." As for the young men who staffed the camps, they came to feel for him a deep trust and affection. He could easily have chosen some other kind of holiday, yet he did not. One can only conclude that in the camps he was renewed and restored in some special way.

In 1929, when he was thirty-four and his term as Administrator of the Transvaal had expired, he decided to go into politics. He could have joined the ruling party, the National Party, under the leadership of General Hertzog, or the opposition, the South African Party, under the leadership of General Smuts. He decided to join Smuts, but in 1933 Hertzog and Smuts came together in coalition, and in 1934 they finally fused their parties and formed the new United Party. Hofmeyr became Minister of Education, and soon thereafter became responsible for the reformatories in South Africa. It was therefore to him I wrote to ask if there was any prospect that I might get a post at one of these institutions.

I think it would be right to say that Hoffie had innumerable friends but no intimate. He was able to hide himself behind his thick-lensed spectacles, which were for him a kind of guard against those who might want to pry into the secrets of his private self. Perhaps half a dozen times in his life he made a remark to me that I recognised as a dropping of his guard. When the first South African soldiers went north in 1940, Hofmeyr, who was then Minister of Education and Finance, stood behind General Smuts on the saluting platform. He said to me of this occasion, "Do you know, Smuts isn't much taller than I am?" This became for me a clue to the complex relationship that existed between these two men, two of the most gifted Afrikaners of their time, geniuses in fact. The one was a soldier and a man of action, looked up to and respected by tens of thousands of men, the other was an administrator without equal, but mother-possessed and lacking whatever quality it is that attracts and almost overawes other men. He did, however, attract and influence the young men of the camps. He was also at home in yet another world, that of cricket. This was not because of his prowess but because of his utter devotion to the game.

I have been called an intimate friend of Hofmeyr, but I was not. I would, however, claim to have known him as well as any other man did. This was not only because I saw a great deal of him but because the complexity of his personality fascinated me, and because I am, by temperament or gift or whatever it is, an observer of human nature.

Two personal relationships to a large extent ruled his life. His attitude to Smuts was ambivalent; sometimes he came close to veneration and sometimes close to hostility. Hofmeyr was like a great hill under a great mountain. He was twenty-four years younger than Smuts, yet he died two years earlier. He had in fact spent his life as Smuts's lieutenant, and in Smuts's shadow.

If Hofmeyr had outlived Smuts, would he have become Prime Minister? He had two great handicaps. One was his liberalism, which frightened and antagonised white South Africa. The other was his phenomenal childhood and boyhood, and the possessiveness of his mother. This was the second personal relationship that to such an extent ruled his life.

As a biographer-to-be I was lucky to be able to study this relationship at close quarters. I stayed many times as the guest of mother and son, and could observe with fascination the independence of Hofmeyr the cabinet minister and the dependence of Jantjie the son. Mrs. Hofmeyr was a dominating woman of implacable will, charming to her friends and relentless to her enemies and the enemies of her son. To me she was very gracious, but I knew that one wrong step would have been the end of me. Except for the members of her intimate circle of women of her own age, I never met one person who did not treat her with caution mixed with a dash of fear, not so much fear of her perhaps as fear of losing the friendship of her son.

I did not have to wait long for an answer to my letter to Mr. Hofmeyr. His fame for swift replies was immense. His custom was to keep all unanswered letters in the inside pocket of his jacket, and therefore swift reply was essential. This habit was extremely bad for the smartness of the jacket, but that did not worry him. What *did* worry him was the crime, the scandal, of unanswered letters, a strange kind of blend of quixotry and puritanism.

In his reply he advised me to apply for all the four principalships, Tokai White and Tokai Coloured, Houtpoort White and Diepkloof African. He told me I would not get Tokai White because it was intended for a man who was already a principal in the Union Education Department. As for Diepkloof African, he had been to see it himself, and he wrote, "It is hard to know what can be done with it." I therefore applied for all four principalships, hoping that I would not get Diepkloof.

Dorrie did not approve of my new aspiration. She said to me tearfully, "What do you know about reformatories? What do you know about African delinquents? Why do we have to leave Natal, where all our family and friends are? I don't want to go."

We were estranged by this event. It was the only time in our married life that she did not approve of a decision of this kind, and did not want to accompany me in it. She did not want to leave the security of Pietermaritzburg, and the countryside of her birth. She did not want to venture into the unknown world of the Cape or the Transvaal, and of reformatories and delinquents. And especially she did not want to go to Diepkloof, to a place of which a great man like Hofmeyr could say, "It is hard to know what can be done with it."

Therefore when I received a letter to inform me that I had been appointed principal of Diepkloof Reformatory, I went into the garden to hide myself, and to summon up courage to tell her. When at last I told her, she was much upset, and would not be comforted. But I was excited. At the age of thirty-two I was being given the chance of turning a prison into a school. I forgot my ambition to become headmaster of Maritzburg College, something of which Dorrie heartily approved. I went off to Diepkloof, not soberly and regretfully but almost light-heartedly, leaving Dorrie to pack and follow. A large crowd of my friends came to see me off at the railway station. I must record an act of conceit and vanity. I had bought myself a new suit and a new overcoat, befitting this up-and-coming young man who was travelling to Johannesburg to take over the biggest reformatory in the whole continent of Africa. The outfit was sober and dignified, and to it I added a pair of eye-catching yellow gloves. If someone said to me now, "That reformatory must have gone to your head," I would not be offended, but if someone had said it to me then, I would have been. It must be confessed that I held the opinion that the yellow gloves gave a touch of class. What a mixture it was, ambition, vanity, and high purpose!

So the train pulled out of Pietermaritzburg station, into the great hills to the north of the city. I stood on the open platform at the end of the coach, and as we turned and twisted there came one view after another of the lights of the town below. I stayed there until we had reached the summit of the hills, and my birthplace disappeared from sight. I knew that some great change had come over my life, even though I did not know just how great it would be. I went into the dining saloon for dinner, and sat opposite another young man who was going to a new job. It was Arthur Keppel-Jones, lecturer in history at the Natal University College, who was going to the University of the Witwatersrand. Some ten years later he was to write a prophetic book called *When Smuts Goes*. With him, as with me, the future of our country was going to become an overriding concern. If you have a high purpose, even though it is blended with ambition and vanity, you can't help it happening to you.

Chapter 18

I was met at Johannesburg Station by a remarkable man with the name of Cornelius Olivier, the senior probation officer of the city. He had been given the task of introducing this greenhorn from Natal to the reformatory and to Johannesburg, which besides being called the City of Gold was called the City of Crime. Olivier was about forty years of age and unmarried, and the possessor of a splendid tenor voice. He was completely devoted to his work, and would say of his devotion that it was no virtue, but was the result of *oversocialisation* by his parents, who in addition to having a number of children of their own, had also a number that they had adopted.

It was good luck, being met by a man like that. I took to him at once. He put me in his car and took me to see Diepkloof Reformatory. It was the first of July, 1935, and it was my first day as its head. I have suddenly remembered as I write that I was not appointed its *principal*, but its *warden*. The change in title came some months later. I was appointed at £600 per annum, which was actually £20 less than I was earning as a schoolmaster. Such is ambition.

On the way to Diepkloof, Olivier told me briefly about the reformatory. I was the warden and my next-in-command was the deputy warden. Under us was a white chief supervisor who was our executive officer, and was responsible for the carrying out of the policy of the warden. He controlled the entire supervisory staff, some forty in number. Under him was a white head supervisor who controlled some twenty white supervisors and a black head supervisor who controlled some twenty black supervisors. Directly under the warden and the deputy warden were the white chief clerk and his assistants, and the white farm manager. Under us all were four hundred African boys, drawn from every part of South Africa but mainly from Johannesburg and its satellite mining towns. There were also some twenty Indian boys who would have been far more at home at the Coloured reformatory at Tokai, to which institution they would eventually be moved.

We travelled seven miles from the City Hall of Johannesburg, along what was then the main road to Potchefstroom. From the road nothing of the reformatory was visible except the gum trees on its northern boundary. We took suddenly a small road that turned to the left, and in less than a minute we had drawn up in front of the custodial block of Diepkloof Reformatory.

It was something to see. It was a great square building, and it was built of what is called in South Africa "wood and iron." The uprights and beams were of wood, and the roof and walls were of corrugated iron, all painted in a kind of Public Works Department yellow-brown. These wood-and-iron buildings were set round the four sides of a hollow square. The one side, the one before which we had now drawn up, was used for administration. The other three sides were composed of some twenty dormitories, whose barred windows were set high in the otherwise unbroken walls. The entrance to the hollow square was a huge security gate, through the slats of which one could see through the hollow square which was called the yard.

Round this enormous building ran a thirteen-foot-high barbed wire fence, inclined at an angle towards the building. The fence was supported by great iron stanchions set in concrete, and entrance was by the outer security gate, which was set parallel to the inner gate and about ten yards from it, thus leaving a security lane that ran round the entire building. The plan of the main block was roughly as shown at the top of the next page.

When I arrived the whole reformatory came to attention. The black, uniformed warder at the outer security gate stamped and saluted, and opened the gate with a great rattling and jangling of keys. Out came Mr. J. H. Laas, the acting warden. He did not ask me for any identification, but I suppose he should have. He shook hands and escorted us through the outer gate, which was then shut with a great clang and some more jangling of keys, while to right and left other warders stamped and saluted, causing the ground to tremble.

When the first warder reported that the outer gate was shut, a second warder opened the inner gate with further rattling and jan-

DIEPKLOOF REFORMATORY MAIN BLOCK

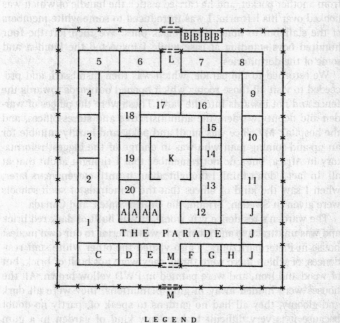

LEGEND

1–20 — Dormitories
x — Iron stanchions supporting
    security fence
A — Solitary Confinement cells
B — Hospital Isolation cells
C — Yard stores
D — Warden
E — Deputy Warden

F — Main office
G — Storeman
H — Bulk stores
J — Hospital
K — Kitchen
L-L — Gates for exit of
    dirt, sewage, etc.
M — Main gates

gling, and I entered the yard itself, where some four hundred boys were drawn up on parade in order to do homage to their most high lord. Mr. Laas introduced me to Captain Stewart-Dunkley, one-time brigade major in Poona, India, and now chief warder* of Diepkloof Reformatory. He had a tall soldierly figure and was a recent recruit, not to the old Prisons Department, but to the new Education Department. Therefore he was not in uniform but was dressed in a smart

* Later chief supervisor.

grey suit, with a white handkerchief peeping from the top outside pocket of his jacket. His accent was aristocratic, a monocle dangled from another pocket, and he carried a stick the handle of which was hooked over his left arm. I was introduced to some white members of the staff but to none of the black ones. We then left the four hundred boys standing at ease while I inspected the kitchen and some of the dormitories.

We returned to the parade, which was then dismissed, and proceeded to visit all those rooms which opened outwards towards the fence and not inwards into the yard. These were the offices of warden and deputy warden, the administrative and stores offices, and the hospital. My office was small and poky, and hardly suitable for an up-and-coming man who was in charge of the biggest reformatory in Africa, but I do not remember that I thought about that at all. In fact I don't think I thought about it until eleven years later, when I saw the kind of offices that the principals of such schools were given in Sweden, Britain, the United States, and Canada.

The warden's residence was worse. It was built of dark red brick and was unattractive and gloomy. It was inferior to our own modest house in Pietermaritzburg. I also visited the other white staff residences, of which there were three; they were not built of brick, but of wood and iron, and were painted in PWD yellow-brown. All the houses were hidden away in gum plantations, they were all dark and gloomy, they all had no gardens to speak of, partly no doubt because it is very difficult to have any kind of garden in a gum plantation.

It was therefore a surprise to see the reformatory gardens themselves, devoted to vegetables and fruit, not to flowers. They were situated on both sides of the valley of a small stream that fed a small dam. The sides of the valley were each a quarter of a mile in width, measuring from the stream, and must have been more than a quarter of a mile in length. These two slopes were terraced from top to bottom, and on these terraces were grown vegetables of every conceivable kind. It was now midwinter, and most of the terraces were bare, but a few were brilliantly green, and gave some indication of the beauty to come.

On this fertile part of the farm were two tremendous orchards, planted with various kinds of peach trees. The countryside around Johannesburg is said to grow the best peaches in the world, and I must say that I never tasted any that were better. There were also two large plantations of pines, venerable trees planted in the previous century. Our tour concluded with a visit to what in South

Africa are known as "the lands," fields which were planted every year with maize.

The last place visited was the school, which I naturally was curious to see. It had no surrounding fence, but two warders stood watch at diagonally opposite corners. They were provided with sentry boxes in case it rained. The whole reformatory went to school, in five equal detachments, one for each day of the week. There was one teacher, Mr. Ben Moloi, to carry out this impossible job. His title was head native warder, and he was responsible for the African staff. For thirteen years he was to be a pillar of strength to me. I shall go so far as to say that I could not have changed Diepkloof without him.

While it was true that the gardens and orchards were beautiful, and that the main reformatory building was stark and ugly, I must record one extraordinary fact. John Wesley, presumably quoting someone before him, placed cleanliness second to godliness. The Prisons Department places cleanliness second to security. Its buildings are almost never beautiful, but they are clean.

The inside walls of this unsightly custodial building behind its forbidding fence were being eaten away by rust; this would naturally never have been permitted to affect the outside walls, because of the need to maintain security. The yard was of earth, and the floors of the dormitory smeared with a mixture of cattle dung and earth. The sanitary arrangements were unbelievable, and I shall describe them later. The yellow-brown paint on the walls was peeling away, and the walls themselves were infested with bugs. Yet this terrible building was kept as clean as such a building could be. In fact it was the daily task, performed one day by the warden and the next by his deputy, to make a tour of inspection, looking into nooks and crannies, uttering righteous condemnation of specks of dust, demanding the opening of never-opened doors, tasting the food in the great iron pots in the kitchen, enquiring solicitously after the health of the patients in the hospital, praising and criticising, being affable and morose, lifting up and casting down. The only creatures who escaped these Olympian judgements were the bugs, which had the good sense to keep out of sight in the daytime. But occasionally a rat could be seen and its presence utterly disapproved.

So the first day of my wardenship came to an end. If I remember rightly, Corny Olivier took me back to Johannesburg thinking that I needed comfort and conviviality. Until Dorrie arrived I was to stay in the acting warden's house and have my meals with the Stewart-

Dunkleys. On the second day of July I returned to take command of this strange place that was to be converted from a prison into a school.

On this tour of the reformatory and its gardens and orchards, the most interesting historical fact was never mentioned. The simple plan of the reformatory shows B, which was a small block of four hospital cells used for the isolation of infectious diseases. In 1913 Mohandas Karamchand Gandhi, later to be known as the Mahatma, was imprisoned in one of these cells for inspiring and leading the protest march of Indians from Natal to enter another province.

Gandhi welcomed the imprisonment. He said it would give him a chance to read and study. General Smuts, the Minister of Justice, provided books for his prisoner, and Gandhi made a pair of slippers for his captor. When Gandhi was assassinated, Smuts said of him that he was a strange phenomenon, an enigmatic figure, and a prince of men. There seems to be little doubt that Gandhi finally left South Africa in 1914 believing that Smuts would make considerable improvements in the status of Indians. This, however, was not to be.

It was really surprising that no mention was made to me of Gandhi's stay at Diepkloof. The Prisons Department would undoubtedly have had some interest in Gandhi the prisoner, but they would have had none in Gandhi the emancipator or in his philosophy. For them he was just another Indian, and no doubt many members of the Prisons Department would have referred to him as a *coolie*, a word which was used much more in 1913 than it is today.

In some other country Gandhi's cell would have been preserved as a national monument. It no longer exists. Some years after I left in 1948, Dr. Verwoerd, Minister of Native Affairs, ordered the dismemberment of Diepkloof Reformatory on the grounds that it offended against the principles of ethnic separation. The beautiful farm was allocated to a housing scheme for Coloured people, but before the scheme got under way the land was handed over to the Defence Force. Its nine hundred acres, six to seven miles from the Johannesburg City Hall, must have been worth a million rands, and its strategic value, situated as it is between white Johannesburg and the great black satellite town of Soweto, must be immense. One of the results of these changes was the destruction of Gandhi's cell. It is probable that no one realised that it was one of the famous buildings of history.

I was at my post on July 2, very early in the morning, in order to see what was called the "opening of the cells." The stench that poured out of these rooms was unspeakable. For fourteen hours some twenty boys had been locked up in each of them, with one bucket full of water for drinking and another for urination and defecation. The lights had been burning all night, and in each door was a spy hole through which acts of turpitude, such as smoking, assault, sharing the same blankets, and homosexual acts, could be observed. It was a great temptation to share the blankets, quite apart from any sexual motive. The boys had two each, and slept on the earthen floor, with a night temperature that on the highveld during July was regularly below freezing point. Some of the blankets had long since worn threadbare, and all new blankets found their way into the possession of bullies, toadies, and "trusties" who worked in the clothing store.

The opening of the cells preceded the first count of the day. This business of the count was probably the most important in the entire routine of managing a custodial institution. Some twenty shivering boys paraded in front of each foul room, clad in nothing but shirt and short trousers. An iron discipline was exercised, but not the greatest disciplinarian could have stopped the boys from shivering. They were silent but the staff were not, especially the black warders in their black serge uniforms, and armed with heavy sticks. Commands and rebukes and what came close to curses filled the air, and the sound of blows could be heard, though I do not remember to have seen one on this my first working day.

After this parade the boys adjourned to the watertaps situated throughout the yard. The water was cold, and in July it was ice-cold. But there was no pretence of cleanliness during the week. On Saturday afternoon hot water was distributed in metal basins, but there was no question of a bath.

Then came breakfast, which consisted of mealie-meal porridge and black coffee. The boys collected dish and mug and spoon and filed into the kitchen for their rations. These they took back to that portion of the yard which on the plan is called the parade, and after grace they ate sitting on the ground.

After breakfast the whole reformatory, except those who had special duties, lined up on the parade ground. Each boy paraded with his own *span*, which is the Afrikaans word for "team" or "gang." Afrikaans was the language of the reformatory. Most of the white staff was Afrikaans-speaking, but in addition to that, Afrikaans was, except in Zululand, southern Natal, and the Transkei, the language of the African delinquent and the language of the African townships. It is a weird and wonderful Afrikaans, far from pure and certainly far from holy, but full of the vitality of the slums of the cities. Many vernacular languages are spoken in the African townships, but the lingua franca has become Afrikaans. This is especially true of the young, and still more true of the young delinquent, whose school has been the streets and the markets. Ten percent of the boys of Diepkloof could speak no other language.

When all the boys had paraded with their *spans,* they were counted. If the count proved correct, the two security gates were opened, this being the only time when they stood open together. As the boys marched out to their work on the reformatory farm, they were counted again. At noon they returned and were counted in. After their midday meal of beans, broken maize called *samp,* dripping, vegetables from the terraces, and meat twice a week, they had half an hour of rest, paraded, were counted, marched out, and were counted again. At four o'clock they returned and were counted in again. At four-thirty they had their evening meal of mealie-meal porridge, a stout piece of bread, and black coffee. At five o'clock evensong was held, taken by Head Teacher Moloi. The boys sang a hymn and the beauty of it, and the earnestness and innocence and reverence of those four hundred delinquent voices, captured me then and held me captive for thirteen years. I may add that it captured many others also, and sometimes visitors to the reformatory could hardly hold back their tears. Then Moloi read a short passage of scripture, and prayed briefly, after which the whole reformatory recited Our Father in Zulu. Moloi pronounced the benediction and the warden or his deputy said "Goodnight, boys" and the congregation said "Goodnight, Sir." The boys then assembled in front of their rooms, and were counted for the last time of the day. Then they were locked in with their two buckets, and the reformatory was handed over to two night warders. My first working day was over.

These countings and these locked doors, these double gates and the high security fence, the high barred windows of the rooms had one purpose and one only, and that was to prevent the boys from running away. When I went there, the boys were called *inmates,* but they were soon to be called *pupils.* The warden and his deputy were to become Principal and Vice-Principal. Moloi was to become Head Teacher, and the *warders* were to become *supervisors.* The reformatory continued to be called by that name in English, but its Afrikaans name of *verbeteringsgestig* was changed to *verbeteringskool.* Its name changed in the language of the boys too. Instead of *die tronk,* "the prison," it became known as *die skool,* "the school."

Over in Pretoria, some administrator sat down and changed all the names. Would this change of names bring about a change in the character of Diepkloof Reformatory? How could this strict custody be reconciled with an educational and reformatory purpose? How could I remain the principal of a school whose pupils were locked up for fourteen hours a day, in rooms that contained one bucket of water and one bucket for urination and defecation? Some magistrates were already telling boys, "I am not sending you to a prison, I am sending you to a school where you will learn habits of industry and cleanliness." That was very nice for the magistrate, but what about the poor fellow who had given up his promising career as a schoolmaster, and exchanged the venerable buildings of Maritzburg College for this foul place?

When I was ill with enteric fever, Dr. Croudace had said, "I wish he would stop thinking." He should have seen me now. I was thinking all the time. I was saluted and stamped at continuously. I was treated as though I were the emperor of some immense domain, majestic and omnipotent. Yet it was all a façade. Behind it sixty pairs of eyes were watching me, sixty men, some of them prison officers with many years of service, watching this young schoolmaster of thirty-two, who perhaps had never in his life seen a delinquent until now, who could not have clapped a pair of handcuffs on anybody if he had tried, who had no doubt read many books in the seclusion of his study. What did he know about crime? Did he perhaps think that *mooipraat*, "pretty talk," could change the hearts of criminals? Didn't he know that some of these boys would cut your throat for a shilling?

Some of the white prison officers had left already, having no desire to change the known for the unknown. Some had stayed, and among them was Mr. H. J. Laas, my deputy warden, who had not been a warder but a prison schoolmaster. He was a simple and upright man, a loyal subordinate, and an elder of the Nederduitse Gereformeerde Kerk, which is by far the largest of the Dutch Reformed Churches. He was in politics a Nationalist, and held the Nationalist views on apartheid and racial separation. He lived for the day when a Nationalist Government would come to power, when all the past wrongs of the Afrikaner would be righted, and when the racial policy of the Union of South Africa would approximate more nearly to the policies of the defeated republics: "no equality in Church or State." But in the best Public Service tradition he kept his political views to himself while maintaining his right to hold them. He was neither adventurous nor imaginative, and I was to lead him into deep waters. He never refused to follow me, though he did on occasions suggest that I might have taken a safer route. Soon after I arrived he asked to go on leave, and left me alone with my new estate.

Of the black staff members who stayed, all except Head Native Warder Moloi* were illiterate. They were Zulus from Zululand, there being a tradition in those days that the illiterate Zulu was the most reliable subordinate in the world. There was some truth in this, and I have no doubt that as warders they were outstanding. But many of them were to have difficulty in understanding the new and revolutionary ideas that were to be loosed upon them.

It did not take me long to understand what Mr. Hofmeyr had meant when he had written, "It is hard to know what can be done with it." It was unthinkable that the place should be left as it was. But I knew from my reading that reformers of reformatories could be broken. It was hard enough to change a white school in a white environment. But Diepkloof was a black school, and its immediate environment in those days was largely white. On our southern boundary was the white village of Comptonville, whose inhabitants were soon to hear of the mad experiment that was to be conducted on their borders.

I had come to Diepkloof believing that freedom was the supreme reformatory instrument, yet most of white South Africa believed that a reformatory was a place to which you sent troublemakers to get them out of the way for a while. *Freedom* was a sweet word, hallowed through the ages. But *escaping* or *absconding* were harsh words and they could bring a man's career to an end. If a boy absconded from Diepkloof and murdered a white woman in Comptonville, that would be bad enough. But if he absconded because he had been granted a measure of physical freedom under this new dispensation, that could be the end of me. My colleague Z. went to Houtpoort Reformatory, and under his new dispensation two boys broke into the school armoury, stole a gun, and killed a white storekeeper who resisted their entry. The effect of this on Z. himself was disastrous, for he also had believed that freedom was the supreme reformatory instrument. He had to take long leave, and at the end of it a generous department sent him to an easier job.

Was there to be a new dispensation at Diepkloof? If there were not, then what was I doing there? And if there were, and if it did not work, then I would have proved myself a fool and a failure, and would have to creep back to Natal—without the yellow gloves.

I had three assets. The one was an overwhelming determination to do something about this foul place. The second was an aptitude for wrestling with problems, an indispensable element of which is

* *Later titled Head Teacher.*

foresight. The third was a physical energy that amazes me when I look back upon it. It reached its peak at some time during the next thirteen years.

I also had two assets extraneous to myself. One was that Hofmeyr was my minister, and that he wanted a new dispensation. But Hofmeyr in his ministerial capacity was remote; my second asset was nearer at hand. His name was Professor M. C. Botha, and he was the Secretary for Union Education, the permanent and administrative head of Hofmeyr's Ministry of Education. He was the child of poor parents, and had now risen to one of the highest posts in the Public Service. He had said to me, "You're going to a hard job, and you must not hesitate to come to me if you are in trouble." He was as good as his word, but I knew that if I got into big trouble, there would be no one who could save me.

There is a last element, but I don't think I can call it an asset. It was luck. I was to have many disappointments and suffer many anxieties, but I was never struck the kind of blow from which I would never be able to recover, the kind of blow that exposes the vain ambitious young man with the high purpose as nothing more than a self-deluded fool, playing with forces the strength and nature of which he just did not understand.

Chapter 19

My first days at Diepkloof were days of exhilaration. Freedom was hardly the characteristic of this grim reformatory, but I had an extraordinary sense of it. For one thing I was no longer tied to a teaching timetable. Yet I would be down at the yard at 7:30 A.M. for the breakfast parade and for the work parade at 8:00 A.M. After the boys' work had begun I would go home for breakfast, and after that would go walking on the farm, visiting the various teams of boys and their supervisors.

The respect shown to me was excessive. This had nothing to do with my character or personality, but was paid to my office. It was in fact the tradition of prisons. When I visited a *span*, supervisor and boys would come to attention with military precision. The parade was in fact an important instrument of order and discipline, and indeed it would have been impossible to organise such a large number of boys without it. There were the breakfast and other meal parades, the work parades at 8:00 A.M. and 1:00 P.M. and the evensong parade at 5:00 P.M. The parades were in fact the events of the day, and their role was made all the more important because we had no assembly hall and no dining hall.

After this walk in the freedom of the highveld air, at a time when all my colleagues at Maritzburg College would be incarcerated in their classrooms, I would return to the main building and attend to the mail of the day, which was always tremendous, and dealt with committals, releases, relapses, probation reports, and all staff matters. At 12:00 noon the *spans* would return and at 1:00 P.M. they would all march out again. At 4:00 P.M. they would return, and I would have to deal with the problems of the day.

With few exceptions the staff members had all been members of the Prison Service, and many of them were waiting to return to it.

It was only a few days after my arrival that three new white staff members arrived to take the place of three warders who had elected to stay with the Prisons Department. These three were young men in their very early twenties, and had been members of a unit called the Special Service Battalion. Although they were in civilian clothes, they came into my office and came to attention with a deafening crash that threatened to bring down the building. Stewart-Dunkley, who clearly highly approved of this, ordered them to stand at ease, and then introduced them to their warden. So these young Afrikaners came to a job of a kind they had never dreamt of, that of being supervisors at a black reformatory, and of helping in the re-education and rehabilitation of black delinquent boys.

In 1935, the year in which I went to Diepkloof, South Africa was emerging from the Great Depression. One of the most severe effects of this had been that large numbers of scholars leaving school could find no employment, and Mr. Oswald Pirow, Minister of Defence, established the Special Service Battalion for white boys. This was to keep young white men from drifting to the towns and cities and becoming loafers and worse. It was typical of the ruling white mentality that it was not thought necessary to do the same for all other young men. The battalion was to give a military training, to prevent moral degeneration, and to keep young men off the labour market. A sergeant-major of the Grenadier Guards was brought from England to organise the military training, and instruction was therefore given in English.

All this sounds very militaristic, and it was. But if it had not been for these young sergeants and sergeants-major, and all the others from the battalion who followed them, Diepkloof Reformatory would never have been changed from a prison into a school. With few exceptions, these young men were Afrikaans-speaking. Ninety percent of the boys of the reformatory could speak Afrikaans. Ten percent of them could speak nothing else. Afrikaans therefore could be said to be the language of the reformatory. This meant that for the next thirteen years of my life I spoke more Afrikaans than English.

My idiomatic knowledge of this language, after a second sharp ascent and the reaching of a second plateau, increased at a fast pace, and this gave me considerable satisfaction. I would now be able to speak to J. H. Hofmeyr in his home language. The opportunity came when I was asked to the Hofmeyr home in Pretoria for the weekend. I brought out my Afrikaans, but each time I used it Hofmeyr responded in English. Though feeling rebuffed I persevered; it was in a way a kind of gift that I was bringing him. He determined to make an end of it, and after perhaps my fourth attempt, he gave that characteristic snort that I have described in my biography of him, and said, "You speak with a very strong Transvaal accent." I never tried it again.

The arrival of the battalion young men enabled me to do one thing, that was to forbid all shouting in the yard by members of the staff. The young men from the battalion did not find it necessary. They transformed the parades from subdued affairs interrupted only by the shouts of black warders upholding law and order to silent and orderly assemblies which on the command "Dismiss" erupted into carnivals of shouts and mad chasings by small boys. Later these carnivals were to be further enlivened by the sounds of cornet, flute, harp, sackbut, psaltery, and dulcimer. Under the Department of Prisons such instruments had been forbidden, no doubt because they could be used as weapons.

That was another thing that held me captive for thirteen years, the transition from the silent parade to the bedlam that followed it. It was almost as though four hundred boys had unanimously decided that in return for the uproarious bedlam they would offer a total silence. In thirteen years it was broken a few times, always by boys of disturbed mind. There was one exception, and that was when a magistrate committed two offenders who had not only been to prison more than once, but who were in their late twenties or their early thirties. They resented bitterly being sent to an institution for boys and made this loudly known during one of the parades. Only my undertaking to ask for a review of their sentences persuaded them to observe the silence. They asked not to be made to sleep in a dormitory, but to be allowed to occupy two of the solitary confinement cells, shown on my rough plan as A. The problem was solved when they were finally discharged "from the provisions of the Children's Act." How the magistrate ever determined that these two had not yet reached the age of twenty we never discovered, but we heard that he had said in passing judgement that because previous prison sentences had failed, it was time to try a reformatory.

I think that one of the reasons for the transformation of the parade was that our new staff members were themselves highly self-disciplined. They were also to be admired for their masculinity and their efficiency, and many of the boys did admire them for these reasons. Ex-Sergeant-major Grobler would march the whole reformatory out for drill, and all that could be heard was the sound of feet and of his voice when he gave a command. Ex-Sergeant-major Naudé became Captain Stewart-Dunkley's second in command, and he was the master of the silent yard parade. Ex-Sergeant Oosthuizen was a physical training expert, and we added that to the curriculum also.

Comparisons are odious, but the *primus inter pares* was ex-Sergeant-major Isak Engelbrecht, six foot four inches in height and proportionally built, one of the two or three matriculants, and a young man of strong character. His understanding of human motive and behaviour grew daily, and though untrained he became our psychologist. There was only one word to describe his discipline and that was "perfect." When I left Diepkloof in 1948 he was a young man in his early thirties, and he decided to take a degree and to train as a teacher. I have seen him only once in the ensuing thirty years, but I heard that he became the principal of a very large school. I would guess that the discipline there was perfect also.

It did not take me long to realise that I, and to a lesser extent my deputy warden, would be the only links between white staff and black. My young white supervisors were with few exceptions Afrikaners, and most of these were Nationalists, and therefore strong believers in apartheid. Stewart-Dunkley, the brigade major from Poona, was certainly no believer in integration. Therefore I was the principal of two staffs, one white and one black. The principal and vice-principal were superior to all, and so was Captain Stewart-Dunkley, who was now called the Chief Supervisor. The Head Teacher, Mr. Ben Moloi, was superior to all blacks, but to no whites. The greatest source of difficulty could have been those supervisors who were in charge of the *spans* that worked on the farm. Some were white and some were black, and they were, so to speak, equals, though not in salary. Yet in South African terms any white supervisor would have been regarded as superior, and would have regarded himself as superior, to any black supervisor. In all my years at Diepkloof we probably had an average of perhaps two cases a year where a white supervisor complained to the Principal about a black supervisor, or a black about a white. The complaints were invariably of "insolence" on the part of the black and of "insulting behaviour" on the part of the white. A white man could not be "insolent" to a black; he could only be "insulting." The same distinction was made in Afrikaans; a white man and black man could be *beledigend* towards each other, but in addition the black man could be *astrant* or *parmantig* towards the white.

The colour-bar has strongly influenced the Afrikaans language, and to some extent South African English also. A white girl is a *meisie*, a black girl is a *meid*. A white boy is a *seun*, a black boy is a *jong*. I started to use the word *seun* of the reformatory pupil, and not long after the Education Department, in its statistical returns, did the same. However, I made no rule about it, and I was astonished to hear Engelbrecht, in one of our staff meetings, use the word *seun*. Slowly some staff members came to use it, but some could not. It would be hard to explain to a non–South African that for many Afrikaners it would be psychologically almost impossible to use the word *seun* of a black boy.

A black boy would not use the Afrikaans word for "you" to a white man, and sometimes not to a white boy. There are two forms of "you," the respectful *u* and the colloquial *jy*, but they are not used. The black boy would say, *"Meneer, I am asking Meneer if Meneer will lend me a pencil."* It would also have been unusual for a black man to address a white man except in this indirect way.

This is not entirely a matter of white and black. Mr. Laas would address me as *u*, but most white staff members would use the indirect method. What is more, most white children would address any older person, even their own parents, by the indirect method. I might add that for thirteen years I had the utmost difficulty in bringing myself to address Mr. Laas as *jy*.

One word I would not allow, and that was the word "kaffir," in English, or *kaffer* in Afrikaans. Today, thirty years later, it has come to be regarded as an insult, and very recently a judge has awarded damages to a black man addressed as *kaffer*. Equally insulting are "coolie," or *koelie*, used of an Indian, and "tottie," or *hotnot*, used of a Coloured person of mixed race. In 1940 the polite word for a black man was "native," or *naturel*, but a few years later it was replaced by the official word "Bantu," or *Bantoe*, which is a plural noun meaning "people." But because white people cannot be expected to know African nouns, one speaks officially of "a Bantu," and of "two Bantu." African people resent the use of "Bantu," strongly insisting that it means "people" and not "black people." Today African people want to be called "blacks," a word that in 1948 would have been regarded as derogatory. And today there are Indian and Coloured people, who in a revulsion against white domination wish to be called blacks also. As I write this, the Government has announced its decision to use the words "black" and "blacks."

I must record that I did not try to change overnight the racial practices of South Africa. If I had tried to do so, I would never have been able to perform the task of turning a prison into a school. For example, I held two staff meetings, one for whites and one for blacks, and a third and special kind of staff meeting for senior whites and blacks. My first tactical error was made in ignorance. An itinerant photographer wanted to take a staff picture, and I assembled the entire staff, with the white members in front and the black members behind. I think the whole thing might have passed off reasonably well had I not invited the two African laundry workers, wives of black teachers and in fact themselves teachers, to join the group. They were placed well away from any possibility of physical contact, but their presence was an offence to some. I was made aware of this by the photographer himself, who told me that many of the staff members refused to buy the picture.

The white staff view was put to me by Mr. James Barry, who had arrived to take on the newly created post of Farm Manager. He was what is called a "red-hot Nationalist." He was a big shambling man, with a high voice and not a great intelligence. He accepted the surname Barry because it had been hallowed by General James Barry Munnik Hertzog, the creator of the National Party and Prime Minister from 1924 to 1933. But for some reason he did not feel the same about the name "James," and Afrikanerised it by calling himself "Ya-mus." I heard staff members poking fun at this, and I never heard any of them commend it. Mr. Barry also rejected the English pronunciation of place names, such as the name of the Cape province town of George; he gutteralised both "g"s and called it "Georg." He explained to me that it was impossible for any decent Afrikaner to have the photograph of a black woman in the house, and that was why so few had bought it. I told him that never again would such a photograph be taken, and this satisfied him, because he did not know that I had also decided never to have any other kind of photograph taken.

I offended Mr. Barry on yet another occasion. He was a typical white boss, and if he called a black boy, he expected him to come running. What is more, he could not stop shouting. He was quite incapable of issuing a quiet command. On one occasion I said to him sharply in Afrikaans, "Do you never say please or thank you?" It was not long after this that I heard that he had been deeply affronted by this. I think it was bad enough for him to be expected to say "please" and "thank you" to any black person, but to be expected to say it to a *delinquent* black boy, who was putting the State to enormous expense, was intolerable.

At last my behaviour as principal became so obnoxious to him that he took his stories of the reformatory to Dr. Hendrik Verwoerd, who was then the formidable editor of the "red-hot" newspaper, *Die Transvaler*, and was later to become the formidable Prime Minister who was to refashion the whole of South Africa according to the immutable doctrines of race separation. I guessed that it was Mr. Barry's work as soon as I read Dr. Verwoerd's editorial entitled *Diepkloof wysheid*, which is "Diepkloof wisdom." I shall tell later how I recoiled when I first saw the editorial, with its boundless contempt for all the *vertroeteling*, the "pampering" of the new principal, who thought you could reform criminals with sweets and softsoap. But the most striking passage of all described Diepkloof as a place where you said "please" and "thank you" to the black ladies and gentlemen who loafed about the farm. So Dr. Verwoerd revealed—intentionally or not I do not know—his attitude to black people, an attitude which became enshrined in one draconian law after another. Amid the adulatory cries of his followers, he constructed for them a prison from which now many of them cannot escape. To use another metaphor, he set them digging for themselves a grave so deep that it is doubtful whether they will ever be able to get out of it. In his obsession to preserve the identity of the Afrikaner, he gave him a security which is now seen to be the security of chains and fetters. It was the security of apartheid, which having done so much to destroy the happiness of black people, is now slowly and surely destroying the happiness of whites as well.

I was given one more example of Mr. Barry's intense nationalism, and of the difficulty of assuaging wounded feelings by words of reason. Every six months or so all the worn-out and obsolete items of stock of the reformatory were assembled, to be condemned by a member of the Board of Management, after which they could be written off the books. Mr. Barry had assembled a collection of farm implements some of which must have dated back to the beginning of the century. Mr. A. S. Andreassen, who had come out to inspect the items, said to me in a jocular way, "These should be sent to the Africana museum."

After Mr. Andreassen had gone, Mr. Barry stormed into my office. He was beside himself. He told me that the visiting member had insulted the Afrikaner nation, and that the white staff was seething with rage. The implements which were obsolete and useless were considered by the visiting member to be fit only for an Afrikaner museum. I explained that the word used was "Africana," not "Afrikaner," and that there was an Africana Museum in the public library in Johannesburg, not intended specifically for Afrikaner items, but for anything pertaining to the continent of Africa. I took a piece of paper and printed clearly on it the word "Africana." I could see that Mr. Barry either did not believe a word or that he was too enraged to listen to reason, and I assembled the white staff at the close of work to explain that no insult had been given or intended. Those were inflammable times, because the hundredth anniversary of the Great Trek was approaching.

Mr. Barry's attempt to make himself the spokesman of the Afrikaners at Diepkloof, and to exploit his acquaintance with the powerful Dr. Verwoerd, came luckily for me to a sudden end. He and I had Chevrolets of similar colour, and one day I climbed into his car by mistake, to find myself face to face with a very large milk can, the property of the Union Education Department. I invited Chief Supervisor Stewart-Dunkley to inspect the can, and to ask Mr. Barry to come to my office. This instruction he carried out with unconcealed pleasure, for although he was not anti-Afrikaner, he had found Mr. Barry's Afrikaner zeal a bit too much.

Mr. Barry did not have much time to think up a story, and he told me blandly that all he was doing was advertising the quality of Diepkloof milk to his neighbourhood, and making known the immensely valuable rehabilitative work that was being done at the reformatory. "I do not need to tell you, *Meneer*, that many people think that delinquents should be treated severely, especially if they are black."

Whether he meant me to believe this story, or whether he knew very well I did not, I do not know. But with the memory of the *black ladies and gentlemen* fresh in my mind, I said to him coldly, "I shall report your efforts to the department; I think they will be interested." The next morning it was a very chastened Farm Manager who reported for work, and he was accompanied by his wife, a very nice-looking woman. She was presented to me by Stewart-Dunkley, and when he left us alone she said to me, "You must not be hard on my husband. He is a simple-minded man, and he gets these storms. If he loses this job he will not easily get another, so you must be merciful." Before such words I am defenceless, and not just because they were spoken by a nice-looking woman who had appointed herself the protectress of a simple-minded man. I said to her, not grandly, but indeed quite simply, "Mrs. Barry, the matter is finished."

This little affair added to my status as principal. Mr. Barry became a faithful servant, and in fact confided to me that he was not an extreme Nationalist. He was a Freemason, and the Nationalist Party and especially the secret Afrikaner society known as the Broederbond frowned on Freemasonry for the simple reason that it permitted a loyalty outside the rigid frame of Afrikanerdom. But he was a weak man, and again got caught up in 1939 in the fierce antiwar feelings of many Afrikaners who resented bitterly General Smuts's action of taking South Africa to war on the side of Britain, especially as Smuts had done it once before, in 1914.

I have mentioned ex-Sergeant-major Naudé, who presided with unchallengeable authority over the yard parades. I offended him too. I started a Zulu class at my house, and our teacher was Head Teacher Ben Moloi. During the class tea was brought in, and Naudé being a young man of manners drank it, but he never came to a Zulu class again. He did not object to being taught by a black man, but he objected to drinking tea with him. I close this story by adding that Naudé was a young man of erect bearing, of great but unassertive dignity, of upright character, and was held in great respect by the four hundred members of his silent parades.

One of my earlier official acts was to raise the status of Head Native Warder Moloi. It was some time before he was appointed to a new post called Head Teacher, and was given a substantial increase in salary. When I arrived at Diepkloof, any white warder who required boys for any task simply went to the school and took as many as he wanted. His only obligation was to sign for the number taken. One of my first instructions was that no one except the warden or his deputy would have the power to do this. Under the regime of the Prisons Department, Moloi was accorded a certain amount of recognition in that the white staff called him Teacher Ben. So he remained for the thirteen years of my principalship. It was to be another quarter of a century before the Government authorised the use of the titles Mr., Mrs., *Meneer,* and *Mevrou* in addressing black people, but that was only in official correspondence. Up till then white officials had used such evasions as "Greetings!" or "Friend," or later still *"Mnumzana."* There is nothing wrong with the word *mnumzana* but its use is also an evasion if the rest of the letter proceeds in English or Afrikaans. In speech the titles were not so polite; they were "boy," "girl," "John," "Elizabeth," or plain "You." White speakers of African languages were able to use African titles, and thus avoid giving offence. I may add that at long last the use of the words "boy" and "girl" as forms of address is going out, though not so fast as it might be. And I shall add also that the average Afrikaner found it much easier to use towards black men the titles of "Doctor," "Professor," and "Reverend" than the title of "Mr."

I shall conclude this chapter with an account of my first important reform, which, however, I would not have been able to make had I not had permission from above, by which I mean not Heaven, but Pretoria.

This first reform was introduced on my first Thursday afternoon. I returned from lunch to find about two hundred boys lined up outside my office. I asked Stewart-Dunkley what was going on, and he told me it was Offences Day. Each of these boys was to be brought before me, charged, and tried. Evidence would be led, and I would have to pronounce him guilty or not guilty, and if he was guilty I would pronounce sentence. This sentence would then be written up in an enormous book.

"But what have they been doing?" I asked.

Stewart-Dunkley smiled in his inimitable way, which gave his face a look of incredible but very cultured cunning. "Sir," he said, "sodomy, indecency, insolence, use of bad language, assault, smoking of dagga, smoking of tobacco."

His eyes twinkled as he recited this account of human depravity. He had a slight dent in his forehead and this made him look more cunning than ever. He was a man of the world, confident and assured, and of course an Englishman at a time when the British Commonwealth was at or about its prime. Of struggle, aspiration, poetry he knew nothing. Yet he had something, that indefinable quality that characterised the Englishmen of those times who had had the luck to be born into the upper or upper-middle classes.

"It seems a serious list," I said.

"It's not so serious, Sir," he said. "Most of them are up for smoking tobacco."

"How many?" I asked.

He ran his eye down the line.

"About one hundred and eighty," he said.

"And I have to sit here the whole afternoon and try them? Have you got witnesses?"

"Sir, in some cases yes. But in most cases the witness is the supervisor who caught them."

"And when do we finish?"

"Sometimes we finish before the afternoon is out. Sometimes we resume on Friday."

"And all this time these boys are withdrawn from work?"

"Yes, Sir."

He was totally unmoved. He had not made the system. Like a good British soldier he wanted to do and die but would not reason why.

"We shall have to wait a bit," I said. "I am going to ring Pretoria."

It was my good luck to get my boss, Professor M. C. Botha, on the phone.

"You told me to ring you if I was in trouble," I said.

"Well, what's the trouble?" he asked.

And so I told him.

"You told me to change this place," I said, "and I shall spend today and part of tomorrow deciding the guilt of one hundred and eighty boys who are charged with smoking tobacco. And I shall do this every week."

"You can issue tobacco tomorrow," he said.

I wanted to tell him he was a genius, but it did not seem proper. I thanked him and called in Stewart-Dunkley.

"Tobacco smoking is no longer an offence," I said. "You may dismiss all those who are charged with it. Tomorrow you and I shall discuss the conditions under which we shall issue tobacco. You will please see Mr. Kruger and arrange with him to order it. Nobody under the age of sixteen will be allowed to smoke it. I shall ask the department if we may issue sweets to the small boys. There will be one strict rule and that is that no boy will be allowed to smoke during working hours."

Stewart-Dunkley looked at me with what might have been a glint of respect in his eyes. That night at evensong I announced that the smoking of tobacco would cease to be an offence, and that an issue of tobacco would be made as soon as possible. The next event was monstrous and unprecedented. The whole reformatory broke out into a storm of cheering. Naudé, stern and unsmiling, looked to me for instruction. I nodded, and he struck the hanging iron rod that served as a bell. The noise stopped almost instantly, and we proceeded to our religious observances.

When I said goodnight and the boys went to their rooms to be counted, I was aware that something had changed somewhere, perhaps only in myself. It seemed to me that many of the boys looked at us out of new eyes, almost as though they were astonished to find that we were human. That day also had lasting consequences for myself. After that I never again smoked in working hours.

The lifting of the ban on tobacco smoking was perhaps in itself not a great reform. There was still the challenge of those foul-smelling dormitories. There was still the proposition which seemed to be unassailable that you can't train boys for freedom in an atmosphere of detention. There was the hardest question of all—would it be safe to create conditions of freedom?

All I can say is that the minor reform of lifting the ban on smoking prepared the way for others more dangerous and difficult. For the first time I began to feel that my hope would be confirmed, that amongst these four hundred young offenders there was a willingness to give a reasonable obedience to a reasonable authority.

What luck I had to have Professor M. C. Botha as my boss!

Chapter 20

What must be done next? I thought about it night and day. How do you open up those foul-smelling rooms?

Of those four hundred boys, one hundred were children. The youngest was nine. A boy could commit a crime at the age of seven, but we had no seven- or eight-year-olds. The offences of these children were trivial. They should never have been there at all. They had pilfered from shops and fruit stalls and at the markets. One of them had been so foolish as to steal a tin of jam from the pantry of the magistrate's wife. Most of them were children in need of care, but what was to be done with them? There were no industrial schools for black boys, no orphanages, no hostels. In fact in 1935 J. L. Hardy and M. W. Richards of Johannesburg were planning the first hostel for black delinquent boys.

The offences of the three hundred older boys were of every kind. Some of these boys were also petty pilferers, and constituted no real danger to society. Some had committed murder, for reasons of passion or after a quarrel, especially a quarrel during a gambling session, or because of a girl. Some had committed rape, but some of these rapes were not really rapes at all, or had been committed under provocation. Some had raped white girls, and this in South Africa was considered a most serious offence. Some had stolen or killed cattle or sheep, and if these had been the property of a white farmer, the offence was also considered most serious. But the really dangerous offenders were those who would not hesitate to kill for material gain, or to kill anyone who interrupted them in the robbery of a warehouse or shop. There were probably fifty boys who belonged to this dangerous category.

These hundred small boys had a humanising effect on this grim place. Some of them if I came near them on the parade would be conscious that the great *meneer* had taken notice of their existence. They would observe me watchfully, not directly or fully, but obliquely and secretly. Sometimes I would surprise them at it and make some small sign of recognition, which would satisfy them so that they would cease to observe me, and would give their full attention to the parade.

Sometimes I would stand still by one of them, usually one of the very smallest. He would look straight in front of him with a little frown of concentration that expressed both childish awareness of my nearness and manly indifference to it. Sometimes I would tweak his ear, and he would give me a brief smile of acknowledgement, and frown with still greater concentration. It was as though I had tweaked the ear of the whole reformatory. These small outward expressions of affection were taken as symbolic, and many of the other older boys would take themselves to be included. These were the irrefutable proofs that the aim of the reformatory was not punitive. But quite apart from that, they were to many the only signs of affection they had ever known.

Would these small boys run away from me? It seemed unlikely. Then why not open up their rooms? But where would they perform the natural functions? Would the buckets have to be left in the open rooms?

The department came to my aid. I was to be allowed to build a bucket latrine with eight units. Within the week the contractor was there and we decided to build the latrine in the rear exit passage shown on the plan on page 141 as L-L. Hardly had the contractor left the reformatory when another arrived with an order to build a latrine with eight units. We decided to build this second latrine onto the first and now had a magnificent latrine with sixteen units. This second contractor had hardly gone when the PWD inspector arrived.

"Who gave you permission to build a second latrine?"

"Nobody. The second contractor told me he had been instructed to build a latrine."

"Why didn't you stop him?"

"You must understand," I said, "that I have no authority to interfere with contractors."

"There'll be hell to pay," he said.

But there was no hell to pay. Dear Miss Chattey, Inspector of Hygiene and Domestic Science, ridiculed the idea of eight buckets for four hundred boys. She was also part of my luck. It was she who revolutionised the diet, abolished the prison caps, introduced jerseys and sandals, devised special diets for the hospital and those who had come in suffering from deficiency diseases. She abolished the washing of clothes on stony slabs, and introduced the laundry, and a personal ration of soap. We had many departmental inspectors, but none did more than Miss Chattey to show my staff that the Union Department of Education meant business, and that there was no place in the department for any person who disapproved of the new policies.

So now we were no longer totally dependent on those unspeakable buckets that often overflowed nightly on the earth floors, impregnating them with a smell that it was impossible to eradicate. On a Friday the first dormitory of small boys, shown on the plan as No. 11, was left open after the evening count. For seven nights they had the monopoly of the freedom of the yard. If there had been more than twenty of them the noise would have been indescribable. They laughed and shouted and chased one another round the yard. At ten minutes to nine o'clock the warning bell was struck. At nine o'clock the bell was struck again and every boy had to return to his room. This was also the time for individual evening prayers; how many said them I do not know, but the sound of them was audible, like a great hum throughout the yard. At five minutes past nine the silence bell was struck, and the silence was absolute, for the promise had been made at evensong that if this new freedom was respected, it would be extended throughout the yard. It was again the offering of a total silence in return for a gift. Is the modern young offender so generous? So amenable? The answer is I do not know.

It was easy to open five dormitories of small boys who had stolen sweets and fruit and bicycles, many of whom had frequented the markets of Pretoria and Johannesburg and Durban and Bloemfontein trying to make both an honest and a dishonest penny. Like small boys in their circumstances in any part of the world, they were as smart as monkeys, full of tricks, plausible, and some of them very attractive. Yet if left alone, most of them would graduate further in the university of crime, passing on from petty theft to breaking in and robbery, and some of these would finally commit murder, not the honest murder of passion, but the worst crime of all, murder for material gain, usually of some person unknown except as the possessor of desired goods. And worst of all no doubt the murder of some person well known, even a father or a mother, for these desired goods, a terrible account of which is given in my story "The Waste Land."

One thing was certain. One could not open five dormitories of small boys and hope to stop at that. After that the opening of the dormitories depended no longer on age, because it was only the young who had been separated from the rest. Therefore from now on I would be giving the freedom of the yard to boys and young men some of whom were experienced in breaking in and therefore might not hesitate to try their hands at breaking out, some of whom indeed might not hesitate to attack or kill an unarmed night supervisor who stood between them and freedom. The yard was by no means absolutely secure against breaking out. It was reasonably so, because the Prisons Department tried to foresee every such eventuality. But if the night supervisors had been overpowered, it would have been possible for determined boys either to seize from them the keys of the main gate, or with the assistance of one's mates to scale the walls. This would have been a self-sacrificing act on the part of those lower down, for they would not have been able to escape themselves. In any event the successful ones would have had to surmount the obstacle of the thirteen-foot barbed wire fence, inclined inwards to make climbing almost impossible. It was the final precaution to keep wire cutters and such tools in a special cupboard which could not be locked at four o'clock until every item was hanging in its place.

Some of the staff members wanted a siren installed, but I resisted it strongly, and decided to stick to the police whistles. I was sure that the sounding of a siren would itself create a kind of feverish situation, with unforeseen consequences. It was also a matter of pride, for if we were in difficulties, I would not want the people of Comptonville to know about it. The sensitiveness of the reforming principal to public opinion is a recurrent theme in reformatory literature. What was more, there were members of the white staff who would not have hesitated to take tales to Comptonville. The new members of the white staff were not all young men from the Special Service Battalion. Many of them were of farming stock, and had been forced out of agriculture by the continually decreasing sizes of the farms, caused by the ancient custom by which the owner was obliged to divide his land equally among the members of his family. These supervisors were on the whole antagonistic or indifferent to the Diepkloof experiment; white farmers, and there are of course exceptions, do not in general concern themselves for anything more than the material welfare of black people, let alone the welfare of delinquent black boys. On the other hand the young men from the battalion, though most of them also were of farming stock, were energetic and ambitious, and had acquired through their own training the appetite for training others, and they naturally enjoyed occupying positions of authority and responsibility.

In August 1935 Dorrie and David arrived at Diepkloof. Dorrie came to the miserable small dark house allotted to the principal, and she didn't like it, but she didn't say so. She came because it was her duty to follow her husband, who for some reason had given up the sweet life of Pietermaritzburg and the college, and had come to this barred and alien and forbidding place. But her protest had been made and now she was done with it.

She entered into the life of the reformatory with zest. With all its forbiddingness it was an exciting place, always lively, sometimes turbulent. She could not speak Afrikaans, but the young Afrikaners did not hold it against her. When she got to know them she treated them as she once had treated me, with that urchin-like mischievousness. We entertained some of them at dinner every week, and after dinner we played bridge or monopoly, which was then at the height of its popularity. It was now almost spring, and there was great activity on the terraces of the vegetable gardens, and Dorrie took her small son there regularly on their walks. The semimilitary parades led by ex-Sergeant-major Grobler were always dramatic spectacles. I would not be able fully to explain the extraordinary fascination that this highly disciplined activity had for these wayward children of the black townships. It must have satisfied something very deep in them, for their response was total. Naudé, who was a man of few words, said to me, "It's as good as the Special Service Battalion." This must be regarded as praise indeed.

I well remember the day when we first discussed the possibility of parading the whole reformatory outside the security of the barbed wire fence. Mr. Laas kept silent; it was a proposition wholly outside his ken. Grobler was emphatic that nothing would go wrong, and in this he was supported by all those young ex-battalion men who assisted with the drill. Head Teacher Moloi and Chief Supervisor Stewart-Dunkley were not opposed, but were prepared to leave it to me. So I decided, not without some twinges of anxiety, to hold a parade on the open ground in front of the main building. We invited Major Maynard Page, Chief Magistrate of Johannesburg and Chairman of the Diepkloof Reformatory Board of Management, to be the guest of honour and to take the salute. I explained to the boys the significance and dignity of such an occasion, but did not mention the twinges of anxiety. Four hundred boys marched out, and four hundred boys marched in. It was another step forward, and we all knew it.

It was with greater confidence that we opened the sixth dormitory, and then the seventh, and then the eighth. It was at this point that I reached a crisis in my private life. I shall not find much pleasure in writing about it, but there can be no excuse for not doing so, for I have done it already in *For You Departed*. William Plomer in one of his autobiographies made a fascinating remark; he wrote, "I never feel that candour is a constant necessity." I do not quite share this feeling. From a literary point of view there is only one kind of candour that is not permissible, and that is boring candour; and from a moral point of view, the only kind that is not permissible is that which does harm to others. There is no fear of that now. And indeed a little more candour from William Plomer could have done no harm at all. I had a great liking for this quiet, industrious, gifted man, but his extreme reticence about his sexual life was often exasperating, especially as his last autobiography was written in the "seventies," at a time when public attitudes to homosexuality were far less harsh than they had been in the days of E. M. Forster.

Joan Montgomery was the daughter of one of Dorrie's friends. She was nineteen years old, a student at the Natal University College, and was training to be a teacher. The University College opening term began in March, but student teachers had to teach during the month of February. Joan was appointed to a school in Pietermaritzburg, and because the university residences did not open till March, she came to live with us for the month of February. She was very beautiful, and her name was not Joan Montgomery.

When I left Pietermaritzburg to go to Diepkloof at the end of June, we were in love with each other, though not one word had been said on the subject. In August she came with a students' hockey team to the Transvaal, and came to stay with us at Diepkloof. I would take her into Johannesburg in the mornings, and go to fetch her in the afternoon or evenings. It was on one of these return journeys that we admitted our love for each other. We did not discuss the consequence of this event. When she returned to Pietermaritzburg we wrote every day to each other, and I found a reason to go down to Natal for a long weekend. We became lovers.

It was soon after this weekend that Dorrie suddenly said to me,

"Are you in love with Joan?" and I said, "Yes." She said, "What are you going to do about it?" and I said, "Stop it." She said, "Surely she must be consulted about it," and I said, "We have already spoken about it." Then I said to her, "I ask only one thing, and that is to go down to Natal and say good-bye to her," to which she replied, "I am willing that you should." Sometime later she said to me, "What did I do wrong?" But I cannot remember what I answered, or if I answered at all.

I arranged with the department to take a few days' leave, and I handed over the reformatory to my deputy warden. Then I drove along the four hundred miles to Pietermaritzburg. It was both relief and pain to say good-bye to each other. I watched her for the last time open the gate of the house where she stayed, and walk up the path, and let herself in at the door. She turned and gave, hardly a wave, but something more like a sad salute. So it came to an end. It was a brief encounter, but I dreamed about her two or three times a year till the year that she died, and on occasions I still do, though it all happened forty years ago. She was in her early fifties when she died, with a devoted husband and children.

I did not think of her often in those later years, unless something happened to remind me of her. Then suddenly, out of the deep depths of wherever it is that such things lie, comes in sleep this memory of the past, strange and surrealistic like the scene in "Wild Strawberries" that I shall never forget, of the old man who visits the scene of his first love, yet it evokes in me an emotion so strong that it leaves me disturbed for a while.

I knew more clearly than Joan what was happening, and I should have drawn back from it but I did not. Was it because she was young and beautiful? Or was I taking some revenge, or giving myself some reparation? But whatever I had done, I had no wish to lie or temporise when Dorrie asked me her question. When I answered it so unequivocally, was I just being honest or did I wish to hurt her? I don't know the answers to these questions.

Before I close the story of this event, let me now confess that many years later I transgressed again. But I have decided not to relate the story of it. Perhaps, only a few pages after criticising William Plomer, I have come round to his view that candour is not a constant necessity.

The day after I had said good-bye to Joan, I drove back the four hundred miles to Johannesburg, subdued and quiet. Dorrie met me at the door of the house, and took me into her arms in that strange fierce way she had when she meant something intensely, and held back her head so that I could see the earnestness in her face, and said to me, "I am going to make it all up to you."

I cannot remember when I first noticed that she was no longer wearing her first wedding ring, but that night when we went to bed it had gone from her finger.

That was the beginning of our Diepkloof life, thirteen years of disappointment and achievement, of failure and success, of labours prodigious and now almost unbelievable. Dorrie's resentment against Diepkloof, and the way it had interrupted the sweet tenor of her life, disappeared completely. We were later to embark together on still another dangerous adventure, but she never again showed that reluctance to take a new road and to leave the old. Our son David was now five years old, and his companions were the small boys of the reformatory. He was given a *span* of his own, and marched it in and out of the gate. By that time the small boys were allowed to spend the afternoon in play. Our second son, Jonathan, who was born nine months after our emotional crisis, actually grew up at the reformatory, and the playmates of his later childhood were also the small boys. In fact the reformatory was our home and our life.

Those thirteen years at Diepkloof were among the happiest of our life. I remember what Francis of Assisi wrote in his will, he whose life was utterly changed when some tremendous compulsion drove out his fear, and he came down from his horse to embrace a leper in that road on the Umbrian plain. He wrote,

The Lord Himself led me amongst them, and I showed mercy to them, and when I left them, what had seemed bitter to me was changed into sweetness of body and soul.

That was true of Diepkloof and ourselves.

I must record that with the coming of the Children's Act, and the placing of young offenders in the care of the Union Department of Education, magistrates were beginning to make greater and greater use of the reformatories. Diepkloof grew from four hundred boys to five hundred, then to six hundred, then to seven hundred. This had an important consequence: the department was forced to consider new buildings, and these were to be of a kind very different from the big custodial block in its faded yellow-brown paint. But of that in due course.

The steady growth of Diepkloof gave satisfaction to its enemies. This growth was a clear result of the *vertroeteling*, the "pampering," the issue of tobacco, the opening of the dormitories. The word had gone out, to the boys of the slums and markets of Johannesburg and Pretoria and Durban and Capetown, that crime now really paid, and they were eagerly committing crimes in order to get into these new reformatories. There were even a few members of my own staff who believed it too.

The morning after my return I went to the reformatory block to be present at the morning parade. My deputy warden met me with a solemn face and told me he had closed all the open dormitories while I was away. He said that he had not felt able to bear the responsibility of having 160 boys free in the yard.

Was he giving me notice that he could no longer support my policies? Or was he, after half a lifetime spent in the Prison Service, with its discipline and its rigidity, unable to adapt himself to this programme of change and experiment? Or was he just plain afraid? I think it was the last two, not the first. After half a lifetime in the Prison Service, you do not tell your chief that you cannot support his policies.

Because I thought he was afraid, I did not reproach him. Instead I took a step which in retrospect seems to me to have been extraordinary. I gave orders that every dormitory should be opened that night. I realised that this was in a way a rebuke to the deputy warden. However, I had a job and a responsibility, and I suppose an ambition too, and I knew it was make or break with me. If it didn't work I would be broken.

I spent the first hours of the evening in the yard, amidst a noise indescribable, of laughter, shouting, singing, and the first crop of dulcimers. I made several rounds of the yard, being greeted on all sides with the Afrikaans, *"Goeie naand, meneer,"* "Good evening, sir." When the last bell was struck at five minutes past nine, the silence was absolute. It was again the gift being given for the gift.

As I write these words, I find my eyes are wet. Why did it happen that way? I just don't know. How was I to know that four hundred boys, of whom at least a hundred would become the hardened occupants of prisons, and some of whom had no regard for human life at all, would in return for this gift of an open dormitory observe this total silence? It was a popular reformatory theory of course, that if you treat prisoners well, they'll treat you well too. But it was a theory pooh-poohed by all the realists; the only thing to do with a prisoner was to trust him no further than you could throw him.

Within a few weeks of the opening of the dormitories, typhoid, which had been the scourge of the reformatory and the cause of many deaths, almost completely disappeared. This was because the latrine buckets were no longer needed in the rooms. The opening had one other consequence. My deputy warden, who was soon to become my vice-principal, and who was a quiet and shy man, became even more quiet and shy. I realised that I had wounded him by my reversal, and total reversal, of his decision to close the dormitories. I realised too that I could no longer rely on him to carry out any plan that involved change and risk. I must in the future rely on my young Afrikaner supervisors and my African teachers. So I put him in charge of all the records of the reformatory, and gave him the task of admitting all newcomers, opening their files, telling them what the reformatory was all about, allotting each to his dormitory and his work *span*, supervising the school, sharing the rounds of inspection with me, and preparing all boys for release. There was one other duty that he could not evade performing, and that was to take over the control of the reformatory when I was not there. All these duties he performed faithfully, and never again did he reverse any change that had been made in the policies of the reformatory.

I must also add that I treated him with the most careful consideration. I would have thought a dozen times before countermanding any order that he had given in my absence. I never discussed him with any member of my staff, nor I am sure would he have discussed me either. Yet there were times when I resented having to accept a prisons man as my chief collaborator.

In fact my two main co-architects in the rebuilding of Diepkloof were Moloi and Engelbrecht. I should have had a third, and he should have been Chief Supervisor Stewart-Dunkley. He, however, had no interest in education; his job was discipline. I resented his presence more than I did that of Mr. Laas. He had been given this job by a very powerful man in the department, Dr. van Schalkwyk. He was an expert on children but couldn't stand them at any price. He angered me on the occasion when I invited him to take the salute at one of our ceremonial parades by coming onto the parade ground smoking. He was one of the most insensitive men I ever knew, and here he was occupying a very high post in a department that dealt with children and education.

I resented the fact that though the department had appointed me as warden, it had given me no say in the selection of my senior colleagues. One was a prisons man, and the second was an army officer. Later on I discovered that it didn't matter. Engelbrecht was a man in a thousand, and so was Moloi. Both were heart and soul in the new adventure. My vice-principal could look after the records and the admissions, and Stewart-Dunkley could look after the discipline while Engelbrecht and Moloi and I, with much support from our juniors, would change the reformatory.

My impatience with Stewart-Dunkley reached a climax which now seems very funny but did not seem so then. When I decided to open up all the dormitories on the first day of my return, he looked at me with that incredible cunning which did not really exist at all, but the look of which was created only by the dent in his forehead. To me he appeared the incarnation of that upper-middle-class English superiority which in those days angered white South Africans and especially Afrikaners. In addition to that, the dent in his forehead gave him a look of knowing cynicism, of contempt for the unpractical ideas of theoretical reformers. Our conversation went something like this:

SELF *(goaded)*: I suppose you think it is foolish.

STEWART-DUNKLEY *(smug, proper, infinitely wise)*: Sir, it is not my place to criticise the orders of my commanding officer.

Then, or some time later, frustrated to explosion point, I repaired to the staff lavatory—the white staff lavatory—at the rear of the main block, but outside the fence. There I wrote on the immaculately whitewashed wall, with what instrument I don't remember, the words "To hell with Stewart-Dunkley."

It was that day or the next that he came to me, his face full of high duty.

STEWART-DUNKLEY *(pained)*: Sir, I have an unpleasant matter to report.

SELF *(innocent)*: What's that, Captain?

STEWART-DUNKLEY: Sir, some person has written on the wall of the staff lavatory the words "To hell with Stewart-Dunkley."

SELF *(very grave)*: Have you any idea who is responsible?

STEWART-DUNKLEY: No sir, I have not.

SELF *(very emphatic)*: Captain, I take the gravest view of the matter. Take any measures you wish to find who is the culprit. And if you find him he will be dealt with severely, both by me and by the department.

STEWART-DUNKLEY *(satisfied, as indeed he had to be)*: Sir, I am gratified that you take the matter so seriously.

SELF *(with a cunning of my own)*: Captain, the health of the reformatory depends on its discipline, and that applies just as much to staff as to boys.

STEWART-DUNKLEY: Thank you, sir.

The culprit was not discovered. Not till more than forty years later has his identity been revealed. The Captain never knew (at least I hope not) who had committed this act of gross insubordination. He has now passed on to a service higher than that of the British Army in Poona. Whether he knows now, or whether he knew at the very moment of his promotion, I do not venture to state. That was the second and last time in my life that I wrote on a lavatory wall. The first had a painful consequence. The second had a useful one; it gave me courage to go on.

Another question was engaging my mind. Freedom inside the custodial block, well and good. But what about freedom outside it?

Chapter 21

Freedom within custodial walls isn't the real thing. How could one introduce freedom outside them? This was the question that now exercised my mind. There was one great asset—another piece of luck—and that was that we had a farm of nine hundred acres. Some prisons and reformatory schools have no land but that on which they are built. For them the problem of freedom outside the custodial walls is difficult indeed.

My first plan was not a good one. It was to invite all the supervisors to pick from their *spans* those boys who would be unlikely to abuse such a freedom. This freedom they would be given with due ceremony at evensong. Each boy would be given a shirt the pocket of which had been covered with a piece of green cloth. This green pocket soon became known as the *vakasha* badge, the word *vakasha* (pronounced *va-ga'-sha*) meaning in Zulu "to go for a walk."

On Fridays at evensong these chosen boys would be paraded before the whole congregation, and facing me. As the names were called out, each boy in turn would come and stand in front of me. I would say to him, "Today you are receiving your *vakasha* badge. What do you have to say?" The boy would then turn to face the congregation and say:

Today I receive my *vakasha* badge.
I promise not to go beyond the boundaries of the farm.
I promise not to touch anything that is not mine.
I promise to obey the rules of the school.

He would then turn to me again and be given a shirt with the green badge. When all the badges had been given, I would say to the congregation, "Today these boys you see before you have received the *vakasha* badge," and the congregation would applaud.

The *vakasha* badge now enabled supervisors to use the free boys as messengers, or to allow them to work apart from the main *span*. But the big privilege was to be signed out at the gate at two o'clock on a Sunday afternoon, to have the freedom of the farm, and to return to the gate at fifteen minutes to five. On the first *vakasha* afternoon, some fifty boys were signed out and the same number were signed in. The actual signing out was a great event for the whole reformatory, and a large crowd gathered to watch the lucky ones go out.

But the plan did not work out as well as I had hoped. Some boys who had been picked out by their supervisors as trustworthy used the *vakasha* badge to abscond. Its weakness was further exposed by a boy who absconded without the *vakasha* badge, and the only way to do that was to make a sudden bolt for freedom. He was apprehended and brought back, and when asked why he had absconded, he gave the answer: "You gave Johannes the badge and he had been here only a month; I have been here for a year and have behaved myself, but you gave me nothing. So I ran away."

I had in fact failed to realise the importance of *time* to those who have been deprived of freedom. Time is the overriding interest of their lives. In strict prisons the granting of privileges, the right to send a letter, even the issue of a spoon of jam, all depend on time. Although the aim of the Children's Act was to substitute an educational for a custodial aim, the Diepkloof boy still thought in terms of time. Under the act the *sentence* had been abolished; children were now *committed*, and the time for which they were committed was called the "period of retention." This period was not determined in any way by the nature or seriousness of the offence; it was determined solely by the age of the child. If for example a boy of ten committed an offence, he could be *retained* until he was sixteen, and he was under *further supervision* until he was eighteen. If a boy was fifteen he could be retained until he was eighteen, and would be under further supervision until he was twenty-one.

However, the length of his stay in the reformatory was determined by quite other considerations. One was the number of pupils that the reformatory could accommodate. Another was an unexpected change for the worse or the better in the boy's home circumstances. A third was an offer by some responsible person to adopt him.

The reformatory had its own period of retention, and this was determined largely by the number of pupils it could accommodate. It was finally decided to fix the period at twenty-one months, except in the case of very young boys who had no home to return to. This period of twenty-one months then came to be regarded by the boys as their *time,* and almost every boy in the reformatory knew the month of his release.

The boy who had absconded because I gave him nothing brought about a big change in the free plan. From then on behaviour was not the sole criterion; the two criteria were now *behaviour* and *time.* The time was fixed at nine months, and after that period any boy whose behaviour had been good would receive the *vakasha* badge.

The second plan was a decided improvement on the first. The boy who had already done nine months of his reformatory term was less likely to abscond than the boy who had done one or two months. Further, the fact that the free badge would in all likelihood be granted after nine months meant that the urge to make a bolt for it before that time was lessened. The absconding rate *after* freedom settled into a steady pattern that was to be consistent for thirteen years. Of every hundred boys receiving the badge, *one* would abscond on the first occasion that he was signed out at the gate, *one* would abscond within the next four weeks, *one* would abscond at some later date, sometimes when his reformatory term was almost completed. *Ninety-seven* boys would not abscond at all.

Why was that? Why should a promise prove so binding on the delinquent population of the slums and the markets of South Africa? I do not know the answer to that question. It was again a part of my luck, for if it had turned out otherwise, even perhaps disastrous, I would have had to return to freedom within the custodial walls.

But whatever the right answer was, a very epigrammatic one was given by a boy who had been a determined absconder until he received his freedom. "When I made my promise," he said, "it was like a chain on my leg." And for many it was undoubtedly true. The most extraordinary example was that of a boy who after receiving his freedom absconded and made his way to Durban 450 miles away. He then gave himself up at the police. "Why did you do that?" I asked. "Because of my promise," he said.

Absconding is the preoccupation of every reformatory principal. Especially is it the preoccupation of the principal who has, in his reforming programme, made it easier for his pupils to abscond. The

Department of Education would have been very patient with the reforming principal, but it too had to reckon with public opinion. Members of Parliament, and especially those representing the farming districts, could ask difficult questions of the Minister of Education. Such questions could easily intimidate a reforming principal.

In countries like Sweden and Britain, it was in a way the controlling departments themselves that determined the kind of custodial supervision that was to be exercised, and the responsibility of the principal was thereby lessened. But even then, heavy absconding casts a gloom over any institution. I visited the Borstal Institution in Rochester, England, in 1946, and a senior officer, maybe the Governor himself, apologised to me for the lack of cheerfulness, and the taciturnity of the staff, which had been caused by a mass absconding the previous day. But in South Africa in 1935 the responsibility was still largely that of the principal himself. There had not yet been time to devise general regulations, and reforms were left almost entirely to him. This gave him a greater measure of freedom but also a greater measure of responsibility than if he had been acting according to regulations.

Absconding under the prisons regime was in fact common. It involved a sudden break from the *span*, except in the isolated cases of "trusties," who could abscond with ease, but there were few of these. Before my arrival absconding had been at the rate of thirteen per month. When an abscondment occurred all the *spans* were recalled to the main block, and members of the staff were thus enabled to join in the pursuit. It was of course my ambition to bring this number down.

When an absconder was returned to the reformatory, he was greeted with howls of execration, and was assaulted, sometimes severely. The boys of the reformatory held the belief—or acted as though they held the belief—that each time a boy absconded the discipline became harsher. How the discipline became progressively harsher thirteen times in one month I could never discover. Among those joining most heartily in the assault could well be some boy who would abscond the day following. After the reformatory had dealt with him, the boy would be officially punished by the warden, and would be made to wear a red shirt till further notice.

After one severe assault, the chief culprits were brought to me, and the conversation went something like this.

SELF: Why did you assault this boy?
BOY: Because he ran away.

SELF: I believe you ran away yourself once.

BOY *(a trifle disconcerted)*: That was two months ago.

SELF: What has it to do with you that this boy ran away?

BOY *(now sure of his ground)*: He makes it harder for us.

SELF: In what way will it be harder?

BOY: It will be harder.

SELF *(to the others)*: Do you all agree?

OTHERS: We all agree.

Under the Prisons Department these assaults had been winked at. They were certainly regarded as useful curbs on absconding. But now they were to be no more. The red shirts were also withdrawn and were used to make pocket badges for a new breed, the *head-boys*, who were appointed to be in charge of the open dormitories. The twenty rooms were divided into four houses, each in charge of a *house-captain*. At the head of the hierarchy was the *senior*, who was inevitably a young man rather than a boy, and was regarded with the same awe with which I had regarded Arthur Clayton at Maritzburg College, twenty-one years before. It was an aristocracy of course, but it eased the tasks of discipline. It also helped still further to reduce absconding, because it meant that each supervisor now had an assistant. The new head-boy was also brought before the congregation, and made appropriate promises, after which he received his badge and a round of applause.

The head-boys, house-captains, and seniors were very powerful, and one had to be continually on the alert to prevent any misuse of their power. Here Engelbrecht was the tower of strength. He trained them in the proper exercise of authority, of which he, with his six foot four inches and his quiet personality, gave a magnificent example. He once said to me in a rare moment, "*Meneer*, I wish I were not so tall. Six foot would be enough." I said to him, "I. Z., you can give the rest to me."

Before a boy received his *vakasha* badge, his supervisor had to write a report on his progress. This was the beginning of a system that was to record his progress from his admission to his release. In this final report we would predict his future, whether he would relapse, whether he would relapse into serious or less serious crime, and whether if he relapsed he should be sent to prison or returned to the reformatory. Engelbrecht took charge of this report system, and he acquired a knowledge of our four hundred boys that was invaluable. It was a matter of intense disappointment to us that the final release report, often so accurate in its assessments and predictions, was in the case of relapse seldom called for by a court. Therefore the courts sent many a boy back to the reformatory who should have gone to prison, and many a boy to prison who should have had another chance with us. There was one notable exception and that was the Johannesburg Juvenile Court at Auckland Park, with whom we established a close relationship.

There was one other invaluable service rendered by Engelbrecht. Of our four hundred boys some suffered from ungovernable rages, and when possessed by them they could be dangerous, especially when they were physically powerful. Some would have no compunction in inflicting grave bodily harm on an opponent, and some would kill if they were not prevented. I was lucky in my thirteen years that no boy was killed. When it happened that one of these older boys had done serious bodily harm, or that one of them seemed to lose for a while all self-control, there was only one thing to do, and that was to confine him. In Chapter 18, in my sketch of the main block, there are four cells marked A, and these were for solitary confinement. However, I determined that we would never have more than four, although there was often pressure from the staff, especially in turbulent periods, to build four more.

The advantage of having only four solitary cells was that if you wanted to confine a fifth boy, you had to let one of them out. The task of looking after the confined boys was given to Engelbrecht; he saw them daily and was able by the strength of his personality to persuade them to abandon their intransigence, for there were some of them who in the uncontrollable moods would willingly have died rather than submit to authority. Some indeed would have killed themselves.

I did not foresee in 1935 that the consequence of increasing the amount of physical freedom would be to reduce absconding drastically. I *hoped* that it would, but at times it seemed like some utopian ideal. I did not know that the rate of absconding would drop from thirteen per month in 1935 to three per month in 1948. In 1935 boys could not abscond easily from the reformatory, whereas in 1948 more than half of them could. At Diepkloof I became addicted to statistics. With fascination, and with thankfulness, and of course with pride, I watched the monthly average decline year by year, except for one year when it went up slightly, causing me a pang, and spoiling a perfect curve.

Yet I did not foresee it. I was too deeply committed to see that the setbacks were only falterings in a ceaseless moving forward. It is impossible to recapture now the times of depression, sometimes approaching despair, or to recapture the intense disappointment—concealed as far as one could—when one of the *vakasha* boys failed to return to the main block on a Sunday afternoon. I had no means of knowing then that he was only one of three in a hundred who would not be faithful to the promise given at evensong. My reader can imagine how intense the disappointment would be when all three chose the same afternoon for their abscondment!

I can see it all clearly now, though it happened forty years ago. If Engelbrecht and Moloi and I were on weekend duty together, we would take up a position at the gate at about four-thirty. From the gate one could see at least four roads radiating from the main block, and at about that time the first boys would be seen returning from different parts of the farm. By about four-thirty most of them would be in, and we would—inevitably, perhaps surreptitiously—be scanning the four roads, and if there was no boy visible, be hoping that the remainder would come from behind the main block. When the last one, or the last two, came in sight, Engelbrecht would permit himself a small smile of satisfaction, for he was the one who now received each supervisor's recommendation and prepared each candidate for his new freedom. And sometimes the last one or the last two would not return, and after evensong the principal would go sadly home.

I do not remember what was the cause of the deepest depression that I ever experienced at Diepkloof, but it was certainly due to what I thought was an ominous bout of abscondment. Between the main block and the principal's house was a pine plantation through which I had cut a pathway home. I stopped in the plantation on the way home and said (rather than prayed) to God, "Don't You want this to happen? Because if You don't want it to happen, I'm going back to a safer job."

But apparently He did want it to happen; otherwise I would not have dared to set the story down.

Of course the deepest cause of the fear of abscondment is not that a cherished educational theory will have to be abandoned. The deepest cause is the fear of the consequences for oneself, the disgrace, the loss of reputation, the nasty question in parliament, the nasty article in Dr. Verwoerd's newspaper, the exposure of one's sentimental and entirely unfounded belief that freedom is the supreme reformatory instrument. Therefore when one felt sick at heart, it was not because some lofty educational theory was in danger, but because one was in danger oneself. And luckily for me, the theory worked.

So the first six months at Diepkloof drew to their end. The atmosphere was changing from one of grimness to one almost of gaiety, and a very industrious kind of gaiety. The closed dormitories were no longer there to reproach us. The morning stench had gone. Typhoid fever was going. Small boys did not any longer tremble when one approached them. The clean whitewashed walls were no longer sacrosanct; pictures could be painted on the dormitory walls. And what pictures they were! Of boys with stolen handbags fleeing from the cops, of planes and cars and trains, of the streets of Johannesburg both rich and poor, of courts of justice with august magistrates on the bench and naughty boys in the dock. Some boy from Durban would paint a nostalgic picture of ships on the ocean, and a boy homesick for the country would paint an idyllic picture of cows and horses and birds, in a meadow under a willow, weeping into some river of home.

But how could one boast of all this, and to what extent was it real, while the main block stood behind its thirteen-foot barbed wire fence, inclining inwards, so that it was impossible to scale? That was the next step to take.

The barbed wire fence enclosed the entire main block, as shown on page 182, ABCD being the fence, and EFGH the main block. Ga, Ga, Ga, Ga are the gates. On New Year's Day, 1936, the front fence AD was taken down, and short fences AE and DH were erected.

At first it was like being naked. The great main gate was taken down, and the administrative offices, including my own, were now open to the world. Mr. H. C. Fick, known to all, boys and staff, as Oubaas, a man of about forty, was now put in charge of all the gardens that were to be. His first job was to make a garden where the fence AD had been. Prominent in his first garden were geraniums, and I became known as "The man who pulled up the barbed wire and planted geraniums," although it was only half my doing.

The establishment of the gardens was the first attempt to diversify the occupations of the reformatory. Oubaas Fick was given five supervisors and a hundred boys. He was a kind of genius. All our roads were lined with gum trees, but now they all came down and were replaced by ornamental trees set in lawns. He established a nursery, and raised seedlings of many kinds. It became one of my greatest pleasures to visit it on my inspection rounds.

Mr. Barry watched this new development with disapproval. So far he had had almost a monopoly of the boys' labour. I should explain that under the Prisons Department almost every boy was appren-

DIEPKLOOF REFORMATORY BEFORE
FRONT PORTION OF SECURITY FENCE WAS REMOVED

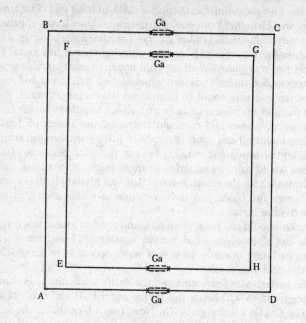

DIEPKLOOF REFORMATORY—
FRONT PORTION OF SECURITY FENCE REMOVED

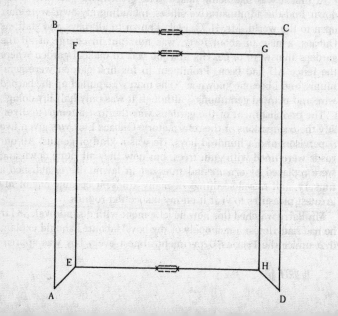

ticed to a white farmer on his release, and there he had to complete
what was then called his "sentence." The wastage was unbelievable. After one month fifty percent of the apprentices had absconded to the cities. After two months barely ten percent were left
on the farms. Quite apart from the question of the advisability of
sending to the country urban delinquent boys who were more used
to the sight of a magistrate than to that of a cow, the system was
grossly abused by many farmers, and amounted to a form of slavery.
Some boys would not abscond to the cities but would run back to the
reformatory, and the tales of hunger, scant bedding, and brutal
treatment were endless. To verify them was impossible, to rectify
proven wrongs equally impossible. The entire system was wasteful
and intolerable, yet the Prisons Department persisted with it year
after year. The arguments were simple: the boys still needed discipline, their sentences had not expired, the farmers needed labour.
These arguments were considered more cogent than the plain fact
that within two months nearly ninety percent of the apprentices
had melted away.

Mr. Barry came to me to advance these very arguments. He also
pointed out that farmers did not want horticulturists; they wanted
boys who understood cattle, maize, and vegetables. The reformatory
was doing a disservice to its boys in not training them for useful
occupations. I pointed out to him that an urban black boy was more
likely to become a gardener than a farm labourer. He pointed out to
me that the reformatory was thus encouraging boys to return to the
cities and to shun the healthy useful life of the farms. I pointed out
to him that ninety percent of them did not like the healthy useful
life of the farms, and ran away from it. He persisted that if I took
away a hundred boys, he would not be able to provide great and
important institutions like the famous Johannesburg prison known
as the Fort with much-needed vegetables. I replied—and I was now
growing warm under the collar—that it was not the task of the
Union Department of Education to provide vegetables for prisons. I
then delivered the knockout blow for poor Mr. Barry, namely that
the Department of Education, on the recommendation of the Diepkloof Board of Management, would from the end of the month abolish the apprenticeship system altogether and that only those boys
who chose to do so would go to the farms. He left my office with the
look of a man to whom a great injustice had been done.

The removing of the front portion of the reformatory fence had
no untoward consequences, and after a while we grew used to the
feeling of nakedness. I must record that Miss Chattey was delighted,

but not so Inspector Mr. T., a man much older than myself, who explained to the young principal that liberty was not to be confused with licence. When I asked him what evidence he saw of licence, he said that he was merely giving me a friendly warning. I am quite sure that he was not doing this at the instance of my Chief, Prof. M. C. Botha.

I must mention one other inspector, Mr. B. de Klerk, responsible for agricultural instruction. During the Second World War he resigned from the department rather than from the Afrikaner secret society, the Broederbond, from which General Smuts had ordered all civil servants to resign. He was what was known as a "red-hot" Nationalist, and an uncompromising believer in racial separation. Yet in all my time he was the only white man who raised his hat in response to the salute of the head-boy in charge of the gate.

Chapter 22

Our Farm Manager watched with dismay the diversification of the educational programme of the reformatory. With a few exceptions all the boys had been under his control, but now he lost all the small boys, of whom there were about one hundred. They were sent permanently to school, and that meant the appointment of three new black teachers, and incidentally, the removal of the two sentry boxes.

These hundred small boys formed the *Kleinspan*, and in the afternoons they played and did small chores, such as weeding and wood carrying. They were put under the supervision of one of the older boys at the school, Daniel Bob. His nickname was Majohnnie, and he was another genius. He stood less than five feet, and was never to grow any taller, but his discipline was perfect, and his understanding of small boys profound. When the time came for him to leave the reformatory he came to see me.

"*Meneer*, I do not want to go back to Kimberley."

"Why not, Majohnnie?"

"Because I shall be back here in a month."

"Why should that be?"

"*Meneer*, I know Kimberley and I know myself. I shall be back in a month."

"Then what must I do?"

"*Meneer* must employ me here to look after the *Kleinspan*."

So I asked the department to allow me to employ four reformatory boys as supervisors after their discharge. This in fact was in line with its own policy of appealing to employers to give a chance to boys and girls released from reformatories and industrial schools, and it would have been difficult to refuse me. Of these four, Majohnnie was an outstanding success, and remained so all his life. Why a delinquent boy from a derelict home should have come to cherish, almost fiercely, such qualities as punctuality, reliability, loyalty, and honesty I do not claim to understand. After I left Diepkloof he married, and had seven children, with whose education I helped him. In almost every letter he wrote he told me that his committal to the reformatory was the luckiest event of his life, and that he was trying to teach his children the lessons that the reformatory had taught him.

For Majohnnie Diepkloof was like some heaven on earth. In fact it was very like the world itself, where virtue and vice live side by side. The authority of the principal had to be firm, and it had to be perpetually vigilant to control and prevent offences. In a monastic institution like Diepkloof there were inevitably cases of sodomy and other homosexual relationships. The principal had to be vigilant to make sure that the head-boys, to whom he had delegated authority, did not become bullies and despots. Boys frequently brought false accusations against their fellows in order to satisfy personal grudges. Yet in this mess a child of the Kimberley slums found a guiding rule for his life, and followed it as faithfully as any of the saints. And indeed this miracle can be seen every day in this strange society of ours, so corrupted by the racial arrogance and callousness of those of us who rule, so disfigured by that fear and distrust that has destroyed all peace and happiness in Northern Ireland and the Lebanon, and may one day destroy them here.

For many years after I left Diepkloof Majohnnie had been promising to spend one of his holidays with me, so that he could tell me in person what he had so often told me in his letters. But some five years ago he died, so that I have never had a chance to find some clue to the nature of the miracle.

The other three ex-reformatory boys turned supervisors did not do so well. Two had eventually to be dismissed. The fourth survived many threats of dismissal for drunkenness, homosexuality, and womanising, because he had a genius—I am sorry to use this word again, but that is what he had—for smoking out absconders from the dens and hideouts of Johannesburg. Some of my staff—both black and white—took a dim view of his immunity, and supposed that he exercised over me some kind of malign and occult influence.

A large unisexual institution shut off from the world is bound to be the home of homosexual practices. The prison method of control was to provide each locked dormitory with a spyhole and an electric light which burned through the night. Before we opened all the dormitories at night, this led to practices just as repugnant as the homosexuality. I had one young white supervisor, Mr. O., who spent his hours on night duty trying to trap offenders. His ostensible motive was to prevent sin and protect virtue. He himself was a very ordinary young man, and his goodness did not irradiate his personality. I told him it was his duty to inspect regularly, but it was no part of it to stand for long periods at a spyhole. I must record that after he gave up the snooping he became one of the most popular supervisors in the reformatory.

It was comparatively easy for a head-boy to commit a homosexual act. Very often the boys in his dormitory would be afraid of him. Sometimes he would allow himself to commit such an act but no one else. The rules were simple—no sharing of blankets, the doors to stand open, no boy to sleep in any other dormitory except the one to which he had been assigned. These rules could be evaded, but their evasion was preferable to a reign of snoopery and an encouragement of informers. If a free boy were discovered in a homosexual act, he would for a time lose his freedom. For a head-boy the disgrace was greater; the rank which he had received publicly was taken away publicly, though the principal would express the hope that he would one day be considered fit to receive it again. I never had the experience of seeing any boy indifferent to the loss of his badge; some could not raise their eyes from the ground.

I shall relate one more incident while on the theme of homosexuality. One day Engelbrecht, accompanied by "Doc" Gertenbach, the supervisor in charge of the hospital, came with grave faces to my office to tell me they had just admitted a boy with fully developed breasts. He was kept in the hospital, and the department came to our rescue by asking the minister to discharge him from the provisions of the Children's Act. This was fortunately easy, as his offence was not a serious one. Thus we were rescued from what might have proved a difficult situation, and as far as I know the boy did not break the law again.

Further blows fell on the Farm Manager. Miss Chattey decided that the Diepkloof boys, who had so far gone barefoot, must wear sandals. So was opened the shoemaker's department, with twenty boys under a black instructor. But where was the workshop? It was easier to get additional teachers and instructors than to get a workshop. The cost would have been placed on the estimates, and in the first year a token five pounds would have been voted. But with the connivance of Mr. Linscott, the Inspector of Trade Training who later married the inviolable Miss Chattey, which no doubt explained everything, we built a workshop with timber, mud, and thatch from the farm. It cost twenty pounds and it lasted for ten years, after which it was replaced by a prefabricated workshop from a white school that had decided to give up shoe-making.

The provision of new buildings for new activities would have extended over many years, but the department now appointed the brothers K., two Afrikaners from the western Transvaal, which was a stronghold of Afrikaner nationalism. This meant taking away yet more boys from the farm to become builders' assistants, but Mr. Barry did not mind this so much, because many of the new buildings would be for the farm. One of these would be new stables for a herd of Friesland cows transferred to us by one of the white agricultural schools. This also was Miss Chattey's work, because she had made milk an item in the new diet.

The brothers K. were farmers turned builders. This was quite a common change for a man to make and was due to the traditional practice of dividing a farm among all the members of the family. So the farms got smaller and poorer, and the more adventurous would move on. The elder brother K. was a rough, tough man who didn't believe in taking nonsense from blacks, yet he and his brother began to take a kind of pride in the reformatory. One day after work I asked the elder brother K. for a sundowner drink to celebrate the finishing of a big new store for the farm. He became mellow and expansive, and said to me, "*Meneer,* this is not a bad place." He considered that for a moment, and then plunged forward and said, "These boys aren't bad either." Then he added, in order to correct the balance, "except the one who stole the seven pound ten from my wife."

It was next decided that we should make our own clothes, and then our own tin dishes, mugs, and spoons. The tailoring instructor was black, and the tinsmithing instructor was white, and the white one earned twice as much as the black. In 1936 this was not a great source of grievance, because the salary scale for black instructors was a considerable improvement on the scale for black supervisors. In present times such disparity causes black resentment, and increasing pressure for equal pay for equal work. Yet it is the continuing disparity in earnings and possessions that makes evolutionary progress towards a common South African society in the highest degree unlikely. The hard truth is that black earnings cannot go up appreciably until white earnings come down. There are very few white South Africans who would acknowledge this truth, and still fewer who would preach it. Economists are always urging increased productivity, but no amount of increased productivity would enable black workers to earn the unreal wages and salaries now paid to whites. Another hard truth is that white affluence is not so much due to their know-how and the richness of the country's natural resources as it is due to the standard of black wages. The wealth of our great gold-mining industry is not so much due to the richness of the gold as it is to the poorness of black wages. In no other capitalist country in the world could such an industry be continued.

I must, in the interests of that candour that William Plomer did not regard as a constant necessity, record that I tried for a brief period an experiment of racial separation. The suggestion was made at a white staff meeting that we should try allotting separate dormitories to Xhosas, Zulus, Basotho, and so on. I do not remember what period had elapsed before we had the first fight between two tribal groups, and I do not even remember which groups they were. But I knew at once that the experiment was dangerous, and it was stopped. In any event it was not a reasonable experiment. The great majority of our boys were from the towns and cities, where the common experiences of the struggle to live and the common resentment against the discriminatory laws are far stronger to bind together than the tribal differences are strong to separate. Especially was this true of delinquent boys, whose common language was the picturesque Afrikaans of the townships, and who either could not speak any other language, or who spoke the vernacular languages badly. By separating them racially from one another, one was in fact trying to put back the clock of history, and one was pitting the puny strength of the reformatory against the giant strength of the cities.

It was understandable that some of our white staff should support the programme of racial separation. When Hertzog and Smuts amalgamated their two parties to form the United Party in 1934, Malan stayed outside and set himself the task of rebuilding Afrikanerdom through what was known as the Purified National Party. Its cardinal political belief—which was hardly separable from its religious belief—was that it was called upon to build a South Africa in which each race would realise its own racial self, with its own language and with its own culture. There were at least three Afrikaner prophets who shaped the thinking of Purified Afrikanerdom. They were Dr. N. Diederichs, later to become President of the

Republic of South Africa; Dr. P. J. Meyer, later to become Director of the South African Broadcasting Corporation; and Dr. G. Cronjé, Professor of Sociology at the University of Pretoria, and Chairman of the Suid-Afrikaanse Akademie vir Wetenskap en Kuns. To all three the individual had no meaning apart from his race. The greatest God-given treasure was not individuality, but one's racial inheritance and being. Therefore racial mixture was intolerable. It was this thinking that was determining the growth of the new Afrikaner nationalism that would triumph politically in 1948, and would rule South Africa from then until now, 1980. It gave intellectual, even spiritual content to the much older practice known as apartheid, and gave birth to the new doctrine, separate development. In 1980 it is seen by anxious Afrikaners not so much to be intellectually untenable and spiritually wrong, but to be politically and economically impossible. It is seen by these anxious Afrikaners not only to have incurred the increasingly active hatred of the world, but also the hatred of those races on whom it had been imposed, who see it as the supreme instrument for their oppression, and for the maintenance of white supremacy.

It was lucky for me that in the 1930s the new Afrikaner Nationalist conviction of the divinely ordained nature of the doctrine of separate development was not felt with the intensity which it was to acquire in the 1950s and the 1960s, when it became almost treasonable to question it. What is more, my young Afrikaners, except perhaps Engelbrecht, did not know what their prophets were saying. Therefore my decision to stop the racial separation in the dormitories was accepted without overt opposition.

In fact opposition to the programme of education through freedom and responsibility had now almost disappeared. On New Year's Day, 1937, the barbed wire fence was removed entirely and the massive iron supports were torn out of their concrete. The reformatory block seemed more naked than ever, but the feeling of apprehension was largely absent. The announcement that the fence was to be removed was greeted with shouts and applause.

Chief Supervisor Stewart-Dunkley had given the department a month's notice, having obtained a better-paid job on the mines. We gave him a grand farewell and he made a little speech. He said to me with that incredibly knowing smile that I had come quite to like, "Sir, when you started your changes, I didn't think they would work. But now I think you'll bring them off." So off he went with his stick and his monocle, which device I had never once seen him put into his eye.

I do not remember the year in which home leave was introduced, but I think it was in 1937. It was done with the goodwill of the department, whose new head was Mr. F. D. Hugo, who had been my Superintendent of Education in Natal. Home leave was to be given once a month to any boy who had held his *vakasha* badge for three months, and who had money to go home. There must have been some magic in the number 97; the reader may remember that out of every hundred boys receiving the *vakasha* badge, ninety-seven would reach the end of their reformatory term without absconding. Now of every hundred boys given home leave, one would return late, one would return drunk, and one would not return at all. Ninety-seven would return at the given time, and sober. Most of the leaves were given to the townships of Johannesburg, to Pretoria, and to the string of mining towns known as the East Rand and the West Rand. But some went as far afield as Bloemfontein, Pietersburg, and Durban, which city was eight hundred kilometers (say five hundred miles) away. When I finally left Diepkloof, ten thousand boys had been given home leave and plus or minus one hundred had not returned.

It was one of these hundred who did the kind of thing that I feared most. His mother worked as a domestic servant on one of those small holdings that are common in the Transvaal. White people driven off the farms by economic pressure try to keep their contact with the land by buying a small holding and building on it a humble house. On the Sunday of his special leave we heard over the radio that hundreds of police were searching the region for a young black man who had killed a white woman in the pantry of her house. It was supposed that she had heard a noise in the pantry and had gone to investigate. Pantries usually have only one door and she was standing in it. The young man, using either some weapon of his own or, if I remember rightly, a bottle of her own preserved fruit, struck her down and when found, she was dead.

A grave-faced Engelbrecht brought me the news that the boy had not returned. He and Moloi and I decided that he might well be the murderer. And so he was. He was sentenced to death, but if I remember rightly the fact that he was a Diepkloof boy, and worse still, a Diepkloof boy on special leave, was not given publicity. By this time many special leaves had been given, but if this had happened on the very first occasion it would have filled me with the gravest anxiety for the future of the policy of reformation through freedom. It is deeply disquieting to know that one's experiment in freedom has meant that hundreds of police had been called back to duty.

Luckily this Diepkloof boy was not really one in a hundred. He was one in ten thousand, for such a thing never happened again.

In 1938 the whole character of the reformatory changed, and the main block ceased to be the main centre of the reformatory. The Public Works Department built on an open piece of land below the main block four free hostels, each to accommodate twenty-five boys. Each hostel consisted of a cottage with rooms for an African teacher and his wife, and a communal dining room for the twenty-five boys. Arranged in a semicircle around the cottage were five huts or *rondavels*, each housing five boys. The new free buildings looked something like the drawing on the next page.

The walls of these buildings were white and their roofs were thatched. The teacher's wife became the housemother, and she and her husband were given generous rations (by Miss Chattey of course) and lived rent free. One of the housefathers was the first African staff member to buy himself a new car.

One can only describe the free village as an architectural gem. The spacing of the buildings, the simplicity of their design, the white walls and the thatched roofs made the village something to be proud of. In the moonlight it was—in my opinion—as beautiful as the Taj Mahal. One no longer had to explain to visitors the free system that would function only when they were not there. They could now see part of it for themselves.

I left Diepkloof in 1948, and the final step of its transformation was taken in that year, when the department agreed to build in Orlando, the great African township and the forerunner of Soweto, a hostel for twenty Diepkloof boys. Here, after having spent nine months in the main block, having survived the temptations of the *vakasha* badge and the home leave, and after having lived for six months or more in a free hostel, a Johannesburg boy would be allowed to spend his last six months in a working hostel, where he could work under our supervision and learn to earn, spend, and perhaps save money. If it worked well, other hostels would follow.

We had as far back as 1936 begun a kind of aftercare section, which was intended to keep in touch with the homes of all Johannesburg boys. It was begun by another young man from the Special Service Battalion, "Lanky" de Lange. He served as the model for the young white man in *Cry, the Beloved Country* who worked at the reformatory and hid his gentler nature behind the fierce and frowning eyes. It was his task to visit the homes, to recommend the granting of the home leaves, often to visit the home after the leave had been granted, and to prepare both the boy and the home for the final release. The value of his work was immense, and he was often able

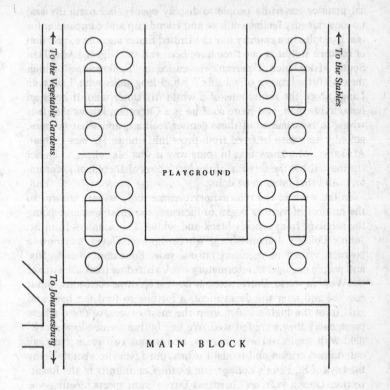

To the Vegetable Gardens ←

↑ To the Stables

↑ To Johannesburg

PLAYGROUND

MAIN BLOCK

to restore relations between boy and home where these had broken down. The delinquent boy was not always the product of a derelict home; sometimes his delinquency was the result of his rebellion against the discipline of the home.

The building of the working hostel in Orlando was in a way the crowning of de Lange's work. It would enable us to prepare for the release of boys who either had no home or whose return to their homes would have been useless or harmful. In 1948 de Lange's aftercare section had grown, and he then had about five assistants. In other words, seven percent of the staff were in his section; in some schools I visited in the United States the figure was thirty percent.

It is not uncommon for white people who are engaged in black social work to hide their gentler natures behind fierce and frowning eyes. This is because they live in a country where it is not a universal practice for white people to display openly and naturally and unconstrainedly feelings of love and friendship and compassion for black people. In a country like the United States such an expression of concern would at one time have been called "Nigger loving." In South Africa such a person was called a *"kafferboetie,"* which means "little brother of a kaffir." I had long talks with Lanky de Lange about the inhibitions of a white Afrikaner who, if he is an honourable man, and more so if he is a Christian, knows that it is wrong to be ashamed of these gentler feelings, and what is more, actually desires to be freed from these inhibitions. He was such an Afrikaner, who knew that in some way it was his calling to be not the master, but the servant, of the black boys of Diepkloof Reformatory. And that takes some doing.

As the work of the reformatory became more widely known, so the number of visitors began to increase, the most welcome being the scholars from schools black and white. The scholars from St. John's College, Johannesburg, where our son David was now a boarder, visited us regularly once a year. Educators, sociologists, and people engaged in reformatory work visited us from all parts of the Western world. Dorrie acted as hostess on these occasions, and it cost us, and later the department, a fortune to feed the boys and girls from the high schools, even the most expensive ones, where presumably they were fed well. We had built a tremendous sports-field with spade and wheelbarrow, and it took two years. Now we entertained cricket and football teams, our favourite visitors being the boys of St. Peter's College, run by the Community of the Resurrection. Once a year, on Christmas Day, a giant sports meeting was held, with generous prizes. Then came a big midday meal (Miss Chattey of course); after that we allowed a swim in the dam, and on the second or third Christmas one of the boys was drowned. The swim was not allowed again for many years, and again a boy was drowned. We never allowed it again; even in midsummer (and our Christmas Day is one of the hottest days of the summer) the water at the dam was bitterly cold, and both boys were seized by cramp the moment they dived in. I felt my blame deeply, but more so on the second occasion.

Other visitors to the reformatory were those ministers of religion who were invited to take the Sunday morning service. These represented the Methodists, the big Reformed Church (the Nederduitse Gereformeerde), the Anglicans, and the Congregationalists. The Catholics were allowed to instruct their own members, but not to take the morning services; in any event they would not have wished to do so, for in the 1930s they held aloof from others, and others held aloof from them. I also allowed a Mr. Jansen of one of the Apostolic churches to instruct his own members; on one occasion I allowed him to take the Sunday services, but Mr. Laas objected on the grounds that the Apostolics were heretics, and were not permitted to enter State institutions except for private ministrations. I was sorry to find that Mr. Jansen was officially a heretic, because he was one of those persons whom one describes as holy. I should explain that the South African Government regarded itself as Protestant and that the powerful Nederduitse Gereformeerde Kerk abhorred Catholics and heretics.

Mr. Laas was a devout member of this powerful church, and held the office of *Ouderling*, or "elder." On the Sunday mornings set aside for his church he would make a special journey to Orlando to fetch the black minister, and after the service would take him to his house for refreshments; the minister would enter the house by the back door and have his tea or coffee in Mr. Laas's kitchen. My black staff used to taunt him with this, and ask him if there was a back door into heaven; these taunts troubled him because he knew that he was consenting to be humiliated. That was forty years ago, but today the black Nederduitse Gereformeerde Kerk is calling on its white mother church to renounce the doctrines (for that is what they are) of apartheid and separate development.

It must not be supposed that such humiliations were practised only by the Dutch Reformed Churches. When Michael Scott was sent to the Anglican Mission in Pretoria in 1943, he records his "great despondency" that African priests always came to the back door. When my friend Bill Evans became the Anglican Rector of Howick, Natal, in 1956, he was horrified when his black assistant priest did the same. I cannot speak for other churches, but I should imagine that the Anglican clergy no longer practise or suffer such humiliations.

What part did religion play in the life of Diepkloof? With some individuals, a great deal. In the reformatory as a whole, who knows? As I have written earlier, the evening congregation was outwardly deeply reverent, and their singing was magnificent. I have also written about the sound of prayers when the nine o'clock bell was rung in 'he evening, but it was the silence and not the praying that was compulsory.

It was by no means uncommon for a boy to bring the name of God or Christ into a conversation with someone in authority, such as myself. It would not be a full explanation to say that he did it because he thought it would appeal to me or impress me. He usually did it when we were discussing some problem near to him, his future perhaps, his fear of freedom, his desire to do better. I have already told the story of Majohnnie's appointment as a supervisor, how from that day punctuality, reliability, loyalty, and honesty became his guiding principles; he himself, having lapsed, became a devout and practising Catholic. Much less simple was the story of Jacky, which served as the source of my short story "The Divided House," though the fictional story is by no means identical with the other.

Jacky was brought to me by Mr. Moloi, and told me that a voice had called him to be a priest. Such a literal usage, though not common, was not rare. Nor did it necessarily imply a vision or hallucination; it could well be a way of describing an urge of conscience. I explained to Jacky that his present achievement of Standard IV would not be sufficient, and that he must first pass Standard VI in our own reformatory school. This in fact he wanted to do, so he went to school, where he was not brilliant but worked well.

At last came the great day when he passed Standard VI, and a place was obtained for him at the Grace Dieu High School near Pietersburg in the northern Transvaal. He had to have a suit, a blazer and grey flannels, hat, shirts, socks, shoes, and raincoat, and a suitcase to put them in. Friends of mine provided these readily. He asked for special leave to go to say good-bye to his uncle and aunt, but there was nothing unusual about that. He was one of those who never came back. What had happened? Had he suddenly realised that the claims of the priesthood were something he could not meet?

Jacky served as the model for Gertrude in *Cry, the Beloved Country,* who on the following day was to leave the excitement and temptation of Johannesburg for her brother's quiet church house at Ndotsheni. And in the morning, "He opened Gertrude's door, and held up his candle. But Gertrude was gone. The little boy was there, the red dress and the white turban were there. But Gertrude was gone."

Of Gertrude nothing more was heard, but I had a letter from Jacky in prison. He repented of past follies, saying that he was still determined to be a priest. I answered with words of encouragement. I wrote in the story "The Divided House": "Yet I knew that the boy who wrote the letter would, so far as man knew, always be defeated, till one day he would give up both hope and ghost, and leave to his enemy the sole tenancy of the divided house."

That Jacky had an impulse that could be described as religious I have no doubt. That other boys had such impulses I do not doubt either. That some boys had no such impulse whatever also cannot be doubted, yet many of these were subject to superstitious fears.

Moloi was a devout Anglican, and he and I asked the Bishop of Johannesburg, the Rt. Rev. Geoffrey Clayton, to allow a monthly communion service at Diepkloof. Dorrie and I and a young supervisor, Frank Huddle, were the only white Anglicans, but there were about a dozen black ones, including one or two reformatory boys. Dorrie and I, when we went up on that first occasion to receive, knelt at the extreme left of the altar rail, as seen from the communicants' point of view. The celebrant, a white priest from the Community of the Resurrection, when he saw this, began administering from our side, which is not usual. Much later our regular celebrant was Archdeacon Hugh Rouse, and he began administering from the usual side. I remember that I felt we had been slighted, and it was only when Moloi apologised to me for this change that I realised that such a feeling was unpardonable. I suppose this must be regarded as a further step in the direction of emancipation.

Moloi and I also started a confirmation class for Anglican boys. We would not have excluded any boy who wished to become Anglican, but we did not proselytise. It was a great day for us when our first group of boys was ready for confirmation. The Bishop came to lunch with Dorrie and myself. He was a great, strange, extraordinary man, and we were both in awe of him. He could be childish, petulant, rude, absurd, but if there was one thing that he took seriously and humbly, it was his calling as a bishop. Knowing that he liked beer, I had bought some of the best, made in Denmark. He declined it politely and gravely, and said he would not like any child to remember of his or her confirmation that the bishop smelt of beer. After lunch he confirmed our boys, and spoke to them simply and earnestly. Whether he had ever spoken to delinquent boys before I do not know, but in matters like that he could not go wrong. I shall later write more about him.

In any institutional community such as a school or a reformatory, the most powerful educational agent is the community itself, and participation in its life is the real education. The personal influences of teachers and supervisors are of great importance, but they fashion, guide, and use the impersonal influences of the institution itself. In fact, the reformatory boy who most needs the personal influence of the teacher and supervisor is the one most likely to fail in the outside world. As teachers and guides Engelbrecht and Moloi had few equals, but they would have been powerless without the impersonal educational instruments of the reformatory itself. To be a teacher in an institution that relies on force to maintain discipline, and has no sense of aspiration or purpose, is a task to break the stoutest heart. In the last resort, force is the ultimate guarantor of law and order, but the society or institution that has to rely for its continuance on the ultimate guarantor is doomed.

I shall close this brief discussion of the personal and impersonal influences that operate within the institution, and this evaluation of direct and indirect methods of guidance and education, with a story which my colleague Dr. van Antwerpen told against himself. He was a qualified minister of the Nederduitse Gereformeerde Kerk, and he was appointed as Vice-Principal of the Coloured Reformatory of Tokai, just outside Cape Town. He expected much from the evangelistic sermon, and on his first Sunday he preached to his captive congregation, several hundreds strong. He thought his sermon was good and effective, and when it was finished he asked his hearers if they had any questions to ask. When they did not respond, he said to them encouragingly, "You may ask anything you wish." And a boy stood up at the back and said, *"Meneer, asseblief 'n stukkie twak."* *

* *The English translation, not so pungent, is, "Sir, a bit of tobacco, if you please." Better would be, "Meneer, for God's sake, a bit of tobacco."*

Chapter 23

It is time to bring the Diepkloof story to a close, but it would not be complete if it did not deal with two subthemes. One is the role and purpose of punishment, both in an institution and in society itself. The other is to attempt to answer the questions, how far could Diepkloof Reformatory be said to have succeeded in its reformatory task? And how can one possibly judge the success of such an institution?

What is the place of punishment in the educational institution, and in society itself? Many people hold the view that punishment should be *retributive*. If an offender has inflicted hurt, then he should be hurt also. The extreme example of retributive punishment is the death penalty. Imprisonment can also be regarded as retributive. The official statements of judges and magistrates show clearly that many of them hold the belief that the punishment they inflict is retribution for the hurt or damage done by the offender. On the other hand, the idea of retributive punishment has to a large degree fallen into disfavour among educators. Some educators would regard retributive punishment as totally worthless. In many countries corporal punishment is forbidden. In some countries where it has been forbidden there has been a demand among teachers and prison officers that it should be restored, on the grounds that its abolition has created grave disciplinary problems. The attitudes of schoolboys towards corporal punishment are varied; some resent it bitterly, others take it as a joke.

A second view of punishment, not necessarily exclusive of the first, is that it is deterrent. Its purpose is not only to deter the offender, it is also to deter others who might be tempted to commit a similar offence. If the punishment succeeds in its purpose, then it is socially valuable. I was punished at the age of six for pushing a little girl off the pavement by being made to eat my lunch on the girls' verandah. I never did such a thing again, but I was deterred, not by the actual punishment, but by the attention which I had attracted to myself. That was the idea behind the use of the stocks in bygone times. Yet of course there are offenders who appear to be indifferent to public attention or public disapproval.

There is a third view of punishment, that it should be reformatory. This view has gained much ground in this century. If this view is held, then the word "punishment" becomes inappropriate and is replaced by the word "treatment." The whole purpose of the transfer of the reformatories of South Africa from the Department of Prisons to the Department of Education was to change their goal from one of detention to one of education.

There is a fourth and last view of punishment, and that is that there need be none at all. Steps are taken against an offender for one reason and one reason only, and that is for the protection of society. Does society need protection against the old man who is repeatedly found drunk in the streets? Or the harmless man who dresses up as a woman? Or the prostitute who willingly submits to measures of control? Or against "consenting adults"? If society does not need protection, then such persons need not be punished. Nor should more serious offenders be punished. They should merely be "treated" in such a way as will remove their threat to society.

Diepkloof Reformatory inherited a system of punishment in which the infliction of cuts played the major role, largely because there were so few privileges that could be removed. These were—if I remember rightly—the withholding of a weekly spoonful of jam that was awarded after so many months, the withholding of sugar or some other item of diet, the withholding of the right to attend the reformatory football matches. Another punishment, more drastic, was the ordering of solitary confinement, with or without spare diet, which was usually reserved for brutal and dangerous actions or for persistent homosexual offences.

The decision to issue tobacco and to abolish the offence of smoking, except for boys under sixteen, and except for the leaves and seeds of the plant cannabis known to us as dagga, reduced the number of offences drastically, and reduced the number of cuts by about seventy percent. We discussed at our staff meetings the pros and cons of corporal punishment, and it was clear that among both white and black staffs there was a strong feeling against abolition. It was finally decided to retain it for offences against the person and particularly when the person was a member of the staff, or when a boy absolutely refused to obey lawful orders. This was a rare offence indeed, and could be due to mental disturbance; therefore such punishment was never inflicted except on the advice of our visiting district surgeon.

Here I remember a story of another of our young white recruits from the Special Service Battalion. His name was Chris Botha, and he was another master of discipline. In his *span* was a boy Hendrik who refused to work. Sometimes he had to be carried in and out of the yard. Chris Botha advised against punishment, and gave it as his opinion that there was a deep-seated cause for this behaviour. Hendrik was sent to the hospital, and a week later he was dead. The postmortem revealed an internal growth the size of a small football.

Even today when I have reached the age of seventy-seven, I am unable to decide whether corporal punishment for a brutal offence achieves any good purpose. Such offences are often committed in what appear to be uncontrollable fits of rage, and it is highly improbable that the memory of corporal punishment will prevent another outburst. Sometimes the reformatory community would be outraged by a brutal offence committed on one of its number, as when for example a powerful older boy inflicted grievous injuries on a small one, and especially if the small one was a boy of nine or ten years of age. What kind of notice does authority take of such an offence? Does one do nothing, except reprimand perhaps? Solitary confinement seemed to be the only alternative to corporal punishment, but I developed a far greater aversion to confinement than to punishment. And I held the belief that the infliction of corporal punishment made reparation for the outrage that the community had suffered. That the community could also take a sadistic delight in the punishment is also undoubted.

I still cannot make up my mind about the death penalty. South Africa executes more killers than any other country in what is called the "free world." The overwhelming majority of these are black. Some of these killers are robbers who will kill without mercy any person who resists them. Others are young black men who make their living on the congested black trains and buses that take black workers to and from the white cities. Leaving aside the question of personal responsibility, these killers are the product of a corrupting society, and it is this corrupting society that kills them in return.

George rose to be the senior house-captain of the main reformatory. He was a man, not a boy, powerful in build, and powerful in personality also. He made up his mind that while he was in the reformatory, and especially while he was the senior house-captain, he would obey authority, and what is more, that he would rule firmly and justly. Yet while he was in this position, he was already planning his first operation. This was to be the breaking into and robbing of the Comptonville Store, which was situated on the southern boundary of the Diepkloof Farm, and was guarded at night by a gentle black man called Theophilus. On the day after George's release, he and two companions broke into the Comptonville Store. Theophilus was not knocked unconscious; he was hacked to pieces, one of these pieces being his head. George and his two accomplices were sentenced to death and nothing in me rose to protest against it. On the day after the murder, and before it was known who had committed it, Engelbrecht brought for my signature the final report we had made on George, in which we predicted that he would soon again commit a merciless deed of this nature.

Was George responsible for his actions? If one takes the extreme behaviouristic view that we are all automatons, and that we respond to stimuli, that mind and conscience are man-made words that describe states or organs that do not exist, or exist only as epiphenomena,* then George was not responsible. Was George *in part* responsible for his actions? That too is a question impossible to answer. In fact a belief in responsibility is very like a belief in God; one holds it because one chooses to hold it, it is in fact a *faith*, and is based on "the evidence of things not seen." As I have written earlier, I hold myself responsible for my actions, even while I accept that I am not in full control of them. But I choose not to believe that I have *no* control over them.

It seems to me impossible to find any moral justification for punishment unless one acknowledges the doctrine of personal responsibility. But there are occasions on which the court of law is willing to accept a doctrine of diminution of responsibility, and also occasions on which the court finds what are known as "mitigating circumstances." We are in a way dealing with a secret whose truth is hidden from us. Therefore, although I shudder at the thought of a corrupting society that punishes and even kills those whom it has corrupted, I have never been able to make up my mind finally about punishment, and especially the death penalty. If I were a ruler, I

---

* An epiphenomenon is a secondary phenomenon accompanying another phenomenon and wrongly thought to be the cause of it. Webster gives the following illustrative sentence: "Fate determines what will happen to us, while ideas, convictions, and intentions are no more than phosphorescent epiphenomena—J. W. Krutch."

think I would incline strongly to the view that "punishment" is to be used only for the protection of society.

The amount of corporal punishment at Diepkloof Reformatory declined in much the same way as the incidence of absconding. Every punishment was entered in an enormous book, which was open to the inspection of any authorised person. I soon decided to inflict the punishment myself, and not to delegate it to any official punisher. I never departed from this decision, although on one occasion it had a painful consequence for myself.

Tom was a young man whom we estimated to be twenty-six years old. He greatly resented being sent to an institution for boys, and was hostile and inclined to be violent. One night he flatly refused to obey the orders of the supervisor on duty, and threatened to assault him. It was unfortunately not an Engelbrecht or a Botha who was on duty, but a very young man X. whose selection by the battalion authorities showed that we could no longer expect to be sent any more young men of the quality that had enabled us to change the character of Diepkloof. It also showed that the country had recovered from the recession, and that bright young men could now find ready employment.

X. was unable to control the situation, and sent for Engelbrecht, who eventually had to shut Tom up for the night in one of the solitary cells. Tom was brought to see me the next morning, truculent as ever, and I decided to give him six cuts for insubordination. I had made it my rule not to inflict corporal punishment in the presence of others, and asked Engelbrecht to retire, which he did unwillingly. Tom's first action was to seize the cane and to threaten me with it. I am no boxer, and I gave him a left to the chin, but my fist encountered his teeth instead. One of them pierced the middle knuckle of my left hand, with immediate pain. I recalled Engelbrecht and he took Tom back to the cell. I went to the hospital and had the wound dressed, but two days later the pain was intense, and I was ordered to hospital. That was before the days of penicillin, and the poisoning took some weeks to run its course; when the wound at last began to heal, it left the finger stiff, and I finally had it removed at the root.

The episode was a blow to my pride. Here I was, the apostle of freedom who had come to grief. For a long time I was very sensitive about the loss of my finger, though I now hardly ever think about it, except on occasions such as television interviews.

As far as I remember, in my thirteen years only one other staff member suffered an injury. That was Lanky de Lange, who with an African assistant went to bring back to the reformatory a boy who had been found guilty of a further offence after his release. This boy also strongly resented being sent back to an institution for children and on the journey tried to escape. De Lange tried to prevent him and was stabbed in the shoulder. I was in Port Elizabeth at the time, and I returned by the first available train. I was very attached to de Lange, because he was the one who hid his devotion behind the "fierce and frowning eyes," and with whom I had had such long discussions about the psychological difficulties that faced him in his work. He said he was an Afrikaner, and was born and brought up on a farm in an Afrikaans-speaking countryside. It was not part of his tradition to work for the welfare of black boys, and especially those who had committed criminal offences. Some of his people found it hard to understand how he could do such work, and they found it still harder to understand how he did it with such dedication. De Lange was another of the young men from the Special Service Battalion who helped to change the character of Diepkloof Reformatory.

There was yet a third case in my time. It was reported to me that Native Supervisor H. Zimvu was dying of poisoning, and that he had named the boy who had poisoned him. The boy was promptly confined, and Zimvu was rushed to hospital, where it was discovered that he had eaten a quantity of the wild mushrooms that grew on the farm. When he recovered he was brought to my office and confronted with the boy he had accused. He was deeply ashamed and asked the boy for forgiveness, which was granted immediately. I must record that amongst these delinquents of our towns and cities, it was a common thing for forgiveness to be granted, even sometimes for grave injuries, such as the loss of an eye. This is one of the themes of my short story "Sponono."

Now for the question, how successful was Diepkloof as a reformatory? Does a reformatory ever reform anyone? I have no doubt that a good reformatory can stop a boy in a criminal career and send him off in another direction. It can take a small boy off the streets and away from the markets for three or four formative years, so that in a sense he becomes a different being. Diepkloof took Majohnnie off the streets of Kimberley for two or three years, and he became a model of industry and punctuality; he himself said that if he had gone back to Kimberley, he would have returned to the delinquent life. Yet I do not suppose that Diepkloof *remade* him; it merely encouraged the growth of hungers and aspirations that were there already.

In any case how does one measure success? It can only be done in an arbitrary manner. One can say that a boy has succeeded if he can last two years outside without committing a further offence, or without committing a further offence that could be called criminal; for in South Africa many black offences are purely statutory. If this arbitrary measurement was to be used, then Diepkloof was between fifty percent and sixty percent successful.

But even here the word "successful" must be qualified. A reformatory catering for boys from nine to fifteen years of age will always be more successful than one for boys between sixteen and twenty-one. A reformatory for first offenders will always be more successful than one for second and third offenders. Some of Diepkloof's success must be attributed to the fact that the reformatory was used by magistrates and judges for boys who would have gone to orphanages, farm schools, industrial schools had such places been available. But in South Africa the number of alternative institutions for black boys is extremely small.

I shall close this Diepkloof story with an account of our staff discussions on the purpose, scope, usefulness of the punishment of offences. For many of our staff it was their first introduction to any kind of psychology or sociology or philosophy. Some of them were totally fascinated. Many of them had thought of punishment as the right and proper consequence of an offence. A person offended and he was punished. Whether the punishment had any detrimental or beneficial effect on the offender was almost irrelevant. But now these young white men were working at an institution for black boys, and this institution was styled a "reformatory." It was therefore intended that the "punishment" or the "treatment" should be beneficial. This gave to them a new understanding of the work that had been thrust upon them as a result of the economic recession of the early 1930s. It was the kind of work that few of them would have chosen to do.

I regret only one thing, and that is that I was never able to listen in when they were trying to explain to sceptical parents, uncles and aunts, brothers and sisters, old school friends that they were in fact engaged on a task of national importance. The black supervisory staff had little difficulty in grasping that the reformatory had no punitive role to play. Its sole task was reeducation. What made this new idea easier for them to accept was the fact that the work was being done for the children of their own people.

Chapter 24

In 1938 there happened a great event in the history of Afrikanerdom. The Centenary of the Great Trek was celebrated, that northward migration of the Boers from the British colony of the Cape of Good Hope, so that they could escape from British rule and from the doctrines of racial equality which the British administrator and the British missionary had brought with them. The Boers had not only a fear of equality, they felt also an abhorrence for what Anna Steenkamp, sister of the Boer leader Piet Retief, called "ungodly equality."

The committee responsible for the Centenary conceived the imaginative idea of sending ox-wagons from various points in South Africa to Pretoria, where on Dingane's Day the foundation stone would be laid of architect Moerdyk's massive monument, which was to stand on a commanding ridge just to the south of the city.

These symbolic treks evoked indescribable emotion. There was an upwelling of Afrikaner pride and sentiment such as South Africa had never known. *"Die Stem van Suid-Afrika,"* Langenhoven's patriotic hymn, was sung at every gathering where the wagons were welcomed to town and village. The hymn became familiar to tens of thousands of Afrikaners who had never heard it before, and the reverence accorded to it prepared the way for Parliament to declare it to be the national anthem of South Africa.

The wagons were met in every village and town by men and women in Voortrekker dress. Hundreds of streets were renamed in honour of the Great Trek and the Voortrekkers. Often the mayors of these towns would arrange official welcomes for the wagons, and it happened more than once that non-Afrikaner mayors were rebuffed. What burning Afrikaner zealot would want his wagon to be welcomed by a mayor who was not an Afrikaner zealot too?

Prayers were said over the wagons, meat and *boerewors* * were cooked over the fires, nostalgic Afrikaner *liedjies* ** were sung. Old men and women would weep, and reverently touch the tent of the wagon, its wooden frame, and wheels. Speeches were made of dedication and burning love, and history being what it was, many of these speeches told of past British sins. Relief cuts of the symbolic wagon began to take pride of place in thousands of *sitkamers*.† Small monuments, sometimes cairns of stones, rose all over South Africa to mark the passing of the wagons, but when one spoke of the Monument, one could only be referring to the massive tower that was to be built outside Pretoria.

It was not Hertzog and Smuts with their powerful United Party that played a decisive part in the celebrations. It was Dr. D. F. Malan, with his handful of 27 Nationalists in a House of 153. Afrikaner feelings were intense, and the Nationalists were the most intense Afrikaners. Hertzog could not rival this patriotic fervour. To a large extent his own political battle had been won, but for the Malanites there could be no victory until South Africa had achieved its sovereign independence.

The Malanites opposed the proposal that General Hertzog, Prime Minister and the founder of the National Party, indeed regarded by many as the founder of Afrikanerdom itself, should lay the foundation stone of the Monument. This must be regarded as a bitter period in the life of the ageing patriot; it heralded in fact the end of his influence over Afrikanerdom. He was no longer fervent enough for the other patriots.

Finally three Afrikaner women, descendants of Voortrekker leaders, were chosen for the honour. But it was significant that Malan remained the guest of honour and speaker at the second most important ceremony, the unveiling of the memorial at Blood River. He spoke on the text "The New Great Trek—South Africa's Cry of Distress and the Answer to it." It was clear that for him the black-white struggle was continuing.

The Afrikaans-speaking man of the new Great Trek meets the non-European at the new Blood River, half-armed or completely unarmed, without

---

* Boerewors *is a special South African sausage.*
** Liedjies *are folk songs.*
† Sitkamers *are drawing rooms.*

an entrenchment between them, and without the protection of a river. . . . they meet him defenceless in the open plains of economic equality.*

Malan said further:

Afrikanerdom has found itself again in this year of commemoration. Risen out of the dust of humiliation and self-contempt it now demands full recognition of itself, for its noble ancestry, and their descendants.

He ended with the clarion cry:

Afrikanerdom is calling again.

These events naturally had a great effect on the Afrikaans-speaking members of my staff. Only one, Oubaas Fick, the gardening genius, reacted with ill-concealed hostility to the flag-waving and the great speeches. He was a Smuts man, and he resented the way that Smuts, and Hertzog also, had been pushed to one side. Others like Lanky de Lange and another battalion man, Nonnie Pienaar, were supporters of the United Party, and also resented the contempt with which the new patriots treated the old. One thing was clear, most of the Afrikaners on the staff wanted to go to the Monument for the laying of the stone.

And I wanted to go too. In 1938 my pro-Afrikaner feelings were at their strongest. We got the permission of the department to take the reformatory wagon and oxen to the great ceremony. The flourishing beard became the mark of the patriot and I grew one too, more of an Albert Hertzog type than a Hemingway. The wagon flew the *vierkleur*, the flag of the defeated Transvaal republic, and we wore Voortrekker clothing, carried muskets and Bibles, and great quantities of *boerewors*, *sosaties*, *frikkadelle*, and good coarse loaves which had been baked in an old Dutch oven. I do not remember if we brought wine or brandy, but I think not; and if we did it was most moderately used.

We left Diepkloof on 14 December, and decided to take the more or less quiet road to Pretoria that passes under Aasvoëlskop, and we camped in a pleasant place of trees and grass. After the evening meal we had hymns and a prayer, and retired early to bed, I hoping that Mr. Laas and his skeleton staff were having a quiet time at the

* Natal Mercury, *17 December 1938*.

reformatory. I suppose I need hardly say that there was no black member of our party except the two reformatory boys who looked after the oxen. And should I add that of the quarter-of-a-million people at the site of the Monument, the only black ones were servants? It is doubtful whether any black person would have wished to attend the ceremony, and it is certain that no black person was invited. It was not until 1976, after a troubled year of black unrest, alienation, and hatred, that Afrikaners in larger numbers began to question seriously the views of Dr. Malan as set out at Blood River in 1938.* Some of those who were beginning to rebel more and more strongly against the very idea of celebration called for a Day of a New Covenant, which would be devoted to the cause of racial peace, with services, family meals, and other observances open to all people.

We arrived at the site of the Monument on 15 December, after a very hot journey. I made for the shower and another bearded man said to me, *"Het jy die skare gesien?"* And when I said, *"Ja,"* he said to me with unspeakable comradeliness, *"nou gaan ons die Engelse opdonder."* ** I have often told my friends that the best place to listen to such remarks is under the shower.

The young man was not expressing the official view of the Centenary officials, but his attitude was widely shared. The most notable characteristics of this immense gathering were its fervour and its exclusiveness. The theme of every meeting was Afrikanerdom, its glory, its struggles, its griefs, its achievements. At one remarkable meeting the voice of Mr. E. W. Douglass, K. C., descendant of the 1820 settlers who had given Jacobus Uys a Bible when he set out on the Trek, and who was bringing a message of good will in English, was drowned by the singing of *"Die Stem van Suid-Afrika."* After the singing a man in Voortrekker costume took over the microphone, and began to recite a patriotic verse. There was tumultuous applause, and above it, with the aid of the microphone, the voice could be heard of Advocate E. G. Jansen, Speaker of the House of Assembly and Chairman of the Centenary Committee. He was saying in tones of deep distress, *"Ek is bedroef. . . . ek is diep bedroef. . . .*

* Long before 1976 there were Afrikaners who rejected altogether the idea of celebrating a victory of white over black, but they were for the most part non-Nationalists.
** "Have you seen the crowds?" "Yes." "Now we'll knock hell into the English." The word "opdonder" cannot be adequately translated, but what is more interesting, it was in 1938 regarded as almost an obscenity. I do not know when it first appeared in an Afrikaans dictionary, but it does appear now.

vriende, ek is diep bedroef.'' * His words were drowned by the singing of another patriotic song, *"Afrikaners, landgenote."* * * By this time it was clear that the crowd was in no mood to listen to any English, and Jansen announced that Douglass would say a few words in Afrikaans. This gesture was acclaimed, and Douglass said his few words, which were loudly applauded.

If I remember rightly, the Monument post office was the first which had been allowed since the establishment of the Union of South Africa to advertise itself solely as a *"Poskantoor"* and not as a *"Poskantoor:* Post Office.'' Indeed the Post Office had always had such a reputation for a scrupulous fairness in the use of the two official languages that the making of this exception caused both anger and anxiety, especially among English-speaking people. It was a further sign of the exclusiveness of this Afrikaner festival.

I had also a personal experience of this exclusiveness. The C-to-C Cigarette Company had brought out a series of cigarette cards showing the birds of South Africa and a bird book with empty spaces in which to paste the cards. These books were either in English or in Afrikaans, and Nonnie Pienaar decided to buy the English version as a present for our son David, then aged eight. He asked the girl at the Monument bookshop for an English version, and she said to him, "Why the English version?'' He replied that it was for an English boy, and she said, "This is not an English celebration. You'll find nothing in English here.''

What I had done in good faith and such good will turned to ashes. I wanted only that the celebration should come to an end. It was a lonely and terrible experience for any English-speaking South African who had gone there to rejoice in this Afrikaner festival. Many Afrikaners could not forget that the very founder of Afrikanerdom was not there, but stayed proud and rejected on his farm. Yet I saw the great Smuts there, austere and distinguished. What did he make of it all, the apostle of holism, builder and defender of the Commonwealth of Nations, as he walked through the tremendous crowds, to many of whom he was a traitor? My minister and friend, Jan Hendrik Hofmeyr, was also not there. He was in Bloemfontein saying that the Almighty had ordained that Boer and Briton must live side by side as citizens of one state. He told the gathering: "We should refuse to think in terms of a small South Africa. We have to think in terms of a great South Africa which will become greater.

* *"I am grieved. . . . I am deeply grieved. . . . friends, I am deeply grieved."*
* * *"Afrikaners, countrymen."*

Ons vir jou, Suid-Afrika." That was not the stuff for the new patriots. The real generalship was passing into the hands of the Cape predikant. These fiery believers who were looking for a leader found him in the Afrikaner Malan, not in the biracial Hertzog or the internationalist Smuts.

So the great Centenary celebrations came to an end with Afrikanerdom deeply divided. One might guess that one-third of it followed Malan, one-third Hertzog, and one-third Smuts. Yet under these turbulent waters a new tide was flowing. The Afrikanerdom of Hertzog, with its two streams, its scrupulous recognition of English-speaking rights, its tenderness in spite of indiscretions for English susceptibilities, was ebbing, and the Afrikanerdom of Malan was coming in.

The Afrikaner universities were turning out not Smuts men and women, not Hertzog men and women, but Malan men and women. The Afrikaner schools with their fiercely nationalist teachers were turning out Malan boys and girls. The Afrikaner scout movements and the cultural movements were not excited about the Commonwealth of Nations or the biracial policy, but about being Afrikaners, about the day when Afrikaners would govern, when there would be no more equality in Church and State. South Africa would be ruled firmly and resolutely by the Afrikaner people, for had they not been given a divine mission to bring Christianity and civilisation to a barbaric continent? Those who were sensitive about their chauvinism spoke earnestly about their mission, but it was not the mission or the Christianity or the civilisation that could bring that burning light into the eyes, it was being Afrikaner, it was belonging to a people who after years of struggle and suffering were drawing nearer to the Promised Land. Who could doubt the truth of that? Certainly not any person who had been one of the throng that gathered on the ridge where the Monument was to arise.

I did not return to Diepkloof with the wagon, because I was anxious to get back to the reformatory. I went to Dorrie and said, "I'm taking off this beard and I'll never grow another." It is an irony that it was my sympathy for the renascence of Afrikanerdom that enabled me to escape from the narrow British nationalism of God, King, and Empire, only to find that Afrikaner nationalism was just as narrow. I realised at the Monument that one would be acceptable to Afrikaner nationalism only if one wholly supported its political aims, and to do that I had no wish or intention. I realised too that Malan's kind of Afrikaner nationalism was growing more and more powerful. I have no doubt that if a general election had been held in that centenary year, Malan would have gained more parliamentary seats. From that sixteenth day of December, 1938, I became anti-Nationalist. With Malan's brand of exclusive nationalism, and particularly with his race theories, I wished to have nothing to do.

When I told Mr. Hofmeyr of my disillusionment, he gave his characteristic snort and said, "It took you a long time to find out." That was somewhat unfair, because as a young professor he had been a bit of a Nationalist himself. Yet he was to become, in the words of the Public Orator at Oxford University in 1945, "strength and stay of the British Commonwealth."

Many English-speaking South Africans were shocked by the revelation of the depth and intensity of the new Afrikaner nationalism. But they were frightened also. They were apprehensive of what a triumphant nationalism might do to their security and traditions. Yet as we shall see, the advance of nationalism was arrested—or appeared to have been arrested—by the great world events of 1939. For the years of the war, under the compelling influence of Smuts, the aim of achieving an independent republic took second place to that of the destruction of Nazism.

I must record that though I became strongly anti-Nationalist in 1936, I never became anti-Afrikaner. I never developed any prejudice against the Afrikaner's language or literature. My cultural bonds with people like Ernie and Janie Malherbe of the University of Natal, with Leo and Nell Marquard of the Oxford University Press, with Uys Krige, the poet and troubadour, and later with writers like André Brink and religious leaders like Beyers Naudé, were as strong as with any other South African.* And then of course there was J. H. Hofmeyr, who had put me in charge of Diepkloof Reformatory; but the Nationalists maintained that he was not an Afrikaner at all. We all shared a love of justice and a hatred of exclusive nationalism and racialism.

Now having rejected Afrikaner nationalism, I went in quest of a new nationalism that would be based on the love of one's land, though many would argue, and not without foundation, that a *common land* cannot compete with a *common language*, a *common culture*, a *common history*, as a binding force. Nevertheless, foolishly or not, that is what I went in quest of.

---

* I should like to include Karel Schoeman, whose novel Na die Geliefde Land affected me deeply. But I do not know him well enough. Last time I met him he did not even want his novel translated into English. However, he later authorised an English translation.

Chapter 25

When Hertzog and Smuts went into coalition in 1933 and into fusion in 1934, they left grave constitutional questions unanswered. The King of Great Britain was also the King of South Africa, and if the King of Great Britain went to war, could the King of South Africa stay neutral? Was the Crown divisible or indivisible? Did neutrality in war mean secession from the Commonwealth?

The advantages of fusion were very great. It meant a respite from bitter internal strife. For Hertzog it meant a chance to secure the two-thirds majority of both houses sitting together which would enable him to amend the Cape franchise. This permitted an African to qualify for the right to vote for candidates in the parliamentary elections, a provision which was offensive to the old republics, especially the Transvaal, which had stated in its constitution, "no equality in Church or State." For Smuts it meant a chance to strengthen the loyalty of South Africa to the Commonwealth of Nations.

In 1934 both Hertzog and Smuts had hoped that the questions of war and neutrality would not need to be answered, at least not until the country had enjoyed a generation of racial peace, during which white South Africans would draw closer together. It is clear that in 1938 Smuts no longer assumed, as he had in 1914, that if Great Britain went to war, South Africa would automatically go to war too. On 28 September 1938 the whole cabinet agreed with a statement of policy by Hertzog that in the event of war between Britain and Germany, South Africa would be neutral, but would abide by the agreement which allowed Britain to maintain a naval base at Simonstown.

Minister Oswald Pirow wrote later that Smuts had accepted the policy statement merely to gain time, and in the belief that a European war was still some distance off. W. K. Hancock in his *Smuts* shows that this was not the case. Smuts was convinced that war was near, and it would not be a "foreign war" in which South Africa would have no interest. It would be a war against Hitler, about which he wrote, "To me the wonder is how so small and commonplace a person can wield such influence for evil."

Yet Hitler did not rouse in the Afrikaner Nationalist breast the same anger and fear that he roused in English-speaking South Africa. Many Nationalists admired him. Germany, like the Boers, had been defeated by Britain, and now, like Afrikanerdom, she was rising again. Many of them too sympathised with Hitler's hatred of the Jews. In any case why should South Africa concern herself with the wars of Europe?

Diepkloof Reformatory was affected strongly both by the Voortrekker Centenary and the rise to power of Hitler. The more extreme Nationalists on my staff were undoubtedly given confidence by both these events. Surely if the United Party Government were replaced by a Nationalist Party Government, white South Africa would handle her racial affairs with greater determination. New apartheid laws would be passed to bring about racial separation in every possible area of life. The Immorality Act, which made it a criminal offence for a white person to have sexual relations with an African, would be amended so as to forbid all such relations between a white person and any other. Another scandal, the lack of a law to forbid mixed marriages, would be put right. Separate residential and business areas would be proclaimed for all races. Yet another scandal would be ended—the right exercised by such universities as the Witwatersrand and Cape Town to admit Indian, Coloured, and African students. The racial laissez-faire of the United Party would be brought to an end, and South Africa would enter a golden era of justice and peace, in which every race and nation could fully realise its own identity, preserve its own culture, maintain its own language.

Where was there a greater example of firm orderly rule than Germany under Hitler? Even a man like Engelbrecht was influenced by the mood of authoritarianism that was infecting the National Party.

Men like de Lange and Pienaar watched these developments with anxiety. Oubaas Fick watched them with contempt; if there was war he would be one of the first to enlist.

As for me, who had entertained pacifist ideas in the Great War of 1914–1918, I had no doubt that Hitler must be resisted by armed force. I was now thirty-six years of age, but if they would take me I would enlist too.

My own position as Principal remained strong, though some of my staff received with satisfaction the news in September 1938 that Mr. Hofmeyr had resigned from the cabinet, and was therefore no longer the Minister of Education. If, however, they had expected any change in the departmental policy for Diepkloof, they were to be disappointed. The new minister was Mr. Henry Fagan, who was to prove an enlightened administrator also.

Mr. Hofmeyr resigned from the cabinet on what many thought to be a minor issue. They thought that he should have resigned in 1936 when Hertzog with the help of Smuts removed the Cape African voters from the common roll to a separate and segregated roll where they would now vote for their own parliamentary representatives. These representatives would, however, have to be white. In the general election of 1938 one of Hertzog's faithful supporters, A. P. J. Fourie, lost his seat to Malan's party. Hertzog was determined to get him back. In the Senate there were four special senators nominated because of their "thorough acquaintance with the reasonable wants and wishes of the coloured races." One of these obligingly resigned, and Hertzog appointed Fourie in his place. Hofmeyr decided that this was a "prostitution of the constitution" and resigned.

Hertzog was glad to be rid of him, and Smuts was displeased that his protégé should desert him when Europe was on the edge of war. Malan was delighted with the resignation, because here was further proof that the Hertzog–Smuts partnership was far from being a joyful one. But thousands of men and women were encouraged by this sign of probity in public life. I was one of these, and from that day on I looked for the day when Hofmeyr would be Prime Minister. He, so to speak, became my politics.

The year 1939 was an anxious year for the world, and it further widened the gap that separated the Afrikaner Nationalists from the other peoples of South Africa, and the Nationalists on the Diepkloof Reformatory staff from the rest of its members. The black staff was unanimously anti-Hitler, as indeed were the black people of South Africa. There is one big difference between those days and the ones we live through now. In 1939, if South Africa had gone to war, the internal danger would have come from the Afrikaner Nationalist, but the black people would have presented none. If South Africa went to war today, the internal danger from black people would be considerable. This is not because they hated Hitler and love Russia. It is because the whole world has changed. There is a proverb, "Better the devil you know than the one you don't." But today for many black people the proverb runs, "Better the devil you don't know than the one you do."

It would be wrong to believe that in 1939 the majority of Afrikaners were pro-Hitler. Some undoubtedly were, because they were attracted by his authoritarian rule. But for many their apparent pro-Hitlerism was really a hatred of British Imperialism that in 1902 had defeated and annexed their two republics. My young supervisor, de Lange, who was no fanatic, said to me, "If there's a war I don't want England to lose it, but I want her to suffer."

On 1 September 1939 Hitler marched into Poland. On 2 September Hertzog promised to make a statement in the House. On 3 September Britain declared war on Germany. In the afternoon the South African cabinet met, and it was clear that Smuts and six ministers were for declaring war, and Hertzog and five ministers were against. On 4 September there was a tense debate in the House. Hertzog proposed that South Africa remain neutral. He said that Britain had declared war because she had certain obligations towards Poland, but South Africa had no such obligations. He asked why Britain had not also declared war on Russia, who had also marched into Poland. If the House decided to remain neutral it would be proof to the world and to the Afrikaner that South Africa was truly an independent nation.

It was thought by certain observers of substance that Hertzog might have carried his motion had he stopped there. But (irritated by an objection, it was said) he then defended Hitler's actions. "I know what it is to be driven by humiliation."

Smuts followed Hertzog, and declared that whatever could have been said for Hitler, it could no longer be said after his rape of Czechoslovakia. It was not a problem of Poland. Hitler would next demand South West Africa. His aim was the domination of the world. Smuts moved that South Africa declare war.

All were aware of the grave cleavage in the House. Those who supported Hertzog were overwhelmingly Afrikaans-speaking, and those who supported Smuts overwhelmingly English-speaking. When the count was taken, Smuts won by eighty votes to sixty-seven.

Anti-war Afrikanerdom was dumbfounded. The man who had led them for fifteen years was gone, and in his place was the imperialist Smuts. When they had recovered from their shock, their anger and resentment was openly and defiantly expressed. Throughout South Africa, but especially among the English-speaking, there was fear of violence and rebellion. But Smuts wasted no time on speculation about what outraged Afrikanerdom would do, or whether it would win the next election and make a separate peace. He moved with certitude through these many dangers. In those days the whole of English-speaking South Africa, and probably a third of Afrikanerdom, were under his spell. It is strange to reflect that had an election been held then, he would possibly have lost it.*

The great danger to Smuts and to the war effort was the secret and semimilitary organisation known as the *Ossewabrandwag*, the Ox-wagon Watch, composed of those who stood on guard against the dangers that threatened Afrikanerdom. It was founded in 1938, the year of the Voortrekker Centenary, and its duty was to cherish "the spirit of the ox-wagon." It was called the O.B., and was much more the product of those Hitlerian days than of Afrikanerdom.

With the declaration of war the O.B. had a tremendous accession of strength. They would not fight for Smuts, but they would fight for Afrikanerdom. They held great gatherings on the farms, where they drilled and performed military exercises. As the fortunes of Britain declined, so did the O.B. wax in numbers and defiance. Their leaders expressed the greatest contempt for democracy and party politics, and a belief in the authoritarian state. Whether because of their strength, or whether because they deceived him, Malan came out strongly in their support. For a while the new Hertzog-Malan opposition had to consider the O.B. as a serious rival, and therefore Nationalist politicians made intemperate speeches of a kind that today would be considered treasonable, and held stop-the-war meetings throughout the country. Smuts was urged by many of his supporters to take sterner measures, but guided by a wisdom and courage that belong only to the great, he would not. The O.B. now claimed to have 200,000, even 400,000 members, more than Smuts had in the armed forces. There seems

* The Governor-General, Sir Patrick Duncan, had after the vote in the House refused Hertzog's request for a dissolution of Parliament and therefore for a general election. Had Hertzog resigned as soon as he lost the majority in the cabinet, he would probably have been asked by the Governor-General to form a new Government, from which he could have excluded Smuts and the six ministers who supported him. The Governor-General would then probably have granted the dissolution, and it is possible that Hertzog would have won the election.

little doubt that had Britain's fortunes further declined, the O.B. would have tried to seize power by violence.

It was on September 4 that Smuts defeated Hertzog's neutrality motion by eighty votes to sixty-seven. On September 5 the atmosphere at Diepkloof Reformatory was electric. The day's work started at 8:00 A.M., and usually at a few minutes to eight the whole staff would be assembled round and about the entrance gate, engaged in gossip and good-natured banter. But this morning the feeling of rebellion was in the air. Supervisor Oosthuisen, our physical training expert and normally the most docile of men, came up to me truculently as I came out of my office to attend the morning parade. "Sir," he said, "I want you to know that I shall never fight in this war." "Mr. Oosthuisen," I said, "it is unlikely that anyone will want you to." I could see that others, including the older Keulder, wished to convey the same information, so I postponed the morning parade and asked Mr. Laas to call a white staff meeting in the dining room of the single quarters.

In fact young Oosthuisen had done me a favour. I had come to work that morning knowing that the majority of the white staff would be hostile to the new Government, and fearing that they might be hostile to me also, I did not really know what to do about it, whether to proceed with the day's work, as though nothing extraordinary had happened or to call the staff together. Now Oosthuisen had made up my mind for me.

I told the staff that we as public servants owed exactly the same loyalty to the Department of Education as we had under the previous Government. We were not expected to owe political loyalty to the new Government, but we would be expected to obey its lawful commands. It would be our duty to work as hard as before to produce food and vegetables, and to make economies where it was possible. In fact we might have to work harder if the department allowed some of our staff to enlist without replacement. There was one thing we could not do, and that would be to hinder or obstruct the Government in its prosecution of the war. A most serious view would be taken of any attempt to do so. With Oosthuisen in mind I said that I thought it in the highest degree improbable that the Government would introduce conscription, but I did not add that I thought it would be in the highest degree dangerous as well.

The staff meeting cleared the air, but it in no way lessened the hostility. We had hardly finished when Oubaas Fick, the Head Supervisor of the gardens, came to me and said that he wished to join the army as soon as it was possible. And he was followed soon after by Chief Supervisor James Hope. Ultimately nine of the white staff were allowed to enlist, six Afrikaners and three English speakers. If I remember rightly we were allowed three replacements, all of them of course opposed to the war.

After the white staff meeting was over, the black members were gathered together. Here there was no hostility at all. It was well known that Hitler regarded black people as inferior creatures, fit only to obey. Some of them would have asked permission to enlist, but in South Africa a black man might not bear arms. The black contribution would be harder work, bigger *spans*, perhaps longer hours. This they were fully prepared to make.

While some of my staff members were asking permission to enlist in the armed forces, others were joining the *Ossewabrandwag*. In 1940 Smuts felt strong enough to forbid any policeman to belong to the O.B. Civil servants were then forbidden to wear the O.B. badge. The response of my anti-war staff members, and of many others, was to wear the tops of mineral water bottles in their buttonholes. This was too much for me. I called a white staff meeting and said that the wearing of these tops was in fact an oblique defiance of the ruling of the Government, and I urged those who wore them to stop it. Otherwise I would feel obliged to report the practice to the department. Some took out the bottle tops at once. Others felt it their duty to continue for a few days.

The early days of the war were of great difficulty. As the nine volunteers were allowed one by one to join the army, the white staff was overwhelmingly composed of those who were against the war. I was not the only pro-war white member left, for there was at least one other who was for physical reasons unable to enlist; but I was now the only English-speaking member left. Things were made worse by the early disasters of the war, these being welcomed by the anti-war brigade. I have no doubt that my determination to see it through was greatly strengthened by the fact that we were being led by men like Churchill and Smuts, and of course by the fact that one of Smuts's first acts was to bring back Hofmeyr to the cabinet, as Minister of Finance and Education. Then too there was the unanimous support of the black staff for the vigorous prosecution of the war.

I do not remember when I also sought permission to enlist but it was earlier rather than later. I was thirty-six years of age. The First World War had passed me by, now the Second was to do likewise. The department decided that I was to be placed in the category of "key men," and would not let me go. Therefore I belong to that small group of men who were too young for the first war, and either too old or too "important" for the second. Therefore I have never heard a shot fired in war, nor have I ever been wounded, nor have I ever wounded or killed a man. It happens even today that after I have written for the press some strong political article criticising the Government, some angry anonymous person telephones to ask what I did in the great world wars to protect my country. The irony of such calls is that they are made by men who fought against the race theories and practices of Hitler, but who now object to any condemnation of their own. Their argument is that if I did not fight in either war, then I have no right to criticise the Government of my country. Their argument contains a further irony, in that most of the leading members of the present Government also refused to fight for their country in 1939.

Many white South Africans were seized by a kind of crusading spirit when they went to fight against Hitler. The eyes of some of these were opened, and they saw, some for the first time, that our own racial practices were indefensible. But the majority, when the war was over, returned to acquiesce in, and some vehemently to defend, those racial laws, customs, and conventions that deny liberty to so many of our people. Such, it seems, is the nature of collective man.

I would not wish to live again through that first year of the war. My relations with my white staff became increasingly confined to matters of work and duty, except for the one who was in favour of the waging of the war. Although the first white settlers in South Africa came from Holland, and although Afrikaans is the child of Hollands, the invasion and fall of Holland in May 1940 left the anti-war factions unmoved. Hertzog and Malan, now reunited, called for a separate peace. Paris fell in June 1940, this delighting the Nationalists and plunging many of the Smutsites into gloom. Malan said openly that the defeat of Britain was only a matter of time.

In this year 1940 my brother Atholl joined the army. Though immensely popular with women, he had never married but had for some years been very friendly with a Miss Allison of Pietermaritzburg. When he enlisted they decided to get married, and after a few days together, he was sent to the great camp at Sonderwater in the Transvaal. Dorrie and I went to see him there, and he said to us, "I'm not coming back." And he was right too. On December 16, 1940, Dingane's Day, the holy day of the Afrikaner calendar, he was killed at El Wak in northern Kenya. It was the first South African land skirmish, nothing like a battle, and Atholl and the man lying next to him were the first South African soldiers killed in action.*

The news was telephoned to me from Pietermaritzburg. I had never been very close to my brother nor had I seen much of him since my appointment at Diepkloof. I did not weep, but broke out into a kind of sobbing, which astonished me. Why should that be? Does blood matter all that much? For a day or two I walked about in a kind of daze. My mother never recovered from Atholl's death. The naughty boy of the family, who called her Eunice and his grandmother Bessie, was perhaps the nearest to her after all. She lived for more than twenty years after that, but I think that December 16 became for her also a holy day. In the last year of her life she called me by many names that were not my own, but she never called me Atholl.

I do not wish to give the impression that my white staff went about openly gloating over Britain's defeats and Hitler's victories. They carried out their duties with their customary thoroughness. Although it was our duty to assist and not to hinder the Government in the prosecution of the war, Diepkloof remained as it were a neutral territory. The Japanese attack on Pearl Harbour and the entry of the United States into the war certainly appeared to lighten the atmosphere, for from that day the anti-war factions began to concede that Hitler might lose the war.

There were nevertheless still heavy blows to fall. One was the loss in December 1941 of the two great battleships *Repulse* and *Prince of Wales*, another event that gave great satisfaction to the more bitter opponents of the war. The other came six months later, when on June 21, 1942, the South African army suffered an almost irreparable loss. It lost two out of the three brigade groups of its 2nd Division in the fall of Tobruk. Smuts called for 7,000 men to make good the losses, and again I applied for permission to enlist, and was again refused.

It was on some such occasion, or in a period of depression, that I did a foolish thing. Sister Frances Mary, a member of the Community of the Resurrection and principal of the Grahamstown Teachers' Training College, came to spend the day at Diepkloof Reformatory. We visited every part of the institution, and at a few minutes to one o'clock I took her to the big gate so that she could see the *spans* march out to work. The bell had not yet rung and all the staff were there, ready to resume work. Sister Frances Mary was a tall

* *I believe that other South Africans in other services had already lost their lives in action (e.g., in the air).*

commanding woman, and she was dressed in a black habit and wore a chain with a cross around her neck. To the Afrikaner members of the Dutch Reformed Churches, perhaps more so then than now, she was an alien figure, made still more so by her black habit and her cross. It was then that I heard Supervisor van Wyk refer to her as the *Swart Ma,* the "Black Mother," after which there was laughter. I contained my anger, but at four o'clock when the *spans* returned, I sent for van Wyck, and challenged him with having spoken derogatorily of my guest.

Van Wyck was incredulous.

"What did I say?" he asked.

"You called her the *Swart Ma,* and all your friends laughed."

"*Meneer,* I did nothing of the kind."

"But I heard you."

In his distress he racked his mind for some explanation. I may say that in all these years I had found him not only a first-class supervisor, but a well-mannered young man.

Suddenly he knew what it was all about.

"*Meneer,* the words you heard were *swart mark.*" (These words in Afrikaans meant the "black market," which of course was well known in those war years.)

"*Meneer,* we were joking about the black market. Mr. Keulder needed new tyres for his car, and I was telling him that he would get them only on the *swart mark.*"

What was I to say? I realised at once that only a genius could have invented such an explanation. I realised that it was my beleaguered self that had misinterpreted the sounds, largely because I had been living in what seemed to me to be an atmosphere of hostility, the extent of which I had almost certainly exaggerated. There was only one thing to do and that was to apologise, and I did it properly. I thought I should add a reason for my jumping to such an extreme conclusion, which was in fact the isolation of those days. Van Wyck accepted the explanation but I could see that he did not comprehend it. And why should he have done so? Why should I feel isolated when General Smuts was my Prime Minister and Mr. Hofmeyr was the Minister of Education? The tide of war was slowly turning in favour of the Allies, the Afrikaner Nationalist opposition was in total disarray, and more and more young Afrikaners were joining the armed forces.

It is I think a fairly common experience to mishear words when one is in a position of isolation. If one thinks that people are talking about oneself, derogatorily and with laughter, one may well strain one's ears to catch what they are saying, and hear words that were never spoken. As I have written before, in South Africa of recent years it has come to be regarded as offensive for a white person to call a black one a *"kaffir,"* and the courts of law have ruled that it *is* offensive. In the small Zululand town of Empangeni, a Zulu took a white man to court for calling him a *kaffir,* but the white man, who was a Scot, told the magistrate that he said, "Och man, you're a duffer," and the magistrate believed him.

It was very easy in those war years at Diepkloof for staff members to drop poison into the ears of the principal. It was permissible for senior staff members in positions of authority to make reports on juniors, but if anyone else tried to do it, I would ask immediately if he was willing to make the statement in the presence of the person of whom he was complaining. If he said No, then I would refuse to listen any further. This is a rule that has served me well ever since, and it certainly puts an end to malicious backbiting that wishes to remain anonymous.

It was in these war years that I had my first experience of the security police. They came to see me to get confidential confirmation about Mr. L., who was a temporary replacement for one of our supervisors who had joined the army. I did not like Mr. L. at all, and I knew that he had been a member of the *Ossewabrandwag,* but of his private life I knew nothing. Of course the security police swore me to secrecy, and this gave me a certain sense of importance. I had no idea then that in a matter of ten years or so they would be investigating my own private life, or rather I should say my political life, and tapping my telephone, and opening my letters. Our previous Prime Minister, Mr. B. J. Vorster, was interned by General Smuts during these war years; he complained bitterly of the way in which his life and liberty had been interfered with, but when he became First Minister of Justice and then Prime Minister, he did the same things, and he did them more drastically. He later became a great upholder of law and order, but only because they were now his own.

These replacement supervisors were on the whole hopeless. The trouble with them was not that they were anti-war. It was that they were men who would have had no chance of getting into the public service, if it had not been for the manpower shortage. They could not compare with my own anti-war supervisors. In fact the work of the reformatory would have degenerated if it had not been for these stubborn Nationalists of my own, and of course the black staff whose numbers were not reduced. One of my replacements was my first homosexual staff member, except for the ex-reformatory boy made supervisor, whom I mentioned earlier. However, Mr. V. confined his attentions to boys outside the reformatory, and was a scoutmaster in Johannesburg. Before long he was brought before the court, and his sentence was suspended on condition he join the army. He was next discharged from the army for the same reason, and I was able to get him an job in the Public Works Department of South West Africa, only because anyone could get a job in those years. It was not long before he was again brought before the court, and when he came out of prison he returned to Diepkloof, but neither the department nor the Principal would have employed him. He told me the story of his life, and it is one of the most tragic stories I have ever listened to. For deep reasons, no doubt, he was the slave of his sexual desires. They commanded his attention for almost every waking hour, even when he was at his desk, where he worked satisfactorily. One encountered again the riddle of responsibility, not only as a question for the courts, but for himself too, because he was bitterly ashamed of his activities. If he had confined them to men of his own age, his life would have been easier. The white supervisors regarded him with contempt, and the black with curiosity. Dorrie was the only woman on the farm who allowed him in her home.

I shall close this chapter with a story of yet another replacement supervisor. He was Mr. N., who was a simple man of very little education and of very obliging nature. He was vaguely anti-war, and he drove the reformatory truck, which conveyed goods to and from Diepkloof, took discharged boys to the Johannesburg station, and brought new ones to the reformatory. Mr. N. also did shopping for the Diepkloof wives both white and black, and Dorrie grew quite fond of him. They had conversations in his elementary English and her elementary Afrikaans, and he would regale her with simple tales of his life and times. One day he astonished her by saying, "You know, Mrs. Paton, you can't make a Jew turn in Benoni." "You can't what, Mr. N.?" "You can't make a Jew turn in Benoni." She thought it over for a moment and then she astonished him by going off into peals of laughter, for Mr. N. the truck driver was telling her that one could not make a U-turn in Benoni.

Chapter 26

I suppose that the great majority of Smuts supporters who did not enlist worked twice as hard during the war years as they had before. It was not long after the outbreak of war that I found myself appointed the National Chairman of the YMCA–Toc H War Work Council, our president being Mr. J. H. Hofmeyr. Our work was to establish recreation centres for soldiers at every camp in South Africa, and after our men had moved north, at every camp outside it.

My chairmanship opened up a new world for me, that of money and business. If £20,000 was wanted for a new project, a few of the leading businessmen on the council would raise it in an hour over their telephones. For those years I moved amongst men who earned three or four or five times as much as I did; I should add that Diepkloof Reformatory had been upgraded, and I now earned £900 per annum. One member of my council lived in a grand house in Westcliff, and he earned three times as much as I did, but while I was wrestling with the problems of the universe, he was conducting an agency for china vessels, and his showroom was full of chamberpots. For a short time I wrestled also with one of the seven deadly sins, that of covetousness; also with a sense of injustice that one could get more for selling chamberpots than for running a reformatory. I am glad to say that I won both these contests, but I would hesitate to ascribe this to some kind of inner strength. I think it was because I thought the principalship of a reformatory more prestigious * than the ownership of an agency for china vessels. What was more, the staff of Diepkloof was now nearly eighty, whereas the agency owner had only a lady typist. This worked both ways, however; on the one hand it increased the prestigiousness, on the other it inflamed the sense of injustice. Luckily for me this materialistic phase came to an end, and just as well, for covetousness, like hatred, is a destroyer of personality.**

Ever since coming to Johannesburg I had devoted much of my spare time to Toc H. I made lifelong friends there. One was Tom Savage, full-time padre of the movement, who later became Bishop of Zululand. I am tempted to say that he was the holiest man I ever knew but the description doesn't quite fit, because of the earthiness and saltiness of his humour. He had been an engineer before he became a priest, and told the story of how he took his parish car to a garage, and when he went to fetch it again was presented with a bill that staggered him. He asked for details, and when he was given them he said to the proprietor, "Look here, mate, don't be fooled by this collar; before I took to wearing it, I was an engineer, and I tell you these things you put right didn't need putting right at all." He had innocent blue eyes and an irresistible smile, and he had the extraordinary gift of making men feel repentant without accusing them. He could make a tough believer in the colour bar begin to feel ashamed of it, a gift I have never had myself. His standards were high, and he would judge every act by them, but there was no sanctimony in him because his judgements were salty too. Dorrie and I went to see him when he was dying, and he spoke calmly about death and eternal life. When we left he gave us his last blessing, but while we wept he smiled, and perhaps indeed he was smiling at our weeping. All this strength, these gifts, this earthy spiritual power were there to be discerned in those early years in Johannesburg. I would find it impossible to believe that Tom Savage lived his life in the service of a Power that doesn't exist, that he prostrated himself before the creation of his own imagination. People have said to me, "Where's this Holy Spirit? Show Him to me." It was a question much easier to answer when Tom Savage was alive. One does not point to oneself, yet one's faith is that He is there too.

Then there was Michael Westropp, a layman and also a full-time organiser for Toc H, who later entered the priesthood and in 1976

---

* *This word is not good enough for the Shorter Oxford, but it was good enough for Joseph Conrad.*
** *I never quite understood the difference between covetousness and envy. Is envy worse? I envied my business friend for his wealth, but I never had feeling of ill will towards him.*

retired from the vicarship of Natland, near Kendal in the Lake District. He was a man of inexhaustible vigour, but would drop off to sleep at the most extraordinary moments. He gave his last evening in South Africa to Dorrie and me, and after dinner went to sleep. He would have slept till dawn if we had not known that he had an interview in Johannesburg at midnight, so we woke him up at eleven-thirty. He made no apology but looked at us in a way that seemed to say, "Odd thing, isn't it?"

I shall mention three more friends. One was Ronald Anderson, who also became a full-time organiser for Toc H, and another was Eric Tucker, who went into the newspaper world. I shall always remember these two for one thing above all others—the unselfish and ungrudging pride that they felt in the achievements, and the struggles too, of my later life.

The one Toc H member who was to become known throughout the Christian world was an irreverent young man who had the unbelievable name of Gonville Aubie ffrench-Beytagh. He was born in Shanghai in 1912 and in 1933 came to South Africa on the Chinese quota. He was an agnostic and had no time for the church, but said daily the Collect for the Nineteenth Sunday after Trinity:

O God, forasmuch as without thee we are not able to please thee: mercifully grant that thy Holy Spirit may in all things direct and rule our hearts: through Jesus Christ our Lord. Amen.

He had promised an old governess to do this, and he kept his promise, but he declared it was not religion. It was in Toc H that he met Savage, Anderson, and myself. In those days he had thoughts of marrying, and conceived the strange notion that if he had sons, he would like them to resemble these three gentlemen, if not immediately, then certainly later on.

ffrench-Beytagh affected a deep cynicism, deflated all pomp and pretension, and despised conventional dress. Though not a Christian he joined Toc H and he believed that one's life is wasted if not used in the service of others. When it was time for prayers he shed his irreverence. What happened next, though startling, was not totally out of pattern.

On a dark night in 1936 he was walking through the Braamfontein subway on his way home. He was set upon by thugs who knocked him on the head, broke his jaw, and left him for dead. When he came to himself in a bed in Johannesburg General Hospital, the first person he saw was myself. His injuries were very serious, and his long stay in the hospital gave him time to reflect on the nature and destiny of man, and the nature and destiny of himself. When he recovered he went to live in the Toc H Mark in Johannesburg, under the leadership of Tom Savage. Then he wrote to Bishop Clayton asking for advice as to whether he should enter the priesthood.

Once ffrench-Beytagh had decided to become a priest, he took his vocation seriously, but he remained irreverent, untidy, and careless about his health. I once spoke at evensong for him at St. Boniface, Germiston, a dead parish that he had made alive. His influence over young people was very great, and after evensong the noise in his house was tremendous. He and I sat in a corner and ate our supper, but the crowd took no notice of him nor he of them. Later he became Dean of Salisbury in Southern Rhodesia and finally Dean of Johannesburg. Here a new ffrench-Beytagh emerged. More and more he identified himself with the cause of black liberation, and more and more he opposed apartheid, not least from his pulpit. He became more and more involved in the defence of people charged with political offences and finally in January 1971 he was detained under the Terrorism Act of 1967.

In brief, the charges against ffrench-Beytagh were that he possessed and distributed pamphlets advocating violence, that he had himself advocated violence, and that he had received money from the banned International Defence and Aid Fund. After a trial lasting three months, Judge-President Cillie sentenced ffrench-Beytagh to five years, the mandatory minimum sentence under the Terrorism Act. Some six months later the Appellate Division in Bloemfontein set the sentence aside. That day ffrench-Beytagh flew to London, never to return.

He wrote the story of all these things in his book *Encountering Darkness.* Apparently one of the reasons he became a Christian was myself. It must have been a case of the force of example. I was certainly not aware of exercising it. I was not a conscious evangelist. Nor would I have put myself in the same class as Tom Savage as an exemplar.

Yet the fact remains that Savage, Westropp, Anderson, Tucker, ffrench-Beytagh, myself, and many others devoted a great part of their energy, time, and talents to what could be called "the service of others." We travelled up and down the Witwatersrand founding new Toc H groups. How I did this while trying to make a prison into a school I don't quite know.

When war broke out in 1939 I adopted an impossibly ethical line in regard to the work of Toc H. I considered that whatever services it rendered to members of the armed forces, it must not identify itself with the military arm. Since the war of 1914-1918, Toc H had endeavoured to bring about the reconciliation of past enemies, and I considered that this work would be irredeemably compromised if we regarded the winning of the war as part of the duty of Toc H. In Great Britain they had no such compunction. Hitler was evil, and Toc H must join wholeheartedly in the struggle against him.

My attitude caused consternation in Toc H, the more so because I had come to be regarded as a kind of official expounder of Toc H values. I remember the distress of Les Campling, our South African Vice-Chairman, as good a man as we had in the movement. He respected me and thought I was wrong. The silly part of it all was that I thought that Hitler was evil too, and yet I would for the sake of some ethereal idea have prevented Toc H from joining the struggle against him.

Why was this? It was because I, and only a few other Toc H men, knew the traumatic effect that the war decision had on Afrikanerdom. We were a reconciling movement, and the war had proved disastrously divisive. On the day that war was declared I made a special journey to see the Afrikaans-speaking Commanding Officer of the South African Police at Booysens to assure him that I hoped that nothing would disturb the cordial relations between us, and he assured me that nothing would. What is more, Toc H in the Transvaal had made great efforts to recruit Afrikaners. The members of the group at the Westfort Leper Asylum outside Pretoria were mostly Afrikaners, and some of them were violently anti-war. What would be the effect on them if Toc H, so to speak, declared war too?

Campling's reply to this was that the defeat of Hitler far outweighed any consideration for our members in Westfort. Why, if Hitler won the war, that would be the end of Toc H, and of all the values it stood for. In the end I had to give up my lofty ethical line. And to tell the truth, I was much happier once I had done it. Did I not tell my own white staff that whatever their political views they had no right to impede the war effort in any way? The hard truth is that once you go to war, many of your moral principles can no longer be obeyed. I remember a story of the Great War of 1914-1918; a woman said to Lord Kitchener, "Aren't the German atrocities in Belgium too terrible?," and he replied, "Madame, war itself is an atrocity."

All my life I have hated war. Yet there are times when it has to be made. It had to be made against Hitler, but it didn't make a brave new world, it made one just as terrifying. All through England and Scotland there are, in schools, churches, railway stations, even on the open moors, monuments, memorials, plaques, stones erected in memory of those who have died century after century, but never made a brave new world. Round Ladysmith in Natal the flat thorn hills are crowned with many monuments in memory of the young men of Dorset and Norfolk and Cumberland and Midlothian, who came thousands of miles to this far country to fight the unknown Boers, this handful of men who threatened the power and might and glory of the great Empire. And not far from Ladysmith are the monuments to the Boers themselves, in the land of Weenen, which is Weeping, men and women searching for a new country, slaughtered by the warriors of the Zulu king. And had the black people erected monuments, there would have been hundreds of them too, to warriors and innocent women and children killed by the warriors of other black chiefs and kings. And there would have to be one great national monument to the people of the San, the Bushmen, whom Elizabeth Marshall Thomas called "the harmless people" * — and she ought to know because she lived amongst them—the small diminutive people to whom, with the Khoikhoi, the Hottentots, this whole subcontinental land belonged, with its plains and its mountains, its lions and its elephants, and its antelopes running, a people wiped out by the stronger races, the Dutch, the British, the Zulus, the Xhosas, reduced to the remnant of themselves, living now in the desert lands of the Kalahari where no one else desires to live.

In 1939 war had to be. But from the moment that it was declared there was declared also a moratorium on the gentler virtues, mercy, compassion, kindness. The moratorium was not absolute, for one showed these virtues to one's own and even occasionally to one's enemies. But the supreme aim is to kill. And your young tender son goes to the army and there he is taught, thoroughly and methodically, to kill. One is taught not to overkill, but that is not a virtue, it is merely an injunction not to waste time killing here when it would be more profitable to spend it killing there.

So young men, many of whom had learned in home and school and church the sacred commandment, "Thou shalt not kill," jettisoned their learning for a while, and went out to kill. The cynics and the hostile sneered at them, and at the priests and the ministers who blessed the war and the tanks and the fighting men, but I could not do that, because I had also learned the commandment, and in 1939 I was also ready to kill.

What did Jesus mean on the night of his arrest, when he told one

* *In the book of that name:* The Harmless People. *(New York: Alfred A. Knopf, 1959.)*

of those that were with him who had cut off the ear of the servant of the High Priest, "Put up your sword, for he who takes the sword shall perish by the sword"? * It does not appear to be a moral admonition. Yet in the Sermon on the Mount He clearly gives this moral admonition, and gave advice on turning the cheek, giving the cloak, and going the second mile, which contains the implicit rejection of violence; and also the admonition to love one's enemies, which I have always found the most difficult of all, partly, I admit, because I do not understand what it means. If all this were not difficult enough, Jesus made a whip of cords and drove out the money changers.

These various admonitions create tremendous difficulties today for black Christians. If they are committed to violence, they either abjure their Christianity or they find that the gospels support their struggle for liberation. A third course is to take refuge in pietism. There is yet a fourth course and that is to preach peace and non-violence, but that is becoming a lonely road for a black Christian, for he is then accused of choosing peace above justice, and slavery above freedom.

In these days of racial polarisation (I am writing this in 1980) the maintenance of law and order by white authority in Africa has been given the name of "institutional violence." This it often is and therefore a black man may on moral grounds oppose to it a violence of his own.

It is a proposition gravely disturbing to earnest souls that war and participation in war are totally irreconcilable with a Christian morality, but even more disturbing is the proposition that the institution of government itself is also irreconcilable, and this has been the justification of those Christians, such as the hermits and the desert anchorites, and in our days the Jehovah's Witnesses, who either withdraw from the world or deny the right of governments to demand military service. The Quakers have managed it best, and have achieved a certain amount of immunity from governmental action. Not so the Witnesses. They have incurred the anger of all kinds of governments, and their children suffer all kinds of ridicule and ostracism because they will not take patriotic oaths and sing patriotic hymns. Is this their own choice, or do they wish that they could conform too?

When I was the guest of the Society of Friends in Philadelphia a

* *This is the version of the Gospel of St. Matthew. In that of St. Mark, Jesus does not make this remark. Nor does he in the version of St. Luke, but he heals the ear. In St. John, it is Simon Peter who cuts off the ear, and the servant's name is Malchus; Jesus says, "Put up your sword into the sheath."*

quarter of a century ago, I was told by my host the sly story of the Quaker who kept a pistol under his pillow, in case of contingency. One night the contingency occurred, and he woke to find a burglar in his room. He took out the pistol and said to the burglar, "Friend, if I wert thee I wouldst move, for I am about to shoot where thee art." And that seems to be as perfect a moral blend of violence and nonviolence as one could devise.

I myself found help from Geoffrey Clayton of Johannesburg, in regard to at least one of these difficult sayings of Jesus, the admonition to turn the other cheek. Preaching in St. Mary's Cathedral soon after the outbreak of the war, he said, "I do not think it is right to apply to a State, which consists of many individuals, the maxims and example which is set to a single individual. I may turn my cheek; I may not turn yours." Clayton went on to say that he was certain that if the Good Samaritan had come on the scene earlier, Jesus would have wanted him to resist the attacker.

So Toc H Southern Africa, in a manner of speaking, went to war, and I became the National Chairman of the YMCA–Toc H War Work Council. There is nothing I wanted more in those years than the triumph of Allied arms, and the defeat of Hitler and all he stood for. Few of us saw then the shape of things to come, though Churchill no doubt had seen it already, and had to be silent about it till he made his famous "iron curtain" speech at Fulton, Missouri.

So for these years the journey to that holy mountain, where they do not hurt or destroy, is halted. One is busy with the task of killing or of caring for the well-being of those who kill. One's compassion is kept for one's allies, though one may occasionally show it to an enemy. One may even spare his life if the High Command is not looking. How does one forget easily the scene in "Oh What a Lovely War" when the Germans and the British fraternise in the snow and for a few moments the goodness of men triumphs over the evil of war? How often have I wondered why we tremble before the vision of the ineffable when it is so impotent: And I remember the story of the Indian Mutiny, of the Indian man who greets the British soldier about to bayonet him with the extraordinary words, "And thou too art divine." *

I conclude this chronicle of war at a distance by relating that I was awarded a ribbon and a citation for my services in the Second World War. In 1940 General Smuts established the National Reserve Volunteers, a kind of home guard, and I joined it as a private.

* *Told by James B. Pratt, in* India and Its Faiths. *(Boston, MA: Houghton Mifflin, 1915.)*

On Saturday afternoons I would put on my uniform, beret, tunic, trousers, and heavy boots, and take up my gun and go to the parade ground at Lens. The black staff watched this demonstration of patriotic zeal with pride and approval, and the white staff with a kind of acknowledgement that their English-speaking principal at least did something tangible in defence of his beliefs.

My officers treated me with a certain courtesy. After all I was the most eminent member of the detachment. I must be honest and say that I learned nothing, and I don't think anyone else learned very much. If the defeat of the invasion or the rebellion had depended on me, the country would have been lost. After a while I was promoted to sergeant, and was put in charge of what stores there were. This was a recognition of my eminence rather than of my military prowess.

I remember only three things about my training. On one occasion a machine gun was exhibited, dismantled, and put together again, but as we ourselves did not take part in these operations, the instruction was worthless. On another occasion a tank was exhibited. It was not dismantled but it demonstrated its paces, and we took turns to climb in and out of it; we saw neither machine gun nor tank again. On the third occasion we had an incredible lecture from an academic from the University of Pretoria on the way men and women inevitably formed into groups with common interests, and how the groups mistrusted one another, and how the in-group hated the out-groups, and how one's security and the realisation of one's identity depended on membership of the group. The whole lecture seemed to me to be a defence of the very things that we were fighting against. I said so to our commanding officer, but he looked at me with a total lack of comprehension, and I came to the conclusion that he had not understood a word. In any case it was his job to accept such lecturers and to treat them with courtesy, and it was not part of his duty to criticise them.

I do not remember how long my service lasted, but it must have been for three or four years. After the war was over I was awarded the Africa Service medal and ribbon for my efforts, and I also was given a citation from King George VI. This was not in recognition of military services, but was awarded to those civilians who rendered valuable service to King, Country, and Commonwealth.

So ends my personal chronicle of war at a distance.

Chapter 27

Our family life was a happy one. It was a relief to get home after a day at the reformatory, where I could not discuss the great events that were convulsing the world with any of my white staff except one. Our sons David and Jonathan grew up in two worlds. One was that of St. John's College, Johannesburg, one of the most expensive and exclusive of South African schools. The other was Diepkloof Reformatory, and it was this second world that saved them from the corruption of racial prejudice. It was Diepkloof that gave David and Jonathan a command of Afrikaans, not just the racy argot of the reformatory, but the more orthodox language as well.

We could not have afforded to send our sons to St. John's if we had not been helped by the college itself. It was, and is, a college for the white elite, and today its continued existence as a school for rich white boys is hard to defend. Scholastically it was outstanding. It was ruled by a tall, autocratic, aloof priest, Sidney Clarke, who had an extraordinary shyness beneath an extraordinary arrogance. The boys didn't like him, but they certainly feared him. He was determined that the sons of the elite should learn about the other half of the world, and amongst other things, his top forms visited Diepkloof Reformatory every year.

There was at least one genius on the staff. Tinky Iverson, the choirmaster, who gave David and Jonathan and many others an abiding love of music. After the war was over, a memorial service was held for those St. John's boys who had died, and the choir sang the Russian Kontakion of the Departed, with those sublime words beginning, "Give rest, O Christ, to thy servants with thy saints: where sorrow and pain are no more, neither sighing, but life everlasting." It was one of those occasions in life—how many of us experience them I do not know—when one was near to being overwhelmed by a feeling of unspeakable sorrow and unspeakable joy. Why the joy? Is it because the words of sorrow can have such beauty?

Some of Iverson's friends wanted there to be some recognition of his work and they circulated a petition which was signed by many of the parents of St. John's boys, asking the Archbishop of Canterbury to confer on him the honorary degree of D. Mus. But it never happened. The story was that when the Archbishop consulted the headmaster, the latter refused to recommend it because Iverson had a certain weakness which to some people would have seemed amiable rather than grievous.

It was our custom to have one family holiday a year. Both candour and truth permits me to say that these holidays approached perfection, except that David wanted the car windows closed and Jonathan wanted them opened. David was five and a half years older than Jonathan, and he played the part of the lordly elder brother. He would drive Jonathan to distraction, and finally Dorrie would lose her temper and smack them both as hard as she could. I was able to observe the way in which a mother could rebuke and chastise a son, and a father could not. Dorrie's temper would flare up, punishment would be inflicted, and ten minutes later they would all be billing and cooing. The mother–son contest does not seem to be so much of a conflict of wills as that between father and son, and it seemed—in our family at least—to leave no resentment. When the new principal's house was built, I came home one day to find scribbling on the newly painted walls of the sitting room. I led Jonathan to the scene of the crime and said, "Who did this?" His face—he was then three or four—was immediately contorted by passion. I would not be able to enumerate his emotions, but fury and resentment were certainly among them, as though I were invading some private world of his own. He came at me with his small fists, and I realised at once that I must bring the matter to an end as soon as possible. I cannot remember what I said, but it was probably something like, "All right, son, let's forget about it." Jonathan is now over forty, and his character is marked by gentleness rather than aggression.

David always showed much more self-will than Jonathan, and only once did I oppose him on a serious matter. With one year to go at St. John's College, he asked to be allowed to leave school and to learn to become a farmer. I told him that I would not dictate his choice of a career, but he must first pass his matriculation. This he did in the first-class. Then he studied psychology for five years, and taught it for one. He then decided that he had made a mistake and went back to study medicine for six years, assisted financially by his young wife Nancy and myself. After three years in hospitals, he studied radiology for three years. When he finally graduated at the age of thirty-seven, he had been at school for twenty-six years, and had studied for fifteen more years than he had once intended. I do not remember that he ever thanked me for refusing his youthful request, but I was able to boast that I had the most educated son in South A.rica. This may of course not be true.

During the war years petrol (gasoline) was severely rationed, and David at the age of twelve and I cycled to Durban, a distance of over five hundred miles (eight hundred kilometres) in three and a half days, while Dorrie and Jonathan went by train. David and I did this again two years later, and to recompense Jonathan all three of us rode to Paardekraal, about twenty miles (thirty-two-kilometres) from Diepkloof. Jonathan must have been about seven, and his bicycle was half the size of ours, which meant slow travelling. We took *padkos,* which means "food for the road," and stayed the night in the unpretentious Paardekraal Hotel, returning to Diepkloof the next day. I should record that Jonathan's enjoyment of this simple pleasure was intense; also that he too appears in *Cry, the Beloved Country.* He is the small boy with the brightness in him.

Although South Africa made a notable contribution to the war effort of the Allies, the life of the country was not drastically affected. People made nothing like the sacrifices demanded of the British. Food was never rationed. It was true that white bread disappeared, and that meat was dear and scarce, and that we at home had more and more vegetable dishes, some of which were very tasty. Paper was scarce and newspapers shrank in size. For a while a blackout was applied along the coasts, and bridges and railway lines were guarded, not against the enemy without but from the possible activities of the *Ossewabrandwag* within. Our future Prime Minister, Mr. B. J. Vorster, was interned, and has been able to look back on it with pride ever since.

There were cases of sabotage, but as the war progressed, the fear of Afrikaner Nationalist rebellion died away. On December 7, 1941, the Japanese struck at Pearl Harbor and the United States entered the war. It would have been difficult to find a Nationalist who, because of his hatred of Britain, wanted Japan to defeat the United States. It was Smuts who took South Africa safely through these dangers, but like myself at Diepkloof Reformatory, he had luck too.

Indeed the entry of the United States into the war, and the growing realisation that Hitler would be defeated, did a great deal to decrease Afrikaner opposition to the war, and therefore to strengthen the position of Smuts. In the general election of 1943 Smuts increased his parliamentary majority. Malan suffered a heavy blow when sixteen Nationalist members followed Mr. Oswald Pirow out of the National Party into a group known as the New Order, an Hitlerian organisation with a contempt for parliamentary government. What is more, they stuck to their principles and would not stand in the 1943 election. Thus they disappeared from the political scene and were hardly ever heard of again. So ended the career of Oswald Pirow. His greatest contribution to South Africa was the creation of the Special Service Battalion. Therefore it was he who made possible the transformation of Diepkloof Reformatory, an institution with whose aims he would have had no sympathy whatsoever. He and Mr. Hofmeyr were my benefactors, a most unlikely pair!

Pirow's New Order, had he ever been able to construct it, would have been totalitarian and white-supremacist. He openly declared his belief in a master race. Yet he was by no means alone in wanting a New Order. Many of our white soldiers who were fighting in the deserts of North Africa against Hitler and his herrenvolkism realised that the racial policies of their own country could not bear moral scrutiny. It was not only the soldiers; churchmen, politicians, teachers, and students were beginning to realise that there was something wrong with the world and that it ought to be made anew. On May 22, 1940, J. H. Hofmeyr told a crowd of thirty thousand at a solemn dedication service in Johannesburg that "out of the present travail it is inevitable that a new world will be born." Smuts also declared that there must be a new world order, and he made an extraordinary speech in Cape Town, in which he dealt with matters he usually evaded. He spoke of the neglect of African housing and the lowness of African wages, and declared that there was "the best feeling between white and black in the new big army we have in the north" and that this was the forerunner of happiness to come. Nearly forty years later one can but grieve over such words.

Even Malan could not escape the fever of new-order-making. On January 19, 1940, he moved a social security motion in Parliament, calling for a "speedy and radical reconstruction" of the existing order, with "social security for every individual" and a "more equitable distribution of the wealth of the country." Finally he called, as he might have been expected to do, for the maintenance of the position of the white race and of white civilisation "in accordance with the principle of trusteeship."

The call for the new order was made on the grand scale by Roosevelt and Churchill in the Atlantic Charter. Nearer home it was made on a humbler scale in the Anglican diocese of Johannesburg, of whose Annual Synod I was a member for some thirteen years, being one of the representatives of the Parish of All Saints, Booysens, a suburb on what was then the easternmost fringe of Johannesburg, about three miles from the City Hall, and five miles from the main block of Diepkloof Reformatory.

In October 1940 Geoffrey Clayton, Bishop of Johannesburg, declared in the diocesan synod that there would have to be a new order. The Anglican Church in South Africa had always been a great champion of racial justice, though it could justifiably be said that in general priests were more concerned than laymen. He said, "Our policy is a policy of fear, fear of economic competition, fear of racial admixture. But fear is a bad foundation of policy." Soon after this Clayton, speaking on the same platform with Professor Alfred Hoernlé and Professor J. L. Gray of the University of the Witwatersrand, declared that the old order was one of starvation in the midst of plenty, that it prevented men from doing what they had it in them to do, and caused frustration, unhappiness, and crime.* When Clayton used the word "men" in this context, it was the African people who were uppermost in his mind.

Whether it was his own initiative, or whether it was the brainchild of the Rev. A. W. Eaton, Rector of Mayfair and editor of *The Watchman*, the diocesan monthly, or whether the idea was conceived simultaneously in several people's minds, I do not know, but plans were laid to establish at the synod of 1941 a Diocesan Commission which was to set itself a task no less than to define what it believed to be the mind of Christ for South Africa. The establishment of the commission was agreed to, and it was left to Clayton to appoint its members. He appointed thirty-three, one of whom was myself. Thirty-one of these were white, two were black. This disproportion was not entirely due to the white supremacy that characterised almost every department of South African life. It was also partly due to the fact that the educational qualifications of black priests and laymen were much lower than they are today. The language of the commission was English and a poor command of English would have been a great handicap to a commissioner. Yet a

* At a meeting held in December 1940 of the Johannesburg Society of Jews and Christians, on the theme "The Church and the New Order."

third reason would be given, that the political and social awareness
of the black priests and laymen of 1941 was lower—I am tempted
to write *immeasurably* lower—than it is in 1980. Clayton was in
such matters quite unsentimental, and he would never have appointed or refrained from appointing a commissioner just because
he or she was black.

The Bishop of Johannesburg was an extraordinary man, one of
the few persons in my life of whom I would have used the adjective
"great." I came to know him well because soon after my arrival at
Diepkloof I became one of the churchwardens of All Saints, Booysens, and attended the Annual Synods as a representative of my
parish. To sit under him at synod was something never to be forgotten. He was a chairman without peer. While those sitting under him
did so in something akin to awe, their awe was tempered by their
enthralment. At one point he would speak with great authority, at
another, when some speaker expressed some view which he found
more than ordinarily stupid, he would put his great head between
his hands and groan inaudibly. When synod was debating in 1938
whether to send a fraternal message to the big Dutch Reformed
Church * on the occasion of the Voortrekker Centenary, one of our
anti-Afrikaner priests kept referring to the Afrikaners as "they."
This was during the days of my championship of the Afrikaner
cause, and I rose to my feet and said, "My Lord, on a point of order,
who are *they*?" He glared at me with unspeakable ferocity and said,
"That is not a point of order, it is a speech, sit down." It was
painful to be thus humiliated, but one could console oneself that
one would sooner or later be able to enjoy the humiliation of others.
Synod was very like a big class, sitting under a formidable master,
with all the ingredients of earnestness, jokes, castigations, and
scowlings, and a kind of gay enjoyment at seeing such an exhibition
of petulance and greatness. Today, forty years later, there are still
those who remember the days when they laughed, trembled, admired, suffered under the chairmanship of Geoffrey Clayton. I have
never in the course of my life had any other experience remotely
resembling sitting through synod under Clayton of Johannesburg.

Nor indeed have I had an experience remotely resembling sitting
on his commission.

---

* *Die Nederduitse Gereformeerde Kerk.*

Chapter 28

The commission sat for two years, and if I remember rightly, I went to Johannesburg once a week for the whole of that period. There were nine committees, and I was a member of two of them, Education and Social Welfare. It was one of the seminal events of my life, after which I was never the same again. I had to open my eyes and look at South Africa as I had never looked at it before.

This period is so important in my life that I am going to try to define my thinking at that time. The overwhelming majority of white South Africans are always conscious of the fact that they constitute a relatively small fraction of the total population—in 1941 it was one-fifth, in 1980 it is one-sixth. Yet they monopolise the governmental and legislative power.*

Of those who acknowledged the injustice and the instability of such a situation, there were at least two kinds. In 1941 the only white South Africans who had faced the possibility of radical change were the Communists. The other kind—to which I belonged—clung to the irrational idea that one could maintain white supremacy and yet be just. They had not yet learned to understand that justice might be no more than the interest of the stronger.

One either did not think about these things at all, or one alternated between moods of pessimism and hope. One loved what was right and good and just, but one did not yet understand that these

---

* I have omitted the economic power. While the whites wield great financial power, the blacks wield the great power of their labour. How to use it—that is the question.

things could not be had except at the cost of a change in one's whole life and situation.

It is common in South Africa for those white people who regard themselves as radicals or liberals or progressives to reproach their white compatriots for their ostrich-like mentality.

Yet in 1941 I had this same mentality. The land of my birth was beautiful, my homelife was satisfying, the success of Diepkloof was established, so that one could easily deceive oneself that the future was safe and secure. Hitler was going to be defeated, and the world, including our own part of it, would be made better.

Yet there was Alfred Hoernlé, Professor of Philosophy of the Witwatersrand, and President of the South African Institute of Race Relations, saying the very opposite. Hofmeyr, Clayton, and Hoernlé were the three South Africans who most influenced me during these years. Hofmeyr was the orator, the public figure, who had resigned from high office on a matter of principle, and believed that Christian ethics could be applied in social and political life. Clayton was the interpreter of these ethics, and he had the inestimable gifts of the great teacher in that he could say what he believed in words of the utmost simplicity, and could therefore preach to the simplest and humblest.* In some ways Hoernlé's mind was the clearest and most logical, though all three men had clear and logical minds, but Hoernlé's had a quality of coldness too. This does not mean that Hoernlé had no quality of warmth; it means that he subjected emotions such as faith and hope to the most ruthless scrutiny.

At a symposium held in Johannesburg on the New Order he said bluntly and emphatically, "Have we any reason to believe that as a result of the present war, a 'new order' in the relations between whites and blacks will come into being? My own answer to this question is NO." This was I think what divided him sharply from Hofmeyr and Clayton, that he could say such a thing and they could not. Hofmeyr was the symbol of hope to many South Africans, and Clayton was the leader of a Christian community that is continuously committed to repentance and amendment of life. Neither of them could have said that the war would not bring a new order, because that was their hope.

Hoernlé had some hard things to say about hope too. He had no use for hope that was ungrounded. He saw no intrinsic virtue in the act of hoping. He said in his presidential address to the South African Institute of Race Relations in 1941, "I have no use for a faith

* In one paragraph chosen at random from a Clayton address, there are 98 words, 80 of one syllable, 14 of two, 3 of three, and 1 of four.

which is unthinking, or which can flourish only in an atmosphere of an intellectual holiday." Yet he would not have gone so far as to suggest that the Christian hope of Hofmeyr and Clayton was in that category. He rejected Clayton's contention that the real difference between them was one of religious belief. Though he did not accept "all the details of Christian dogma," he had no hesitation in subscribing to Clayton's phrase, "prepared to allow for the entrance into history of an incalculable factor," and also to his statement that "when we have done our best, the resources of the universe are not exhausted."

I was a mere spectator of these contests. My heart was with Hofmeyr and Clayton, my mind was with Hoernlé. And I meant to keep them both. One thing was clear, and that was that Hoernlé would have had nothing in common with any person who did not *believe* in anything. What Hoernlé thought of the great prophets I do not know. When Isaiah prophesied that the sucking child would play on the hole of the asp, and the weaned child would put his hand on the cockatrice's den, after there had come a rod out of the stem of Jesse, was he taking an intellectual holiday? When Clayton, with that great bald head that housed those subtle mechanisms of genius that enabled him to speak words of such wisdom with such simplicity, read the words of the great prophets, he did so with a kind of controlled passion that could be electrifying, and in so doing bound many of his priests to him with bonds that would never be broken, so that they could forgive him his tantrums and his petulance.

In less than two years Hoernlé was dead. One of his last acts was to publish an open letter to the white citizens of Johannesburg, protesting against the proposal to remove the inhabitants of the African township of Alexandria, eleven miles from the City Hall, and challenging them to protest also. Though he was not a churchman his funeral service was held in St. Mary's Cathedral, at which Clayton read the lesson and gave the blessing. Hoernlé was another of those of whom I would have used the adjective "great." The preface to *Cry, the Beloved Country* called him "the prince of Kafferboeties." * The writer could think of no higher praise than that.

Hoernlé concluded his presidential address with these words:

---

* *Kafferboetie is an Afrikaans word which means literally "little brother of the Kaffir." It is a term of contempt used by a number of white South Africans of any white person who concerns himself with the needs and aspirations and deprivations of black people, to what his fellows regard as an undue and extravagant extent.*

If I am a "pessimist" it is not because I regard our caste society as permanent: change will come to it and transform it. But I am a pessimist in that *I deny that there is in our caste society either the will or the vision for planning and effecting this change.* Only complacency or self-delusion could lead us to believe otherwise. The changes which will come will be forced on us by world-forces and world-events over which humanity has little conscious control. Meanwhile I continue to believe in the liberal spirit and try to be its servant to the best of my ability. . . .

Hofmeyr and Clayton would have regarded themselves as servants, however poor, of the Holy Spirit. Hoernlé regarded himself as a servant of the liberal spirit. And in so doing, each of them cherished the same ideals of truth, justice, and compassion.

This then was the kind of world, and these were the kind of people in it, when the Bishop's commission met to perform "the task of defining what it believes to be the mind of Christ for this land."

Of this time and this experience I later wrote: *

As for myself, having lived for thirty-eight years in the dark, the commission opened for me a door, and I went through into the light and I shut it against myself, and entered a new country whose very joys and adversities were made resplendent by the light. This conversion can in a way never be complete, because one continues to live in a colour-bar society, and to obey its laws and to benefit by its privileges. If one did not, one might leave the country or spend the rest of one's life in prison. Some can bear it no longer, and they go, and there arises an incompatibility between some of them and those who do not go, caused in part by the irreconcilability of the two views, the one that the honourable thing to do is to get out, the other that the honourable thing to do is to stay.* *

Yet another incompatibility is possible and common. That is between the Christian who finally rejects and opposes the policies of racial separation, and *first* the Christian who supports them, and *second* the Christian who regards them as politics and thinks that the Church should not be involved with them.†

---

* *Chapter 15*, Apartheid and the Archbishop. (*New York: Charles Scribner's Sons,* 1973.)
* **There is yet another reason for this incompatibility, and that is that some who have gone resent the fact that there are some who have stayed.*
† *Chapter 15*, Apartheid and the Archbishop.

The final report of the commission was in seven clauses, A to G, of which Clause A was purely introductory. Clause B was largely Clayton's own work, and it was in essence theological. To him it was useless to jump into the fight for a better world, armed only with good will. One had to understand clearly one's nature and destiny as a child of the Creator, and therefore one's duty to other men who were one's brothers. A Christian in search of the new order must take realistic account of sin. Neither intellectual enlightenment nor a change in institutions could save society and man without a change of will. It was not part of the church's mission to plan for the reformation or organisation of society, but it was the duty of Christian man. And it was in that belief that the recommendations of the commission would be made.

I had now to face the realisation that white supremacy and the principles of Clause B were irreconcilable. The other clauses of the report confirmed powerfully this realisation. Clause C dealt with church and state, and criticised white South Africa and its Government. They were fighting for the rights of men, but "the charge of hypocrisy cannot be avoided if through the laws and customs of this land, these rights are refused to any of its people on account of colour."

Clause D dealt with economics and industry, and condemned gross inequalities of income, the shocking state of black wages and housing, and the system of migratory labour; it also condemned the control of a community's industrial resources by a few.

Clause E dealt with racial segregation. Occupational segregation, that is, the reservation of certain kinds of employment for members of certain racial groups, was condemned. The report did not condemn separate schools for separate racial groups, but rather the inequality of funds and equipment; I would add that this inequality continues until today, and the education of a white child costs ten times as much as that of the black child, the difference being defended on the grounds that white taxes provide the overwhelming proportion of the tax revenue of the State.

The report then continued, under Clause E, to deal with the most difficult question of all, that of political representation. At this point I would like to remind my readers of the nature and extent of the parliamentary franchise.* Every white man and woman of twenty-one years and over could vote for members of Parliament. So could any Coloured or Indian man in the Cape Province who had certain qualifications of education and property. So could any African man

* *I have omitted minor exceptions for the sake of clarity.*

in the Cape Province who had these qualifications, but in 1936 all such voters had been removed to a separate roll and they now elected three white members of Parliament. As a quid pro quo, it was enacted in 1936 that four African constituencies covering the whole of South Africa could elect four white senators to the Union Senate. This was the position in 1941.

The Report now recommended:

1. The extension of the Cape franchise for Coloured and Indian men to all Coloured and Indian men and women in South Africa.
2. The extension of the Cape franchise for African men (placed on a separate roll in 1936) to all African men and women in South Africa.
3. A corresponding increase in the number of white M.P.s and white Senators who represented African voters.

But the ultimate aim would be:

4. A common roll for all citizens, so that through a common election, M.P.s should represent *all* qualified voters.

The fourth recommendation was not for universal suffrage. It was for the creation of a common roll for all *qualified* voters, and it should be remembered that white voters needed no qualification except age. The proposals were revolutionary for that time, but they were very far from breaking the white monopoly of power. Today they would be derided by all people not white. And why indeed should they accept another qualified franchise, for they had been given one in 1853 in the Cape Province by the British Government, and in 1936 a drastic step had been taken in its destruction? *

Clause F was the last, and Hoernlé would no doubt have regarded it as the expression of a hope that had never been realised in the whole history of man, for it said that the implementation of these findings demanded first of all "a change of heart within the nation." Hoernlé regarded such a hope as a self-delusion. Only world forces "over which humanity has little conscious control" could bring about such changes. Clause F further expressed the belief that "the nation be called back to God." Would Hoernlé have been prepared to regard this "incalculable factor" as one of the world forces? This debate, between Clayton's hope and Hoernlé's realism,

* *The African franchise was abolished altogether in 1960. The Coloured franchise was removed to a separate roll in 1956, and abolished in 1968.*

fascinated me. I believed in them both, and at some time in my life I would have to synthesise them.

The reading, discussion, and adoption of the report by the synod of 1943 was an event not easily to be forgotten.* There was only one person who could possibly write it, and that was the Bishop. He therefore retired to the peace of Swaziland and wrote "The Church and the Nation." On November 15, 1943, after Clayton had read Clause A, the Rev. A. W. Eaton and Archdeacon Rouse presented it to synod, reading its seven clauses paragraph by paragraph.

There were two ways in which such a report might be criticised. The first would be to criticise its clarity and style. The second would be to criticise its principles, judgements, and opinions. It was now known to most of us that the Bishop had written the report. It was recognised that he was a master of the English language, certainly a master of clarity and brevity and had never been known to make a syntactical error. It would have taken a brave man to criticise the actual language of the report. However, there was such a man, and he was the Rev. Percy Forbes, Rector of Klerksdorp, tall, dark, distinguished-looking, formidable in his own fashion. He was much respected as a scholar, and was in his own way also a master of the English language. If his mastery differed from that of the Bishop, it would have lain in the fact that he was more precise, more exact; some might have said that he was more pedantic.

It was soon clear that he intended to subject the language of the report to the most searching criticism, and that he would be quite capable of adding considerably to the length of the synod. It is well known that a meeting is the worst possible judge as to whether one word or phrase is better than another. However, Forbes intended to make the synod decide.

Clayton's reactions were typical. At first his always mobile face showed good humour, tolerance, and amusement. If Forbes's proposed amendment seemed absurd Clayton would scratch his head in puzzlement and put the proposal with baffled resignation. When it became clear that Forbes was not to be deterred, the first sign of displeasure showed itself. By this time the members of synod were agog. They had now realised that they were witnessing a spectacle not often to be seen, and all for nothing. They settled themselves in their seats and prepared to enjoy it.

Clayton now realised that Forbes would not be stopped. He thought—and so did many of us—that the amendments added nothing to the value of the report. He thought—with many of us—that

* *The following account is from Chapter 15,* Apartheid and the Archbishop.

his own English was of a reasonably high standard. His timetable was being disrupted. As the battle proceeded, his look of displeasure became permanent. He put his head in his hands, picked his nose, scowled, even laughed incredulously that a clever man like Forbes could be capable of such absurdities.

It was not Forbes who precipitated the crisis, though he certainly prepared the way for it. It was those who wanted the report to have teeth, who wanted not grand moralising but plans for action, who wanted a crusading church. Among them were Arthur Blaxall, Tom Comber, Maurice Clark, and, most notable of all, Father Trevor Huddleston and the Rev. Michael Scott, who were both men of action, winning in general the devotion of the poor and the hostility of the rich.

Clayton was no pietist, but the activism of Huddleston and Scott irritated him. His phrase "the gradual removal of the colour-bar" came under heavy fire. If the colour-bar were evil, why should a commission of the church ask for its gradual removal? To Clayton— as indeed to Hofmeyr and Hoernlé—the demand for the immediate removal of the colour-bar was absurd.

The conflict went deeper. What was meant by a change of heart within the nation? Did such changes happen? And if they did not, did that mean that the changes would never be implemented? Was there no other way of bringing about reforms in society? Was the front not wider than that of pure evangelism?

At last Clayton could bear it no longer. He jumped to his feet, obviously under the influence of great emotion. His voice, always powerful, was now tremendous.

The Church is not here primarily to serve society. Its prime duty is to worship God and obey Him. And if it is God's will that we should serve society in this way or that, then it is our duty to do it. Let us therefore be very careful that it is God's will we are trying to obey, and that we are not merely trying to make the Church do something that we want to be done. And let me make it quite clear that I appointed this Commission because I believed it might be God's will that we should serve our society in this and that way.

Then with a strange look, compounded of embarrassment and triumph, he sat down. Rebellion was quelled, and Forbes decided that the language of the rest of the report would have to be accepted.

Another thing fascinated me too. Clayton was more patient with those who wanted the church not to go so far and so fast than with those who wanted it to go farther and faster. Three important lay members of the commission could not accept a paragraph condemning the system of migratory labour on the grounds of its moral evils consequent on the separation of men from their womenfolk. All three were important figures in the mining industry, and could not bring themselves to condemn the system on which the industry depended. Their arguments were also based on moral grounds. They shuddered at what would happen to family life if men were allowed to bring their wives and children to the great city of Johannesburg. Clayton accepted with gravity their decision to oppose. He also accepted gravely the decision of another prominent layman to oppose the recommendation for a common electoral roll. Yet Clayton was by no means a pietist; he just did not trust anyone's activism except his own. One must also record that the diocese of Johannesburg received substantial financial support from some of the mining houses.

So the mighty labour came to an end. All this happened over thirty years ago. One must in honesty acknowledge that a bishop's commission in 1977 would produce a report not very different from that of 1943. Hoernlé was proved right; there was no change of heart. Did the commission achieve anything? Did the lives of Hofmeyr, Clayton, and Hoernlé achieve anything? These are questions that I must try later to answer.

I was not as critical in 1943 as I am in 1980. Today I would ask the question, how does one tell the difference between the man who is trying to obey God's will and the man who wants the church to do something that he wants to be done? Who can be more cruel and more dangerous than the ruler who knows God's will and is determined that all his people shall obey it? Today I trust only one kind of person who claims to be trying to do God's will, and that is the one who does it humbly.

That is the story of the bishop's commission. It didn't change the heart of the nation but it changed me. Ten years later I tried with others to apply its principles in the hard world of politics. I wonder if Hoernlé looked down from on high and said, "Paton, will you ever learn?" Or would he have said, "Paton, it won't work, but it has to be done"?

Chapter 29

The intellectual experience of belonging to the bishop's commission was paralleled by an emotional experience of equal intensity. It came about in this way.

The South African Institute of Race Relations was founded in 1929. The moving spirits were J. D. Rheinallt Jones, Assistant Registrar of the University of the Witwatersrand, and Dr. C. T. Loram, Superintendent of Education in Natal, who had been one of my lecturers when I studied for the degree of master of education.

Jones and Loram were joined by many prominent South Africans. There was Edgar Brookes, Professor of political science at the Transvaal University College; Howard Pim, prominent businessman and social worker; Leo Marquard, founder of the National Union of South African Students (NUSAS); Professor D. D. T. Jabavu of the Fort Hare Native Collete; the Rev. Ray Phillips, missionary and social worker for the American Board; T. W. Mackenzie, editor of *The Friend,* Bloemfontein; J. H. Nicholson, a former Mayor of Durban; Professor J. du Plessis, from the Theological Seminary at Stellenbosch University; and of course Professor Alfred Hoernlé, whom we already know.* In the initial years the institute depended almost entirely on American generosity.

The institute's purpose was fourfold: (1) to accumulate facts on

* Soon after this Sheila van der Horst of Cape Town and Major Lewis Byron of Durban joined the inner circle. Nor should one omit Advocate Donald Molteno, one of the best minds I ever encountered. I must forbear to add any more names.

all aspects of race relations; (2) to combat racial prejudice; (3) to coordinate the work of all persons and organisations involved with race relations; and (4) to function as a nonpolitical body open to all. It is generally recognised that it is the first of these aims that has been magnificently achieved. The institute's *Annual Survey of Race Relations in South Africa* is one of the most notable publications in the country, and is invaluable for politicians, students of politics, social workers, and enquiring visitors who want to know more than they will learn from the glossy brochures.*

There were two remarkable women associated with the early institute. One was Winifred, wife of Alfred Hoernlé. The other was Edith, wife of J. D. Rheinallt Jones. It would be no exaggeration to say that their main concern in life was to serve others. They were what the cynics would call "do-gooders." It was my relationship with Edith Jones that led to the intense emotional experience of which I am going to write.

She was no beauty. She was a woman in her fifties, heavily built, and she breathed heavily after any exertion. If she had not kept her facial hair under control she would soon have been bearded. She had been told almost ten years before that her heart was finished, and that if she wanted to live, she would have to give up her many activities with the institute, with the Wayfarers, which was a kind of Girl Guide movement for black and Coloured children, with the Helping Hand Club, which was a hostel for African working girls in Johannesburg, and a dozen other things too, not to mention the running of a hospitable home where all were welcomed.

Edith Jones decided that although she did not want to die, she did not wish to live without the institute and the Wayfarers and the other things too. Therefore she decided to carry on as usual. Her most demanding activity was with the Wayfarers. She went out into the most remote parts of the countryside to visit little troops of schoolgirls, and to encourage and instruct the Wayfarer leaders, who were mostly schoolteachers. When she was there, she usually visited the chief and the church people and the magistrate and the health authorities as well, so that she became in time the best-known white woman in the whole of South Africa, and one of the best-loved too.

She and her husband were two of our first visitors at Diepkloof, and it was not long before Mr. Hofmeyr appointed her a member of the Board of Management of the Reformatory. She was invaluable,

* The name of Miss Muriel Horrell is inseparable from any mention of the survey.

just as invaluable as Miss Chattey. She had a strength of will and a physical energy that are given to very few, and she used both of these on our behalf. Then came the war, when many of us were willing to work twice as hard as we had been working before. She asked me if, whenever I had a free weekend from the reformatory, I would drive her in her car to visit some of the Wayfarer troops in the more remote parts of the country. So it was that I began to learn what this woman meant to hundreds and thousands of unknown people in South Africa.

One of these journeys remains clearly in my mind. We set out from Johannesburg early in the morning and took the Great North Road into the land of the Bavenda people. We left the main highway north of Pietersburg and took a road that led us into a countryside where long hills lay like tawny lions in the sun. They say this is the country where John Buchan dreamed up his story of Prester John. After driving deeper and deeper into the tribal place, we could take the car no further, and we left it and walked down a steep and stony hill to the school. Edith Jones was not supposed to take walks like this, and her breathing was painful to her, but she had no time for rest or self-pity. At last we could see the school, and the schoolmistress too, Mrs. Takalani, waiting for her visitor with every sign of pleasure. Already some of the Wayfarers had come for the parade and were peeping from behind a corner of the school to see these great visitors.

I did not wait to see the parade, but took a walk through the valley, saluting and being saluted by hundreds of people going to the schoolhouse for the big occasion. After an hour or two I returned and spent some time looking round the rooms that made up the school. There were the usual drawings on the wall, and clay figures of tame and wild beasts, also instructions on cleaning the teeth, washing the hands, and what to do about flies and mosquitoes. Nothing could have been simpler than the building and equipment, and nothing more evident than the atmosphere of industry and aspiration that filled these humble rooms.* In the kitchen next door a village mother was boiling water, and after the parade Mrs. Jones, Mrs. Takalani, and I had tea and cakes. It was clear that we were the Big Three, for no one joined us; and it was also clear that the cakes had been brought all the way from the white town, such grand confections being the only ones considered fit for the consumption of such high people.

* I wrote a poem, "Black Woman Teacher," as a gift for Mrs. Takalani.

Mrs. Takalani was in a state of spiritual intoxication.

"You must bring her again," she said to me. "When she comes she makes things new."

She turned to Mrs. Jones. "Did you hear what I said?" she asked. "I said when you come you make things new."

"Don't talk nonsense," said Mrs. Jones.

"Don't you say I am talking nonsense," said Mrs. Takalani. "Why do you think all these people come here? They come here to see you."

"That is nonsense," said Mrs. Jones. "They come here to see what their children are learning in the Wayfarers."

I listened fascinated. I had never before heard a white woman and a black woman talk to each other in this fashion. It was something new for me. At that time my own relations with black people were extremely polite, but I realised that these two had long passed that stage.

We walked up the steep and stony hill to the car, and Edith Jones had to stop every few paces to get her breath again.

"You should not be visiting such places," Mrs. Takalani told her. "You should be staying at home."

One could see that Mrs. Jones was longing to say "Nonsense," but had no breath to do it with. She had to content herself with glaring at her friend.

At the top of the hill Mrs. Takalani wept for about five seconds. To do this she went off for a few paces, and turned her back to us. Then she blew her nose and came back.

"Thank you for bringing her," she said to me, "and bring her again."

"Next time," she said to Mrs. Jones with authority, "we are having our inspection here, at the top of the hill."

She pointed down in the direction of the invisible school. "You should have said good-bye to the school," she said, "for you will not see it again."

And that came true. A month later, ten years after the doctor's warning, the brave heart gave in altogether. They had a farewell service for her in St. George's Presbyterian Church, Johannesburg.

Black people, white people, Coloured people, European and African and Asian, Jew and Christian and Hindu and Moslem, rich and poor, all came to honour her memory, their hates and their fears, their prides and their prejudices all for this moment forgotten. The lump in the throat was not only for the great woman who was dead, not only because all South Africa was reconciled under the roof of this church, but also because it was as unreal as a dream, and no one knew how many years must pass and how many lives be spent and how much suffering be undergone before it all came true. And when it all came true—if it should all come true—only those who were steeped in the past would have any understanding of the greatness of the present.

As for me, I was overwhelmed, I was seeing a vision, which was never to leave me, illuminating the darkness of the days through which we live now.* To speak in raw terms, there was some terrible pain in the pit of my stomach. I could not control it. I had again the overpowering feeling of unspeakable sorrow and unspeakable joy. What life had failed to give so many of these people, this woman had given them—an assurance that their work was known and of good report, that they were not nameless or meaningless, and there is no hunger like this one. Had they all come, no church would have held them all, the vast, voiceless multitude of Africa, nameless and obscure, moving with painful ascent to that self-fulfillment no human being may with justice be denied, encouraged and sustained by this woman who withheld nothing from them, who gave her money, her comfort, her gifts, her home, and finally her life, not with the appearance of prodigality nor with fine-sounding words, but with a naturalness that concealed all evidence of the steep moral climb by which alone such eminence is attained.

In that church one was able to see, beyond any possibility of doubt, that what this woman had striven for was the highest and best kind of thing that anyone could strive for in a country like South Africa. I knew then that I would never again be able to think primarily in terms of race and nationality. I was no longer a white person but a member of the human race. I came to this as the result of many experiences, but this was the deepest of them all.

"So you thought her a great woman?" Mr. Hofmeyr said to me.

"Yes."

"I didn't," he said.

* This piece, with the paragraphs still to come, was first written just after Edith Jones's death in 1944, and was published by the institute. The phrase "the darkness of the days through which we live now" must have been added at least ten years later, and it refers to the spate of apartheid laws passed from 1948 onwards. The piece appeared again somewhat abbreviated in "Case History of a Pinky," published by the S.A. Institute of Race Relations in 1971. This abbreviated version was published again in Knocking on the Door, by David Philip, 1975. It appeared also in Professor Edward Callan's anthology Alan Paton: The Long View (New York: Frederick A. Praeger, 1968).

"And you think Hofmeyr a great man?" Professor Hoernlé said to me.

"Yes."

"I don't," he said.

There was more than one reason for these judgements. The Rheinallt Joneses had failed to take Hofmeyr's side in his puritanical determination to get rid of Professor Stibbe, a married man who had a friendship with a young unmarried typist at the university*; and Hofmeyr had successfully opposed Hoernlé's appointment as Principal of the University of the Witwatersrand, largely—it was supposed—because the Hoernlés had also opposed him over the Stibbe affair. So the liberal cause, with which I was slowly becoming identified, suffered grievously because Hofmeyr, its leading political light, did not enjoy the support or the admiration of four of the leading liberals in the country. Luckily for me, it was never required of me that I should choose a side.

It was now 1945, and the war was drawing to a close. Smuts as Prime Minister and leader of the United Party, and Hofmeyr as his deputy, were in a position of great power. No one could foresee that three years later they would be defeated by Dr. Malan, leader of the National Party. I certainly did not foresee it, and I made plans for a future the realisation of which would depend totally on the continuance of the United Party. I had been ten years at Diepkloof Reformatory and I was forty-two years old. I therefore determined to qualify myself for the eminent national post of the Director of Prisons. To do this I would have to study prisons in several countries of the world.

Without Dorrie's help and the help of the department I could have done nothing. I had three months leave on full pay due to me, but I calculated that such a tour would take eight or nine months. I had a wife and two sons to maintain. If an acting Principal were appointed from outside, Dorrie might have had to vacate the house, and that would have put the whole venture beyond our reach.

Mr. Hofmeyr was sympathetic and so was the new head of the Union Education Department, Advocate A. A. Roberts. Between them they arranged a further three months on full pay. The department also allowed Dorrie to keep the house, and she took in as paying lodgers one of our young men returned from the war, Stanley Watson, and his wife and child. Then Dorrie herself took a job as secretary of the Transvaal Association of non-European Boys'

* *Nothing more than a friendship was ever alleged.*

Clubs, of which I had been the first chairman. As for myself, I was determined to live and travel as cheaply as possible, and I had a further stroke of luck when the Society of Christians and Jews paid my air fare to London on condition that I represented it at the world conference to be held in London and Oxford in July 1946. My last stroke of luck was when Stan Dench, a Toc H friend of mine in Johannesburg, arranged for me to make his mother's home in Seven Kings a kind of H.Q. while I was in England, at a rate far below anything that I could have found for myself. My last preparatory step was to surrender all my insurance policies and to make out new ones. Thus it will be seen that I was following, but not altogether, the advice of Jesus, "Take no thought for the morrow, for the morrow will look after itself."

It was not long after the end of the war in Europe on May 7, 1945, that I had my first experience of a public attack by Dr. Hendrik Verwoerd, the formidable editor of the Nationalist newspaper, *Die Transvaler*, an experience to which I referred earlier. It gave me a considerable shock. Public praise is very pleasant, and it does not necessarily offend one's desire to remain a private man. Public attack is quite different, for it inevitably makes one a public man. I will not say that Dr. Verwoerd's attack *frightened* me, but I found it extremely painful, particularly as I knew that most of my staff members usually read the paper with approval, especially because of its strong antiwar and anti-Smuts sentiments. I read the editorial only once with pain, anger, and resentment, and I did not read it again for thirty years. But I never forgot it.

The reason for the attack was an address that I had given in Johannesburg on crime and delinquency, and Dr. Verwoerd said that this was the time to state "that Diepkloof as an institution to reform young black delinquents was a colossal failure." It was Mr. Paton's mollycoddling theories that made the work so futile. The public could not see the heaven-shaking results; they heard only of the continuous absconding that was an endless burden to the staff, and of the loafing about the farm of black "ladies and gentlemen" to whom the white staff had been ordered by the principal to say "please do" * when asking them to do some trifling thing.

Dr. Verwoerd ended his editorial with the words, "Is this going to be tolerated?" Alongside the article was the daily box which every day carried *"Gevleuelde Woorde,"* which means "Winged Words." On this day the winged words were *"Die weg van 'n dwaas is reg in*

* *The Afrikaans words* "Asseblief tog," *a stronger plea than just* "asseblief."

sy eie oë," which means "The way of a fool is right in his own eyes."

I felt that I should show the editorial to Mr. Hofmeyr, who snorted and said, "What else did you expect?" He was, I think, surprised to find that I took it so seriously, but then of course he was used to public attack.

Archbishop Clayton said of Verwoerd that he had never before encountered such an alien mind. That puts it well. It would be hard to name one category of thought that they had in common. Clayton could be an autocrat, but Verwoerd was a thoroughgoing authoritarian. Clayton won the hearts of his black Anglican people, Verwoerd never won any black heart that I knew of. He revealed his attitude to black people—intentionally or not, I do not know—in his remark about the use of the word "please," an attitude which became enshrined in one draconian law after another.

Dr. Verwoerd's editorial did no harm to the reformatory. My own position as principal was made happier by the return of our staff members who had gone to the war. Their old relationships with those who had not gone were soon resumed. My own plans to study prisons abroad went ahead, and now included the study of reformatories and institutions for boys and girls, this because of the grant of three extra months paid leave from the Union Department of Education. I now planned first to attend the World Conference of Christians and Jews, and then to visit institutions in Britain, Sweden, the United States, and Canada. While in Sweden I would take the opportunity to visit Norway, not to see prisons, but to see the country where Knut Hamsun wrote *Growth of the Soil,* and the many adventures of August. I would visit Trondheim, and travel down the Gudbrandsdal to Oslo. I would have given much to visit the Lofoten Islands as well, but that was out of the question.

I left Mr. Laas as acting Principal of the reformatory. I remembered—and I have no doubt he did also—that time ten years earlier when he closed all the dormitories that had so far been opened. His readiness to act in 1946 was proof of the confidence he now felt in the open system. What is more, the young white men of the Special Service Battalion were now ten years older, and there were four qualified black teachers, all with confidence that they could manage a reformatory that now had close on seven hundred boys.

In 1946 the South African Airways began its first flights to London. On Monday, 8 June I left on the second such flight. Dorrie came to see me off and wept. It was the first time I had been in a big plane, and I was both excited and nervous. It was a Skymaster, the four-engined Douglas DC4, and it was going to stop at Kisumu, Khartum, and Tripoli. Before starting it revved its four engines to a deafening crescendo, and the whole plane sobbed and trembled. Then we took off and it was some minutes before I realised that we were not going to crash, at least not yet. Another cause of anxiety was that the rhythm of the engines would change alarmingly. On one occasion—more than one perhaps—they seemed to stop altogether, and the end seemed near, but they fortunately picked up again.

At Kisumu we had breakfast and at Khartum we landed with many terrifying sideslips and lurchings, and were taken to a hotel while the plane was serviced. There was the Blue Nile, and I went walking along its banks. There was not another moving soul to be seen. The poor slept under the palms, and the rich slept unseen in great houses, shuttered behind vast and deep verandahs. After half a mile perhaps my face and ears and head were on fire, and I returned very slowly to the hotel, and had two or three showers without effect. We were taken back on the plane, which was like a furnace, and indeed I did not recover until we had sideslipped and lurched again into the upper air. I realised the truth of Noel Coward's famous words that only "Mad dogs and Englishmen go out in the midday sun."

On Tuesday night we landed at Tripoli, after what seemed to be an endless journey over the Sahara, during all of which I kept my eyes glued to the window, looking down at one of the most awesome landscapes in the world. We landed at the airport known as Castel Benito, named for Mussolini. On Wednesday morning we landed at London Airport at 9:00 A.M., after a journey lasting about thirty-six hours. I found my way to Mrs. Dench's home in Seven Kings, and soon afterwards took a bus to the West End, to the great city I had seen for the first time twenty-two years earlier. I had that sense of unbelieving wonder, which grows less with experience, that two days earlier I had been in a city at the southern end of the continent of Africa.

I made it one of my first duties in London to find Mrs. Allen, in whose South Kensington home I had stayed twenty-two years earlier, in 1924, when I was a young man of twenty-one. I first found Elizabeth, who was still true to her first love, the League for Civil Liberties. I then went to see Mrs. Allen, who lived in a flat off Sloane Square, where she was having tea with the woman who came in to help. The family fortunes had changed. The house in South Kensington had been destroyed by bombing, the fine house and grouse moor at Tulliebelton had been sold, there were no servants now except the daily help. The reason was taxation, but Mrs. Allen had no complaints. She was glad that the pomp and power had gone. She was by no means poor, and her flat in Sloane Square was far more luxurious than Mrs. Dench's home in Seven Kings, where all the streets and all the houses looked the same to me.

I saw a great deal of Toc H in London. Their headquarters were at 47 Francis Street in Westminster, and I went there often. The administrator, whose name was Lake Lake, took me to his home in the country at Seven Oaks for the weekend, and persuaded me to shoot a rabbit on the grounds that rabbits were destroying England. I remember, though not well, that I refused to shoot more than one. There can hardly be a sight more peaceful than that of rabbits hopping about a field.

I lunched with the famous Tubby Clayton at Trinity Square. I had heard him speak in Durban in 1934, and he would certainly find his place in a list of my ten most memorable speakers. In Durban he was introduced by Sir Herbert Stanley, a man urbane in the better sense, who could begin a sentence at eight o'clock and end it at ten minutes past, without ever losing his way or making an error. Sir Herbert introduced Tubby with just such a speech, and when Tubby spoke he said something to this effect: "I thank you, Sir Herbert, for your kind—much too kind—words. Not if I lived to be a hundred would I ever acquire such a mastery of the English language." To this he added the punch line, "Thank God." Some of the audience laughed uncertainly, some not at all.

I have already written that Tubby was a genius. At his best he was irresistible, inspiring men to be the masters of themselves so that they might be the servants of others. But he had the fatal gifts of the showman. Bishop Clayton would have been unenthusiastic about Tubby's oratory, and Hofmeyr would have called it "interesting," although he sometimes used oratory himself. The fact is that Tubby was a flawed genius. There was in him, with all his superlative gifts as preacher and teacher and speaker, and as a fisher of men too, a streak of phoniness. His biographer, Sir Tresham Lever, in his book *Clayton of Toc H* either did not know of it, or he concealed it. But at 47 Francis Street they told a cruel story.

In his later years Tubby developed a habit of ejaculating "Good, good," and "Grand, grand," very often after having paid little or no attention to what was being said. The story is told that he paid a Toc H visit to the north of England, and was carefully groomed on the journey by his young aide that the leading Toc H figure in those parts was Jack Featherstonehaugh,* who would meet them at the station. Jack did meet them at the station, and the young aide said, "There is Jack." Tubby advanced and said in that powerful voice of his, "Jack, my dearest fellow, how are you, my dear Jack?" Jack said, "Well, thank you, Tubby," and Tubby boomed, "Good, good." Then memory came to Tubby's aid, and he said "And Jack, how is your dear wife?" Jack said, "Tubby, she passed away last Friday," and Tubby boomed, "Grand, grand."

In 1934, at the age of thirty-one, I was very uncritical of Tubby. Now in 1946, at lunch with him, I was repelled by the boisterous bonhomie, which conveyed, and I think was meant to convey, that the relationship between us was deep and precious.

I attended a quiet communion at All Hallows by the Tower at which Tubby celebrated. There he was a different man. When he came to the words

> We do earnestly repent,
> And we are heartily sorry for these our misdoings;
> The remembrance of them is grievous unto us,
> The burden of them is intolerable.

he spoke them with a great and unfeigned humility, almost with pain. We should always do that, but we do not. I came to the conclusion that somewhere, somehow, something had gone wrong. And I came to the further conclusion that—to him—his sin was that he had not fulfilled the promise of those inspired days at the Old House in Poperinghe, and his incomparable ministry to men who were going, many of them, to certain death. And I have no doubt that the praise of men had come between him and his Creator. The booming voice, the bonhomie were meant to hide it all, but in the chapel he hid nothing, for was he not prostrating himself before One from whom no secrets are hid? Who am I indeed, and who is anyone else, to have judged him at all?

The International Conference of Christians and Jews began in London and then continued in Oxford. Our opening meeting was held in Friends' House in the Euston Road, and the big address was given by Dr. Reinhold Niebuhr, an American of whom I had never heard. He spoke for an hour or more, with no papers, no books, no notes. He was the most enthralling speaker I had ever heard, and now, more than thirty years later, I have not heard his equal. What

* A made-up name.

he said I cannot remember except for one thing, and I quote it diffidently, perhaps because somewhere in some record of that conference, his address was published, and it will be found that I have got it all wrong. He was speaking—for that portion of his address at least—on one of his favourite themes, moral man and immoral society. The one thing I remember is that he told us—in words that I have no doubt much changed—that individual man could become a saint, but that collective man was a tough proposition.

He was thus denying a hope that I had cherished when young, that human society could be perfected by love and devotion; and he was making articulate something that I knew but had never myself articulated—that the immorality of society did not invalidate a belief in the goodness of man, that in fact the inhumanity of man to man could be made endurable for us only when we manifested in our lives the humanity of man to man. At that stage of my life Francis of Assisi meant little to me, but he was later to mean a great deal, and he was going to teach me the same lesson, that there is a wound in the Creation and that the greatest use we could make of our lives was to ask to be made the healer of it. Or to put it one last way, the serving of God must be done with no asking for a reward.

It took me back some twenty-seven years, when I learned from Railton Dent—and believed it too—that service to some cause greater than oneself was the best and most satisfying way of using one's life. But we were innocent in those days, and did not ask ourselves hard questions about the long story of man's inhumanity to man and the tendency of human societies to wax and be great and decay.

Reinhold Niebuhr did not change my life. In a way I knew these things already. It was surely what I had learned from my parents. There is no suggestion that Jesus had any illusions about human society, nor indeed about his own disciples. Nevertheless they were to be his instruments in the making of a new society.

Yet I did not sit there listening to Reinhold Niebuhr and at the same time think these deep thoughts. The experience was as much intellectual as spiritual. I had never before heard a speaker who spoke with such apparent ease, who moved his argument forward with every sentence that he spoke, who used language that could be understood by any nontheologian, who could be witty and grave in one short sentence, who in fact held his hearers in the hollow of his hand. Smuts's speeches always dealt with big ideas but he delivered them badly. Hofmeyr's public speeches were orations. Each was a kind of tour de force and was brought to an end by a powerful peroration, usually with a moral content; but he could be both humorous and witty, and this gift and his sincerity saved him from the danger of becoming pompous. Archbishop Clayton * was not an orator, but when he was moved he could move others; his emotions seemed all the more powerful because they were so firmly controlled. He could be humorous and witty too, and was a master of simple language. Niebuhr had all their gifts and was clearly their intellectual equal; he was nearer to Clayton, though without Clayton's penchant for terrifying people, which I must admit he manifested only when in a bad temper or when confronted by stupidity or what he considered to be obstruction of his own sound and reasonable purposes.

I met Niebuhr and his wife Ursula some three years later in their apartments at the Union Theological Seminary. I told Niebuhr that his Friends' House speech had held me in thrall more than any other I had ever heard. He was both humbled and pleased, and, such is human nature, he became my friend and champion for life.

The conference then adjourned to Oxford, where I met the man become saint. He was Rabbi Leo Baeck, who was born in Poland in 1873, served as rabbi in Oppeln and Düsseldorf, and in 1912 he went as rabbi to Berlin. He served as a chaplain in the German army in the First World War and after the war returned to his pastoral work. In 1933 he declared that the thousand-year history of the German Jews had come to an end, but he refused all offers to go abroad. In 1943 he was sent to the concentration camp at Theresienstadt, where he continued his ministry, and miraculously escaped death.

Leo Baeck was a small man on whose face could be seen the blended signs of courage and suffering. He spoke to us in German about the martyrdom of the Jews in Germany. His address was translated for us, and although many of us did not understand German, his talk was as moving in German as was the translation in English. It made a deep impression on me, and although I do not remember anything but the general substance of it, I shall never forget the occasion, which moved many of us to tears.

At least half of the delegates to the conference were Americans. In fact the conference was largely financed by them, because it was 1946 and Britain had no money. Besides their spiritual and intellectual contributions they brought silk stockings, sugar, candy, and hooch. I could not say they were overbearing, but they were cer-

* Not to be confused with Clayton of Toc H.

tainly high-powered. After all they had emerged from the war one of the two most powerful nations on earth, while Britain was poverty-stricken and great parts of London lay in ruins. Our presiding officer at our plenary sessions was Dr. Henry McCracken, a man deeply esteemed in these circles in America. It was my first encounter with the might of America, with its amazing and sometimes irritating self-confidence, which took such a knock during Vietnam and Watergate, with its idealism and its optimism, which could flare up overnight. Of my enduring debt to America and American people I shall tell later. My first encounter did not dispose me to fall in love with them.

It was also my first encounter with a kind of sociological jargon that I did not like at all. I was appointed chairman of the committee on racialism, and my vice-chairman was Dr. M., whom I frequently could not understand, partly because of his accent and partly because of the jargon. A favourite phrase of his was "area of concern," and if I pressed him—which I did less and less often—to define exactly what he meant, he became irritated, and, I think, a trifle disconcerted, because after all he was a very big shot in the American Conference of Christians and Jews. I think he was accustomed to thinking in packages of words, and he felt lost and affronted if anyone tried to make him express himself more clearly and simply. We often had to prepare material which would be used in the final report, and whatever there had been of fire and enthusiasm, yes, and concern too, in our discussion, was done to death in this tortuous jargon.

So the conference drew to its end. Like so many conferences it did not shake the world. It had great moments and personalities, Niebuhr and Baeck, and Canon Raven, who on the Sunday morning conducted a Judeo-Christian service of worship. If I remember rightly, it had never been done before, but it was done magnificently. Then there were the brilliant Laskis, who were dazzling performers with the word, without, however, the deeper dimension of Niebuhr and Clayton.

Before leaving the topic, I should add parenthetically that the Jewish fear of anti-Semitism, which had been so evident in South Africa since the advent of Hitler, was tremendously abated in 1948 when Dr. Malan came to power, even though he had not been reluctant to use this particular racial prejudice in his time. In due course South African Jewry inscribed his name in the Golden Book as a recognition of his "contribution to better racial understanding in South Africa," and he visited Israel in 1953. Afrikaner anti-Semitism was virulent enough, but it was guilt-ridden. The Afrikaner could not help remembering that it was directed against the people of the Book which he himself revered.

Largely as a result of this change in climate the South African Society of Christians and Jews was finally disbanded. Some of us turned our attention to the much more difficult problems of our country. Anti-Jewish prejudice still exists, but Jews do not fear it now as they did in the 1930s. Cynics would say that this is largely because so many of them have given open or tacit approval to the Government policies of apartheid and separate development.

The conference was now over, and I took up the task that had brought me over the sea.

Chapter 30

From Mrs. Dench's home in Seven Kings I set out on my penological journeys. I first went to the Home Office to present my credentials, in the form of a letter from Mr. J. H. Hofmeyr. I was sorry not to meet Alex Paterson, who had revolutionised the borstal institutions by attracting into the service a new breed of men and women, from the navy and the army and the church and the legal, medical, and nursing professions. It was he who wrote the prayer: "O Lord, help us to be the masters of ourselves so that we may be the servants of others."

These journeys did much to show me the price that Britain had paid for resisting Hitler. Very often I spent a day visiting a prison or a borstal, but sometimes my hosts had not sufficient food to give me lunch, and were both embarrassed and ashamed that they could not. One memorable exception was my visit to the borstal institution at Usk in Wales. It was situated on a beautiful farm, and there was food in abundance. The governor, W. W. (Bill) Llewellin, was an aristocrat and brother of Lord Llewellin, who became the first Governor-General of the ill-fated Central African Federation of Northern Rhodesia (now Zambia), Southern Rhodesia (now Zimbabwe), and Nyasaland (now Malawi).

I will not say I was always hungry in those days, but I was seldom satisfied. I had taken out ration books, and handed these over to Mrs. Dench, who would not accept the coupons for sweets. And I, who was no eater of sweets, would go to get my ration book, buy fourteen ounces of sweets, and eat them all on the way home. If I was away from Mrs. Dench's care, I would go to a cafe for a cup of tea and a bun. The tea was never sweet enough and the bun would fill me up for an hour, at the end of which I was as hungry as ever. Some people had grown used to the spare diet, but others were always hungry. Not the children, however, who received special rations and looked radiant with health. It was generally accepted that the people of Britain had never been healthier in their history.

On September 5, at 6:00 P.M., I sailed from Tilbury on the S.S. *Saga* for Gothenburg. The ship was full of British tourists, who when they saw the first display of smorgasbord could hardly believe their eyes. I myself had been on British rations for only two months, yet even I was astonished. The Britishers could not stop eating, and apologised continually for what they called their gluttony. Is it then true that one's health improves when one actually eats less than the amount that would give one satisfaction? In other words, was British health due to a slight degree of starvation? But my fellow passengers did not enjoy their luck for long. The sea grew rougher and rougher, and a bare dozen of us turned up for the next day's meals. On the morning of September 7 we arrived in Gothenburg, and I took a train to Stockholm, and watched with fascination the countryside through which we passed. I had not seen one like that before; it seemed to be forest, farm, lake, forest, farm, lake, in endless sequence. I had never seen so much water; with few exceptions we have no natural lakes in South Africa. All big sheets of water are man-made.

In Stockholm I made my way to the Diakonistyrelsens Hospitz in Jakobberggatan, where I was to stay for a moderate charge, thanks to my friend the Rev. Eric Hallendorf of Johannesburg. The hospitz was spotless, formal, and, I should imagine, very puritanical. The first day was a Sunday and I walked about the deserted streets of this most beautiful city, trying to read the signs and advertisements. I went to the cathedral for what I suppose was morning prayer, but there was hardly anyone there. I was later told that the decline of organised religion had begun in Sweden.

On the Monday I presented my credentials to the department controlling prisons and reformatory schools, and was handed over to Mr. Uno Eng, an administrative official and a Swedish poet with a good command of English. In 1946 English was not generally spoken in Sweden; the second language was German.

With Uno Eng I visited the big prison of Langholmen, the very modern prison at Hall, and reformatory institutions at Uppsala,

Skrubba, and Skenäs. The programme at Hall was after my own heart. There were three stages, and the third one was one of complete physical freedom within the institution. The plan was the same as that at Diepkloof, but of course the buildings were greatly superior. My visit to Skenäs was regarded as a chance for celebration, and after seeing the school and its activities in as short a time as possible, we adjourned for lunch, which took about four hours, punctuated by drinks of schnapps and beer. You lift the schnapps, you say "Skoal," you take it at one gulp; a mighty and benevolent fire courses through the channels of your body, destroying all that it may devour, but you don't care. No one says—I mean, no one said in 1946—you're a white South African and you stink. We decide that South Africa and Sweden are the finest countries in the world. We decide that South African and Swedish reformatories are the finest reformatories in the world. They don't reform anybody but (hic) who cares? Uno and I leave our hosts in a blaze of international love; racialism, chauvinism, and the Swedish Prison Administration are condemned to everlasting perdition. We weave our way back to the station, Jonköping, Linköping, Norrköping, Nyköping, I don't quite remember. We bid our hosts lachrymose farewells, protesting eternal affection. Uno and I climb into the carriage and the train moves off. Uno looks at me out of eyes, or one eye maybe, shining with beatific guilt, like a cat who has been at the cream. Then he goes to sleep. As we pass farm and lake and forest and lake and forest and farm, I reflect that such a day at Diepkloof Reformatory had never been and would never be.

I wonder if Uno Eng is still alive, my prison host who cared so greatly for hospitality and so little for prisons. He looked after me like a brother, no doubt at the expense of the maligned administration. He took me to Den Gulden Freden, where you could have wonderful food and two Schnapps Reine, which is made from potatoes. After that you could have Schnapps Skone, which is made from wood. If badly made it could cause blindness, epilepsy, dementia praecox, and a host of other terrible disorders, or so they told me. I parted from Uno also amid protestations of eternal fidelity. When I got back to England, punctilious in such matters, I wrote him a generous letter of thanks. But I never had a word from him. I had indeed already concluded that he lived for today, because tomorrow we die. And no doubt he is dead. He did not strike me as being of the stuff of which old men can be made. Probably he never knew that his modest guest from that faraway country was pregnant with child, a story which was to achieve a fame he would have coveted

for his poems. I wrote another generous letter to the Prisons Administration, bestowing high praise on the man they had given me for a
guide. Whether this helped him in his career I beg to doubt. I
should think that the administration already knew that their desk-
bound poet lived only for today, and that he cared more for hospitality than he did for prisons.

The prisons of Sweden were gentle places, not because the
Swedes are such great prison administrators, but because Swedish crime was gentle compared with that of Britain and America.
The Swedes had no Dartmoor or Alcatraz. They could take risks in
their prisons partly because their crime problem was not serious,
and partly because their citizens were tolerant of progressive prison
methods; and of course they were tolerant largely because their
problem was not serious. I was told that drunken driving was the
most serious criminal offence, and have a notion that it still is.

So now I set my face towards Norway, the land of Knut Hamsun.
I said good-bye to the noble city of Stockholm with regret. It was
now September 24, and the inhabitants were making the most of
the declining sun. Wrapped in greatcoats they sat in any patch of
sunlight they could find, their faces turned to the dying god. Although Sweden had suffered little during the war, the date for internal heating had been postponed to September 30. In the streets were
great piles of logs ready for the winter, and the rooms at the Diakonistyrelsens were getting cold. It was my first taste of the northern winter, and I had never realised the tremendous efforts that the
northern people must make to keep themselves warm in winter.

At 9:00 P.M. on September 24, I took the train to Trondheim. I
was in a strange mood. I spoke a great deal to myself, composing
sentences which seemed to me to be very beautiful. As we climbed
higher we encountered snow and rocks covered with many-coloured
lichens. We crossed the following day into Norway at Storlien and
were soon running alongside a river, the like of which I had never
seen before, tempestuous and green and foaming. The daylight had
almost gone when the train drew into Trondheim station.

I found my way to the Hotel Bristol, but the girl at the reception
desk could not understand English. I should add that today it is
unusual to meet a Swede or a Norwegian who cannot speak English.
While I was struggling to explain myself, a man of about my age
asked if he could help me. His name was Jensen, and he was an
engineer. When he had booked a room for me, he asked if I would
like to see the cathedral.

It was now almost dark, and the cathedral itself was in darkness.

The lights had been turned off at four o'clock to save electricity, for Norway in 1946 was bitterly poor, having been stripped of almost everything by the Germans. Mr. Jensen showed me round the famous building with the aid of a torch. It is the most beautiful cathedral in Norway, and kings are crowned there. It has also one of the most beautiful rose windows in the world, and when we had finished our tour we sat down in two of the front pews and looked at it. There was still enough light in the sky to see its magnificent design and its colours. We did not speak, and I do not know how long we sat there. I was in the grip of powerful emotion, not directly to do with the cathedral and the rose window, but certainly occasioned by them. I was filled with an intense homesickness, for home and wife and sons, and for my far-off country.

"Let us go back to the hotel," said Mr. Jensen, "and at seven o'clock I shall call for you and take you to dinner." It must have been about six o'clock when I reached my room, and I sat down and wrote these words: "There is a lovely road that runs from Ixopo into the hills. These hills are grass-covered and rolling, and they are lovely beyond any singing of it."

That is how the story started. I do not even remember if I knew what the story was to be. But the first chapter of *Cry, the Beloved Country* was written in my room at the Hotel Bristol, while I was waiting for Mr. Jensen to come to take me to dinner. The first paragraph was devoted to the hills and valleys and mountains of my distant country, but the tenor of the following paragraphs was quite different. It became clear that the story was to be not so much about the beauties of the land, but about its men and women, and about the gross inequalities that so disfigured our national life.

One of these gross inequalities is that of the land, of which, as a result of conquest, some thirteen percent has been allotted to seventy percent of the people. It is therefore almost impossible for a black man to make a living from the land. The white farms are, in general, large, well-tended, and beautiful; the black farms (if one may use such a term) are, in general, small, ill-tended, and often eroded. I have never in my life seen a black holding that one would properly call a farm, though I believe that there are a handful of them.

The great red hills stand desolate, and the earth has torn away like flesh. The lightning flashes over them, the clouds pour down upon them, the dead streams come to life, full of the red blood of the earth. Down in the valleys women scratch the soil that is left, and the maize hardly reaches the height of a man. They are valleys of old men and old women, of mothers and children. The men are away, the young men and the girls are away. The soil cannot keep them any more.

I had just written these words when Mr. Jensen came to fetch me. Of my excitement he knew nothing, and indeed it is not the kind of thing one tells to a stranger. We enjoyed our dinner, and talked about everything except the tumult of my emotions. I learned that no self-respecting person makes a pilgrimage to Trondheim because of Knut Hamsun. In 1946 his name was execrated because of his pro-Nazi sympathies, and he would have been tried for treason had he not been in his eighties. I also learned that on no account must one drink Norwegian schnapps, which was then made from wood and was even more dangerous than Swedish schnapps made from the same substance.

I never heard of Engineer Jensen again, though I have thought of him very often. I do not know if he ever heard of the book that was begun in Trondheim and was triggered by our visit to the cathedral. It was triggered by something else too. In Stockholm I read for the first time John Steinbeck's *Grapes of Wrath*, and would soon adopt his style of rendering conversations, indicating by a preliminary dash that a speech was about to begin, and omitting all inverted commas. The novel made a deep impression on me and undoubtedly strengthened the urge to write. Because of this it has been said that John Steinbeck has been an influence on my writing but in fact he was not. When I met him two or three years later, he was generous in his praise, but I think he would have been astonished at such a statement.

The next day I took the train to Oslo and went to see the Viking ships and the Vigeland sculptures in Frogner Park. The rain was torrential, and I returned to the hotel—eagerly—because I wanted to write. So began the story, with the bringing of a letter by a small girl to the Rev. Stephen Kumalo, telling him of the sickness in Johannesburg of his sister Gertrude, who went to Johannesburg and never came back.

On September 27 I took the train to Gothenburg to return to England, and on this journey, at the border town of Halden, calamity overtook me. Swedish officials boarded the train to examine the passports, and mine was defective because my Swedish visa allowed for only one entry to Sweden. I was ordered to leave the train in the cold and dark. I was almost in tears because this meant that I would miss the sister vessel of the S.S. *Saga* at Gothenburg, and all my plans for visits to other prisons and schools in England would fall to pieces. I beseeched the officials, I pleaded my ignorance, I emphasised the importance of my journey to the cause of international penology. I told them I was lonely and far from home. All they did was to bark at me, in a manner very Prussian. When I saw that my case was hopeless, I barked at them too—"S.S.," I said, "just like the S.S." This made them angry, and they ordered me to get off immediately. I left the train in anger and hopelessness, and watched it gather speed on its way to Gothenburg.

A young man in railway uniform spoke to me.

"Are you English?" he asked.

"Yes."

"I am pro-English," he said. "When the Germans came we took a small boat and sailed to England, so that we could take part in the war. Norwegians are very pro-English. What was wrong with your passport?"

"It did not allow a second entry to Sweden."

"This happens many times," he said, "especially during the tourist season. These fellows, they always behave like this. They would have made good Germans. We Norwegians do not like this stamping and shouting. But do not worry. Tomorrow we shall go to the British consul in Halden."

"Where shall I stay tonight?" I asked.

He said to me grandly, "You shall stay here, in a luxury coach, with clean blankets, sheets, and pillows, and no charge."

And so I did. Early next morning British Consul Thompson and his wife came to invite me to breakfast, and I conceived a fantastic plan. I would spend all my money on a taxi to Oslo, get a new visa, borrow money (ten pounds, I think it was) from the British Ambassador, take the taxi back to the middle of the bridge into Sweden, be met there by a Swedish taxi, rush to Gothenburg in time to take the sister vessel of the S.S. *Saga* to Tilbury.

The first two stages went well, the taxi to Oslo and the new visa. But the British Ambassador was extremely reluctant to lend me ten pounds. He had been bitten before by stranded Britishers. I produced my letter from Mr. Hofmeyr and said, "If I don't repay you, all you need to do is to write to my Minister and he will sack me." "I should hope so," he said, and with sighs and groans lent me the ten pounds. I told him I had a fanatical aversion to owing anybody any money, but he looked at me without enthusiasm, as though he were saying to me, "How naive can you be?" I said good-bye to him with many thanks, and was escorted to the door by a young man who said to me, "It's a miracle."

On the way back to Halden my taxi driver told me that I would not reach Gothenburg in time for the ship. Consul Thompson told me the same, and I decided to stay in the small and clean hotel, the Marine. There I wrote the story of Kumalo's journey to Johannesburg, and of his first adventures in the wicked city. The next day the Ambassador came to Halden to lunch with the Thompsons and I did my best to improve the impression I had made on him. That evening at 8:00 P.M. I boarded the train for Gothenburg armed with my new visa. I must record that after all my exertions no one even wanted to see it.

In Gothenburg I took a room at a Pensionatet. Although the town was empty of tourists, I had to take a double. But I did not worry, I was in a fever to write. I had nearly three days in Gothenburg, and the story poured out. Why did I choose a humble black priest? Not for any weighty reason, but because such a man had several times visited his son in the reformatory. They used to sit on the benches set aside for visitors, and their conversation could be heard by those who passed by. The father used to urge his son to make the best use of his time at Diepkloof, so that he could return to a law-abiding life. The old man wore his minister's suit when he paid his visits and made no attempt to hide the fact that a priest of the church had fathered a delinquent son. When he left he would say a prayer for his son. No one thought it strange. The son would close his eyes and listen humbly to his father's prayer.

It was inevitable that the reformatory would play a great part in the story, and equally inevitable that the city of Johannesburg and the far distant country would do so. I do not remember how the story took its shape, nor when it became clear that Kumalo's son would kill the son of Jarvis, the white farmer of Ixopo, and that the son of Jarvis would be a young man devoted to the service of the black youth of Johannesburg. Nor that it would happen that the two fathers were in fact neighbours in the district of Ixopo, neighbours, that is, divided by the customs of the land and the gross inequalities of society, and that they would be drawn together because the son of the one had killed the son of the other. This is the creative process, and a great deal of it takes place unconsciously.

Another characteristic of the story was that it was written under the influence of powerful emotion. There are some people who imagine that such emotion can be simulated or manufactured. If it is, then at once it loses its power. After my story was published I did not read it again for perhaps twenty-five years, though I read it probably twenty-five times before publication. When I did read it again, I knew that its emotion had not been manufactured, for the story evoked in me the same emotion as that which mastered me twenty-five years before. One simply cannot hide the fact that it evoked the same emotion in hundreds of thousands, perhaps millions of readers, because the story itself has now sold in millions.

Some people thought it was propagandist, political, polemical. The vast majority of these people were white South Africans. The reason they disliked the novel was that it revealed a picture of South Africa that they did not wish to look at. They disliked the film based on the book also. I sat next to Mrs. D. F. Malan, wife of our Prime Minister from 1948 to 1954, at the premiere of the film; she was clearly disturbed and said to me, "Surely, Mr. Paton, you don't really think things are like that." I said to her, "Madam, I lived in that world for thirteen years," but I did not add, "and you, Madam, have never seen anything of it at all."

Let me make one thing clear at once. When I say that the majority of the people who disliked the book were white South Africans, I am not saying that the majority of white South Africans disliked it. In fact the majority of white Afrikaners did not read it at all. The only Afrikaans newspaper to review it was *Die Burger*, and its review was favourable. But when the book persisted in living, more Afrikaners read it to find out what the fuss was all about. In the last couple of years it received its first public mention from a Nationalist cabinet minister, Dr. Piet Koornhof. With a foresight that is denied to many of us, he saw the day coming when the crying for the beloved country would be changed to rejoicing.

I wrote for three days in Gothenburg under the influence of this powerful emotion. It continued to possess me for three months longer. I do not expect, and for a long time have not expected, to be revisited by it. I assume that this is due to the process of ageing. This is not to say that I have become a stranger to emotion, but it is quieter, partly, I think, because an element of stoicism has entered it. I hesitate to say that it may also be that an element of resignation has entered it, because I should hate to be thought to be saying that I have become resigned to evil. Nor would I be truthful if I admitted it. But I do admit that my anger against injustice is not as violent as it used to be. My story, begun in Norway and Sweden, was becoming a cry of protest against the injustices of my own country. Some thought it mild and some thought it strident, but it was neither. Above all I tried to make a story, not a denunciation or a sermon or a lesson. I do not know if I had then formulated my view on the laws of story telling, that if you want to preach you must go to the pulpit, and if you want to teach you must go to the podium, but if you want to tell a story you must go to the desk and obey the rules of the craft. If your story also expounds some moral truth because of the kind of person you are, that is acceptable so long as it is the writer and not the preacher or teacher who tells the story. If the preacher or the teacher intrudes, that will mean the end of the story.

Does one become more resigned to evil as one grows older? I should with all my heart hope not. Reinhold Niebuhr put it clearly in his famous prayer.

God grant me the serenity to accept the things I cannot change, courage to change the things I can, and the wisdom to know the difference.*

It is not always the wisdom that we require. Sometimes it is the courage to know the difference. Then one does not shrug one's shoulders and say, "What can I do anyway?"

However, none of these thoughts troubled my mind in Gothenburg. I was wholly absorbed in the task of creation. The writer may have several motives, and the two purest of these are first the wish to express something of oneself, and the second is to communicate this something to others. There are at least two others, the need or desire to make money or a living, and the desire to win fame. In Gothenburg I had no thought of making money or winning fame, but I certainly wanted to express something, partly for myself and partly for any who might wish to read it. In this regard the writer is like the actor, the dancer, the singer, the composer; what is the use of practising any of these crafts if there is no one to read, hear, see, respond?

Have there been writers who wrote for themselves alone? Francis Kilvert, curate of Clyro, was presumably one. He was born in 1840 and died in 1879, and kept a diary for the last seven years of his life. His widow, to whom he was married for only a month, destroyed parts of it because she considered them too intimate for publication, but twenty-two notebooks survived. In the 1930s a nephew of Kilvert sent two of these twenty-two to William Plomer, reader for Jonathan Cape, and what he read made him send for the rest. He edited them, and in 1938 Cape published *Kilvert's Diary*,

* Ursula Niebuhr, in her memorial tribute to her husband, gives a slightly different version, beginning, "God, give us grace to accept with serenity the things that cannot be changed. . . ." Perhaps I am presumptuous to use another version, but I like it because I live in a country where there are things I cannot change, but which are certainly not immutable.

and it became a classic overnight. It is a story of simplicity, fidelity, goodness, and deep love of field and river and mountain—and also of the susceptibility of a country curate to the charms of little girls. Kilvert was a master of beautiful and simple prose, and one reads his diary with what one may call delight. When he wrote, did he ever have any wish to communicate his thoughts to others? There is no proof that he did, and there is no indication that he thought of either fame or money, both of which his diary earned sixty years after his death.*

It was now time to leave Gothenburg, and return to the prisons and reformatories of England. I did so with a heavy heart. I did not want to leave my book. But in fact I did not leave it. For the next three months I was to travel all over England and the United States, visiting institutions by day and writing in hotel rooms by night. My energy seemed to be endless. At the end of this time I was beginning to entertain the possibility that I had written something of a book.

---

* *Of these twenty-two notebooks, only three now survive. The others were destroyed by an elderly niece of Kilvert who inherited them from the nephew mentioned above. I have never read any explanation of this extraordinary act. William Plomer's last autobiography (Cape 1975) contains a fascinating chapter, "The Curate of Clyro."*

Chapter 31

I very nearly did not get to America. The military authorities still had first call on all sea transport, and I could not get a berth. I wrote to Dorrie to tell her this, and when I got to Stockholm there was a ticket to New York awaiting me. She had gone to the Chairman of the Transvaal Association of non-European Boys' Clubs for which she was working as secretary. That very day the ticket was on its way to Sweden, drawn from a small pool set aside in Johannesburg for South African businessmen. Therefore on November 6 I set sail from Southampton in that great vessel, the *Queen Elizabeth*. I travelled second class for sixty pounds, but it could only be described as a luxury voyage.

I wrote a great deal on the voyage, but another excitement was also possessing me, the anticipation of seeing the skyline of New York, and of visiting the country of the mightiest nation on the earth. Just as I had gone to Britain in 1924 to see the country of Shakespeare and Dickens, of Scott and Burns, of the cathedrals and the ancient universities, of the Yorkshire dales and the Kyle of Lochalsh, so now I came to America in 1946 to see the country of Mark Twain and Willa Cather, and Emerson and Thoreau, Whitman and Hawthorne, of Jefferson and Lincoln, of *The Bridge of San Luis Rey* and *Gone With the Wind*, Erle Stanley Gardner and Raymond Chandler, of the Grand Canyon and Yosemite and *Sequoia sempervirens* and *gigantea*, of the Deep South and the colour-bar. It was not yet for me the country of the Constitution and the Bill of

Rights and the Supreme Court, but it was not yet that for many Americans either. That was still a shore dimly seen, but it was a shore, not a mirage.

On Armistice Day I got up at three in the morning to see the Statue of Liberty. At five-thirty we docked, and greatly fearing, I took a taxi to the Hotel Granada in Brooklyn. I watched the fare on the taximeter climbing inexorably upward, and with each click of the meter I recalculated the tip. Although I was forty-three years of age I was full of apprehension and I believed—or feared—that the taxi driver had already estimated the depth of my innocence, and would rob me of my last dollar if he could. I had many reasons later to repent of my uncharitableness, but on this occasion I paid $2.70 for a $1.60 fare, urged on by the grumbling of the taxi driver.

The Hotel Granada had been chosen for me by Audrey Kanter, whom I had met at the Conference of Christians and Jews in Oxford. It was in Brooklyn, and she had chosen it so that I would be near the Kanter home, for which security I was very grateful. The hotel terrified me, or to put it more accurately, the prices did. For a single room without meals I paid (if I remember rightly) nine dollars a day, and I fed myself at hotdog stands and streetside cafes. After a while the Kanters found me a room at the Gramercy Park Hotel, which was a dollar or two cheaper, and much nearer the heart of New York. Gramercy Park was rather like an English square, and this in itself seemed to protect me from the rush and the relentlessness of the great city. They awed me, the towering buildings, Rockefeller Center, the two great railway stations, the incessant traffic, the stupendous bridges. In London in 1924 I had felt like an uncouth colonial cousin, in New York in 1946, I felt like a hick from the country.

This feeling of inferiority did not last. No people can equal the Americans in their warmth to strangers. I was at once made welcome in the world of the courts and the prisons and the workers in the field of probation and social welfare. Mrs. Marjorie Bell of the National Probation and Parole Association opened all the doors for me. I began travelling in those fantastic trains that have almost disappeared. You go down into the great concourse, you find out from what gate your train is leaving, you go and stand at the gate until it opens, you descend into the bowels of the earth and take your seat, at the appointed minute your train moves off with not even a tremor, it travels underground for a long time to get out of the great city, then it emerges and you find yourself more or less in the country. I visited Children's Village at Dobb's Ferry, with buildings more substantial than the new hostels at Diepkloof but not so beautiful, with every kind of facility that one could dream of, with thirty percent of the staff engaged on after-care work compared with seven percent at Diepkloof, and a principal's house that made my own look like a cottage.

This travelling I do every day, and in the evening I return to write. Then I have a bit of luck. Mrs. Bell gets me an invitation to attend the National Conference on Juvenile Delinquency in Washington, D.C., to be opened by Attorney-General Tom Clark. I get into a train bound for Washington. We go through Newark, Trenton, Philadelphia, Wilmington, Baltimore. I sit with my eyes glued to the window. I have never seen anything like it before, factory after factory after factory, all blazing with light, such an assembly of industrial might as makes one wonder what the Japanese thought they were doing when they attacked Pearl Harbor. I spent five days in Washington, meeting penologists, teachers, psychiatrists, prison officials, and probation officers. I shall mention only one, Ben Alper, because I have written to him for over thirty years. When the conference was not sitting, I went to see the sights. I mounted the steps to the Lincoln Memorial with a feeling akin to awe, and stood for a long time before the seated figure of one of the greatest men of history, surely the greatest of all the rulers of nations, the man who would spend a sleepless night because he had been asked to order the execution of a young soldier. He certainly knew that in pardoning we are pardoned.

One could not help reflecting that the Lincoln Memorial is something like a temple erected to a human being. To do such a thing is not really very American, but one reflects also that it is a temple erected to the spirit of man at its highest and its purest. One would not experience the same emotions standing before a memorial to Roosevelt or Churchill, and certainly not to Napoleon. Americans themselves certainly do not experience these emotions when they survey the Washington Monument; their feelings are probably romantic and mildly chauvinistic, whereas the Lincoln Memorial evokes nothing of this kind.

I was astounded to see a notice at the memorial asking visitors not to smoke, but I understood it better when I visited the cemetery at Arlington, and saw the smokers dropping ash all around the Tomb of the Unknown Soldier. There is nothing more revolting than to see a fat man with his hat on his head and a fat cigar in his mouth, and to hear him saying to his wife, "Say, Mamie, what do you know, they don't even know who he was."

When I was not at the conference, or visiting memorials and the Capitol and the National Art Gallery and Mount Vernon, I was in my room at the Statler Hotel writing my story. How far I had got with it I do not now remember. But Abraham Lincoln got into its pages, when Jarvis senior visited the house of his murdered son, and read amongst other things "The Famous Speech at Gettysburg."

Back to New York and the penological visits. Mrs. Bell helped me to plan a journey to Atlanta, New Orleans, Houston, the Grand Canyon, Los Angeles and San Francisco and Sacramento, and then to Denver, Boys Town at Omaha, Chicago, Toronto and Ottawa, and back to New York. If I remember rightly, the railway ticket for this tremendous journey cost something like $120.00 and was several feet long. But before I set out, I visited more institutions, the most notable being the great prison of Sing Sing. It was December 2, and it was my first taste of the American winter. As I made my way from the Gramercy Park Hotel to Ossining Station, I felt that my clothes were made of paper. It wasn't arctic at all, the temperature being 18°F, but it was the coldest day I had so far experienced in my life. In 1946 Sing Sing had a tremendous reputation for the toughness of its prisoners and the toughness of its administration. Sentries were posted on its high and forbidding walls. I visited the room of execution with its fearsome electric chair, and did not accept an invitation to try it out. What does one learn from a place like this? Only how to maintain an almost unbreakable security. I travelled back to New York in an extremely sober mood, and was glad to return to the quite different security of the Gramercy Park Hotel.

My eyes and ears and mind were open every minute of the working day, not only to prisons and schools, not only to American history, but also to the relations of black and white in this part of the country. In those days the word "black" was seldom used, the correct words being "Negro" and "Coloured." It would have been insulting to refer to "the blacks," as indeed it would have been in South Africa, but the insult was removed by the black people themselves. I am old-fashioned, and still find such usage derogatory, preferring to speak of "black people" and "white people." A South African term that I find revolting is "the Coloureds," * and I always use "the Coloured People."

---

* In South Africa a Coloured person is a person of mixed ancestry, possibly the Khoikhoi, San, European, and Malay. Many Coloured people do not like the word "Coloured" at all, but the word "Eurafrican" has never taken root. More radical Coloured people now call themselves "blacks," but many others will not do so.

The colour-bar in New York in 1946, though observed in some places like certain hotels and restaurants, was to be strikingly different from that in South Africa. While I was staying at the Hotel Granada, I ate in the hotdog stalls and the cafes where there was no colour-bar at all. Nor was there on the trains and buses. A tremendous struggle was going on in the field of housing. There was no segregation on the trains, but as the train crossed the Mason-Dixon line that separates North from South, a partition screen was erected in the dining coach, and any black passenger travelling in a "white" coach was asked to move to a "coloured" coach. To save coloured passengers embarrassment, they were advised but not compelled to start such a journey in a "coloured" coach.

In 1946 the coloured people of the United States contributed some ten percent of the population, but owing to the social, political, economic, and educational conditions in which they lived, they contributed sixty to seventy-five percent of the inmates of prisons and reformatory schools. But there was no racial segregation in the penal institutions of New York State. I visited the State Training School at Warwick, where there were 400 boys and a staff of 230. The absconding rate would have terrified me, and would not have been tolerated by the South African authorities. Boys had for the preceding five months absconded at the rate of thirty per month. The discipline was very different from that of Diepkloof. There was no marching as such; parties of boys walked from one assignment to another, often in a slovenly manner, some with hands in pockets, some with looks of contempt on their faces for this institution that had temporarily deprived them of their liberty. The punishment block was not open to inspection, and therefore I did not learn how many boys were there. Solitary confinement was used only because of "community pressures," whatever that might mean.

I did not presume to pass judgement on this rather forbidding school. I came to the modest conclusion that Diepkloof was a much easier proposition. Certainly there was at Warwick nothing of the cheerfulness and the vigour of the Diepkloof community. Why should that have been so? I did not delude myself for a moment that if I had been appointed the director of Warwick, I would have been able to change the spirit of the institution. Where did the difference lie? Did New York and the United States of America produce a deeper resentment in their coloured offenders than Johannesburg and the Union of South Africa produced in their African offenders? I did not know the answer. All that I can say is that the resentment of many of the Warwick boys was palpable.

At 4:40 P.M. on December 7, I left for Atlanta on an express train.

One had to sleep the night in one's seat, but the seat was very comfortable. There was a dining saloon, but you could buy food more cheaply from the vendors' wagons that passed up and down the broad middle aisles of the coaches. I sat next to Mr. Frank Groseclose of Atlanta, a man a little older than myself and clearly a citizen of some substance. He very naturally wanted to know why I was going to Atlanta and what I was doing in the United States. He would not hear of my going to a hotel, but invited me to spend my seven days in Atlanta with himself and his wife at 296 5th Street N.W., and I gladly accepted.

We arrived in Atlanta at ten the following morning, on the day after one of the most terrible hotel fires in the history of the United States. This was the Hotel Winecoff in Atlanta, where over one hundred (over one hundred and twenty, if I remember rightly) people were burned to death, or in their terror jumped from their rooms to death in the street below. What made the tragedy more poignant was that many of these were schoolgirls and schoolboys who had come to Atlanta for some kind of educational occasion. One man saved his life by resisting the urge to jump, and by closing his door and windows and barricading every crack with wet towels and sheets. One of the features of the fire was the way in which the elevator shafts acted as giant funnels and carried the fire to every part of the building.

Frank Groseclose and I were two of the many thousands who came to see the burnt-out shell of the Winecoff. But it did not occur to me that the news had been sent throughout the world, and had filled Dorrie with panic because she knew that I was going to Atlanta on the very day of the fire. Unfortunately she did not know where I was staying, nor did the Conference of Christians and Jews in New York; however, they got in touch with the conference in Atlanta and they with me, and I rushed to Western Union and sent her a cable. As J. D. Rheinallt Jones used to say to Hofmeyr (related in my life of the latter), "It's nice to be appreciated."

My week in Atlanta was very full, and according to my diary (a pocketbook, not a real diary) I did not write a word of my story. The highlight was a visit to Atlanta Penitentiary, a federal institution for long-term recidivists and what might be called intractables, under Warden Joe Sanford. A better combination of stern discipline and purposeful industry I have never seen. It was like a great factory with excellent management-labour relations. I should add that because the penitentiary was a federal institution, it did not segregate its prisoners according to colour, even though it was in the state of Georgia.

Alas, my week in Atlanta ended on an unhappy note, and I remember it to this day, although it all happened more than thirty years ago. On Wednesday, December 11, I visited a coloured industrial farm outside the city, which had 154 coloured pupils all committed by the courts, and twenty-four staff who were all-white. All the pupils were trained to work on farms, and when I asked if these were successful, the Superintendent, Mr. P., replied, "What's better than a good nigger on a stand?" I was taken to see the stables and the sties and the pastures, and it was clear that the standard of farming was very high. But so far I had seen hardly a boy, and I had the impression that Mr. P. did not think it important. The reason why I had seen only one or two boys was that this was a day for school, and I asked to go there. In the first classroom the teacher was smoking, but the discipline of the boys was perfect if you like that kind of discipline. The classrooms and indeed many of the rooms were full of biblical texts, and I could not help reflecting on the belief that the display of such texts has some educational and moral effect on the boys who live amongst them. In fact the texts were supposed to do what Mr. P. and his staff were clearly not doing, and I came to the conclusion that the mules and the cows and the pigs were what really mattered. Of rapport between staff and boys I detected no sign whatever. I could not bring myself to ask the educational qualifications of the staff, but I would guess that even those of the superintendent were of the most elementary kind.

I asked Mr. P. the question that the majority of visitors ask superintendents, "How successful is your school?" He replied that it was ninety percent successful, but only eighty percent at that time, and I forbore to ask him what he meant by this, or how he worked it out. Instead I asked to see the dormitories and was taken to see the largest, where some seventy boys slept. This was on the second floor, and the windows were secured by iron gauze. The smell was strong, and the dormitory and beds very dirty. The showers and lavatories were in the basement, with hot and cold water. "Some people think niggers shouldn't have hot water, but I do what I think," said Mr. P.

When I returned to Atlanta I was visited by a reporter from one of the most famous of American newspapers, the *Atlanta Constitution*, with which is associated the famous name of its editor, Ralph McGill, and he asked me for an interview on my visit to Atlanta. I agreed to this in all innocence, and tried to give as true an account as I could. He particularly wanted my opinion of the kind of work being done at the coloured industrial farm, of which he and his editor were strongly critical, and I not only gave him my opinion, but contrasted the standards with those achieved by the State Training School at Milledgeville. This school was roughly two-thirds white and one-third coloured, and the two groups were segregated, but the facilities for the coloured boys were very superior to those of the industrial farm. At Milledgeville there was some attempt to honour the dictum "separate but equal." My strongest criticism of the industrial farm was that the animals received far greater care than the boys.

The publication of this interview greatly incensed my host, Frank Groseclose, with whom my relations had been warm. His opinion was that I had abused the hospitality of Georgia, in which I am sure he included that of himself and his wife. This judgement coming from a substantial citizen of Atlanta was painful, and it was fortunate for us all that I was leaving the next day for New Orleans. I have not kept a copy of the newspaper interview, perhaps because of its painful associations, but of one thing I am certain: it contained no attack on Georgia and the Deep South. I would have thought it unwarranted for a white South African to criticise race policies so like those of his own country. My new Atlanta friends consoled me, saying that Frank Groseclose was an excellent example of the upright white Southerner whose mind was closed in the matter of human relations, that is, those human relations which are also race relations.

All I remember about my last twenty-four hours in Atlanta (memory being aided by a diary) was that I visited Georgia Technical College, was taken to Stone Mountain, and gave a lecture to members of community agencies. Otherwise I remember nothing. I had brought presents for the Grosecloses and suppose I must have given them. I suppose I must have breakfasted there on the morning of Saturday, December 14. Who took me to the station I do not remember, but at 10:00 A.M. I took the train to New Orleans. Within a few days I wrote a letter of thanks to the Grosecloses, but it was never acknowledged. So our brief friendship came to an end.

Late that night I took the train to Houston, and crossed Huckleberry Finn's great river, though I did not see it. I was now on my way to more penological visits in and near San Francisco, but was going to break my journey to see the Grand Canyon. At Houston I spent the day in a room at the Hotel Tennison, and returned at last to my story, which was nearing its end.

From Houston to the Grand Canyon is a long journey of some thirty-six hours, and nearly half of that time is occupied in crossing the state of Texas. The train was the worst I had travelled in. The seats were hard and cramped, and the coaches were packed. I sat next to a heater, and my clothes and I were soon wet through. Seeing my discomfort, my neighbour, a young G.I., asked, "Too hot for you?" When I said, "Yes," he offered to change with me. "It can't be too hot for me," he said. "I'm just back from the Pacific." Later I was able to find a window seat and opposite me was a huge Texan with a tremendous hat. I was willing to converse with him, but he was one of those rare Americans who have no wish to talk to strangers.

When I woke in the early morning we were still in Texas. We were passing many automatic pumps in the middle of nowhere, unattended, and surprisingly small and compact, that hour after hour pumped out the black gold from the bowels of the earth. What a way to make money indeed! But that is not what excited me. What filled me with extraordinary emotion was that we might have been passing through the Orange Free State or the Karoo. I found myself saying to the big Texan, "What a country, what a country!" His taciturnity dropped away. The stranger at least knew beauty when he saw it. We talked without stopping until he left the train some hours later.

After a long day and another night in the train, I arrived at Williams at five in the morning. It was very cold, but an all-night restaurant blazed with light. That was one thing I was learning about America; within generous limits you needn't be cold and you needn't be hungry. I treated myself to a giant steak with eggs and coffee and bought a newspaper. I felt like a king. Three hours later I was looking down on the Grand Canyon. I shall not attempt to describe it. It overwhelmed me, and when I saw it again thirty years later it overwhelmed me again. I think it is the vastness and the silence. Sometimes you can hear the Colorado five thousand feet below, but at that distance it looks like a petrified river. An American friend, thinking perhaps to bolster my ego, said to me, "But you have the Rift Valley, which is at places seven thousand feet deep." But the Rift Valley is not to be compared with the Grand Canyon. A valley five thousand feet deep with walls thirty to eighty miles from each other is not spectacular at all. The majesty of the Grand Canyon, strangely enough, is due as much to its comparatively narrow width as to its great depth.

I conceived the notion of walking down the trail to the river, and then hiring a horse and riding back to the hotel. It was a distance of twenty-eight miles, but what was twenty-eight miles to me? I would show these Americans what a South African could do. I was, however, not put to the test. After three or four miles I trod on a flat stone that reared up and cracked me on the right ankle, with a report that reverberated from wall to wall of the great canyon. I sat down for a while, facing the painful prospect of walking back to the hotel, which I reached four hours later. I struggled on to a bus at Williams, and at nine that evening caught a train that would take twenty-four hours to reach Los Angeles. It was a painful journey. I arrived at L.A. with an ankle which had a circumference two or three times that of the other. Although the flesh was unwilling the spirit was indomitable. I took a guided tour to Hollywood, and caught glimpses of the homes of those who had been made famous by the film industry, some of them even more famous in a way than Churchill, Truman, and Stalin.

That evening I caught the night train to San Francisco and thus was not able to see one of the most beautiful rail routes in the world. The train was comfortable, but I was in great pain. I took a room at the Hotel Somerton, and to my rescue came Sonia Davur, who had been one of the secretaries of the Conference of Christians and Jews in Oxford. She had been brought to the States by Dr. Ulysses Mitchell to work in San Francisco, where she later met and married a student from India, and went to live in that far country. She took me to a doctor, who after an X ray pronounced that no bone in my ankle was broken. Slowly the swelling began to subside.

I now had time to return to my story and found that the deep emotion was still at work. Though I had been very conscientious about performing my professional obligations, and though these had often made writing impossible, I had never feared that the emotion would desert me. All I had to do to ensure its swift return was to read what I had already written. In any event San Francisco was in the grip of the Christmas spirit, and I had a great deal of time for my own affairs. On the evening of December 23 I went to a party given by Dr. Mitchell for his staff, and sat at a small table with Aubrey and Marigold Burns; this was the beginning of a friendship that has lasted till now. On December 25 the Burnses telephoned to ask me to spend Christmas with them in Marin County, and so I crossed the Golden Gate on one of the most majestic structures ever made by man.

The Burnses lived in Fairfax, at 127 Cypress Drive, in a house through the center of which rose up four redwood trees through holes cut in floors and ceilings. The trees were young but were over a hundred feet high, and ended up in the sky. Water coursed down their trunks when it rained, and romance competed with discomfort for the mastery. The Burnses were a few years younger than I, but our interests were similar and we talked incessantly, interrupted seldom and demurely by a beautiful twelve-year-old daughter called Martha and incessantly and vociferously by two irrepressible sons, Hal and Christopher, seven and three. About midnight they were all packed off to bed, but Christopher soon emerged demanding food, drink, and conversation. He would be cajoled, bribed, threatened, and would eventually retire and leave his elders in peace, but after ten or fifteen minutes the urge for conversation or the hunger would again overpower him, and he would emerge as masterfully as ever. At last Marigold could bear it no longer and delivered a couple of half-hearted blows which caused Christopher to retreat to his room, full of recriminations and loud expressions of inconsolable pain and grief. When this had lasted beyond the bounds of tolerance, Aubrey would go to this young hellion and again cajole, bribe, and threaten, and peace would reign. But after another ten or fifteen minutes Christopher would come out again, renewing his insatiable demands, and Aubrey, who obviously deprecated Marigold's use of violence, now had recourse to it himself, while ascribing to his infant child qualities of moral turpitude of which no three-year-old is capable.

It must have been about three in the morning when Christopher decided to call it a day, and peace descended on the exhausted house. During this encounter, which lasted some four or five hours, Marigold and Aubrey and I discussed America, South Africa, Jews and Christians, racial harmony, and racial wrongs, the great passages of the Bible, the scenery of our two countries, but above all the literature of the English language. It came as something of a surprise to the Burnses that their visitor from a place almost as far from California as any place could be, from a continent which in 1946 still had the name of the Dark Continent, should have read so much of their own literature.

It turned out that Aubrey was a poet, and out came some of his poems for me to read. More than thirty years later I wrote a foreword to his collection of poems, *Out of a Moving Mist,* and in it I paid special tribute to a poem which I first read in the early hours of the morning in that redwood house. It was called "Apology to a Spider," and I thought it then, and think it now, to be beautiful.

> *Predatory architect*
> *I am sorry to have wrecked*
> *The inimitable snare*
> *You have woven in the air.*

> *Watcher, waiting on your web*
> *While the tides of evening ebb,*
> *Fisher in the waves of wind—*
> *How was luck today, my friend?*

It then could hardly help emerging that I was a writer too, and that I had in the Hotel Somerton a novel almost finished. The Burnses wanted to read it, and they wanted me to make their home my headquarters, but by this time I had arranged a tremendous programme with the California Youth Authority, which had the reputation of being one of the most enlightened youth agencies in the whole United States. I returned to the Hotel Somerton for another two weeks, but I made arrangements for the Burnses to get my finished manuscript.

Chapter 32

I spent a great part of the next two weeks with Ray Studt and Roy Votaw of the Youth Authority. They treated me like a brother, with all the assiduity of Uno Eng but without the schnapps. Ray Studt is no longer alive, but I have kept in touch with Roy Votaw for thirty-three years. With one or the other, or with one of their colleagues, I visited the Fricot Ranch School, the mountain camps at Coarse Gold and Ben Lomond, the girls' school at Los Guillecos,* juvenile courts and homes of detention, and the headquarters office of the authority at Sacramento. These two weeks in California provided the highlight of my time in the United States, and I came to entertain a great respect for the personnel and work of the authority. Therefore what I write about my visit to Preston School must not be allowed to invalidate anything I had already written.

I visited Preston for a simple reason. I wanted to see it more than any other institution. In my early days at Diepkloof I had read about it, and about the pioneering work of Fred C. Nelles, who later went to Whittier School, and it was a story that both inspired and encouraged me. The reality was devastating. To enter Preston I had to be admitted through a security gate, though not so overpowering as the tremendous security gate of Diepkloof Reformatory which was removed on New Year's Day 1936. It was still more devastating to

---

* This is the name as written down in my diary. I am told that the telephone book spells it Los Guilucos, and that some maps spell it Los Guilicos.

realise that this security gate must be part of a security fence and a very long and substantial one too, because it enclosed an area vastly greater than that enclosed by the fence at Diepkloof. This was because Diepkloof Reformatory in 1935 was virtually nothing more than a compact, self-contained, hollow square building, whereas Preston School was by comparison a tremendous place, with a complex of buildings and a diversity of occupations unknown to us in those early years. No fewer than forty of Preston's eleven hundred acres were enclosed by this fence.

The atmosphere of Preston was one of gloom, and no wonder, for it was comparatively recently that the order had gone out to retrace the brave steps that had earlier been taken. There was no Engelbrecht, no Moloi to be seen here with their conviction of the value of the work they were doing and their air of confidence that whatever problems arose, they would be dealt with. It was clear that Preston was going through a grave crisis, and this could be seen in the evasiveness of those staff members whom I met, most of whom, perhaps all, would not now be alive to be wounded by these painful observations.

In South Africa my extreme critics on the left maintained that Diepkloof was too military and that it therefore destroyed freedom, spontaneity, individuality, and personality. But here at Preston boys got into and out of bed by numbers. Mr. F. described to me in the most exasperating detail how this was done. I asked about the use of detention, as I did at every penal institution that I went to. So I was taken to the detention block, which was known as G Company. There was no evasiveness now; it was clear that this was a discipline to be admired. If there was uncertainty in the other parts of the institution, there was none here. When we reached G Company I was handed over to the man who supervised, as grim and taciturn a custodian of souls as ever I encountered.

All of us have experiences in life which will never be forgotten. Some are remembered with difficulty, perhaps when someone reminds us. Others cannot be recalled at all. My visit to G Company, Preston, was an experience that I have never forgotten. I shall try to set it down without exaggeration, and as honestly as I can remember it, with the aid of brief notes that I made on the spot.

As I remember it, G Company consisted of thirty detention cells, fifteen on each side of a brightly lit passage. The cells contained bed, lavatory bowl and cistern, shower, and protected light. I do not remember if there was a table, but there was possibly none, because tables can be used as weapons. The door was a grille so that one could see everything in the cell at a glance. Every cell but one had an occupant; some boys were sunk in lethargy or melancholy, others totally indifferent, others contemptuous. No one came to attention, and it was clear that these boys were beyond any kind of military discipline. One of them came to the grille and cried out at us, in a voice of agony, anger, supplication, despair, who knows? He shook the bars of the grille with an energy so demonic that it seemed as though he might bring down the edifice on the heads of his enemies. My guide remained impassive, and I tried to do the same, but I wanted to speak to the boy and knew that it could not be done, first because it was clear that G Company had only one function and that was detention, second because I did not know in what idiom to address such a boy, third because if by some magic the boy had responded, what next step was possible for me?

I do not think my guide understood what I was feeling or thinking, but he did know that this display of superhuman strength had made a deep impression on me. Therefore he took me to the unoccupied cell; and there the lavatory cistern and pipe had been torn out of the wall and the lavatory bowl out of the floor by a boy who had no instruments but his own bare hands. It was clear that my guide regarded this as the ultimate in criminal depravity. Of the meaning of this incredible feat he knew nothing, or it may be that he had no interest in knowing, or it may even be that he felt there was nothing to know. I became now as taciturn as he, for what was there to say to such a man?

Before we parted, he dealt me another blow. He told me that Preston School was going to build another thirty detention cells, at a cost of $50,000, and they would be proof against this kind of depravity. I had by now had enough. All I wanted to do was to get away from this place. The official car took me back to Sacramento, and I sat in the back by myself and said not a word.

One does not often have two unforgettable experiences in a space of a few days. On January 8, 1947, I took the ferry to Alcatraz, the Rock, the prison of prisons, a building as well known by name as the Empire State. Alcatraz is situated on an island in San Francisco Bay and was for years a military prison, until in 1934 it became a federal institution for the toughest prisoners in the United States, some of whom had killed guards in other prisons. The iron bars were replaced with saw-proof steel and the new locks were invincible. Electric eyes could follow every movement and four watchtowers surveyed the whole terrain ceaselessly. Some of the more daring prisoners tried to escape, but of those who got as far as the waters of San Francisco Bay, not one is known for certain to have reached the shore. The island of Alcatraz is made still more forbidding by the fog which often hides it from view, just as it often hides the great bridge, and the tops of the two giant towers can be seen riding above the darkness.

It is almost as difficult to get into Alcatraz as it is to get out. My credentials were subjected to rigid scrutiny, and my body, clothes, and possessions were searched. But eventually I found myself in the office of Warden James A. Johnson, the holder of one of the toughest jobs in the world.

It was in 1946 that the prison was turned into a battleground. A prisoner washing windows early in the morning was suddenly offered the chance in a thousand which he had in fact been waiting for. He was able to thrust his implement, which was described as a T-shaped squeegee, through the bars and to catch a guard by the neck. He released two of his co-conspirators, but they were unable to unlock the armoury or to open all the cell blocks. Armed only with pistol and rifle they declared war on the authorities, and killed two guards and wounded thirteen before they themselves were killed. The battle lasted three days and Warden Johnson took me to the scene of it, with its bullet-scarred walls, and the high-level galleries where the guards had fought for their lives. The Marines were called out, and thousands of spectators on the hills surrounding the bay, although they could see and perhaps hear nothing, were held spellbound for the duration of the battle.

The warden took me to see the Alcatraz equivalent of Preston's G Company. I write here from memory, and perhaps faultily, for I cannot find my notes. The block was no doubt the most secure, the most forbidding, the most awesome building in the world. It was the home of what would be called the irredeemable, those who could not be touched or communicated with anymore. The block contained a number of cells, perhaps twelve (and I must repeat that I am writing from memory). Six of these were shining bronze cages and had no secrets from guard or visitor. But six were sealed behind massive bronze doors, each with its judas hole. I looked through one and could see a man sitting motionless on a bed, beyond all human power to move or touch or make laugh or weep. He was there because he would kill if any chance were given him, because he was possessed, day in and day out, during every hour of waking and sleeping too perhaps, by a hatred that consumed him without ceasing, of authority and society and law and guards, of life and joy and the whole creation, of the day that he never saw and the night that covered him, black as the Pit from pole to pole. Was his soul unconquerable? Who can answer such a question?

So I returned from Alcatraz as silently as I had returned from Preston, having been a witness to the ultimate conflict between man and society. We talk about the sanctity of human life, but what kind of sanctity is there that can be preserved only by such means? What kind of life is preserved behind these impenetrable doors? Would it not be better to give such a man a shot of sodium pentathol, and to send him peacefully to sleep in a chamber of gas? Not to this day can I answer such a question. Two irreconcilable moral concepts are in conflict, not only in me but in all those who feel any kind of responsibility for the just ordering of society. The one is the sanctity of life, the other the duty of compassion.

Were the boys in G Company heading towards places like Alcatraz? Was there nothing that could be done to stop it? Had some irreparable damage already been done to them by society, or by some institution, or by some misguided and self-righteous teacher or guard? Or was the boy fated from birth? One stands in awe before such questions.

After visiting Preston and Alcatraz I naturally asked myself an obvious question—why had I never encountered anything like this at Diepkloof? Was there some fundamental difference between black African psychology and the psychology of America? Or did Engelbrecht, with his six foot four inches, know some secret or understand some magic that they did not know at Preston? Why did Preston have to build thirty more detention cells when we could do with four?

It was three years after these events that I spent two months in a cabin in a redwood grove at Lane's Flat, California. I went there to read and to write, and produced three poems. Two of these, "Meditation for a Young Boy Confirmed" and "A Psalm of the Forest," appeared in the anthology *Knocking on the Door*, published in 1975. The third, which received no title, is published for the first time here today.

> My Lord has a great attraction for the humble and simple,
>   they delight in his conversation,
> The insane stop their frenzies and look at him unsurely,
>   then they crowd round him and finger him gently,
> Their wistful eyes capture something that was lost, they are
>   healed for a moment of the hurts of great institutions.
> The half-witted press their simple thoughts upon him, and
>   he listens with attention to the babblings of imbeciles,
> He knows their meanings, and they observe him trustfully.

> *He passes through the great gates of Alcatraz, there is*
> *no searching machine that can prevent him,*
> *He goes into the cells that have the iron doors, where*
> *the wild men are shut in completely,*
> *They put their wild teeth on his hands, but take them*
> *away again from his wounds with wonder.*
> *Oh Lord teach us your wisdom, and incline our hearts to*
> *receive your instructions.*
> *Then the maniac would stay his hand from the small girl,*
> *and the drunken man from the throat of the woman,*
> *And the father his hands from the growing son, and the*
> *son his hands from the father.*
> *And the wild boys could be brought out from the cages,*
> *and the wild men from behind the unutterable doors.*

I do not know why I wrote of iron doors. My clear recollection is
that they were made of bronze. Alcatraz prison was closed in 1963.
It was only a day or two ago that I read an extract from *Here Is the
Golden Gate,* by Neill C. Wilson, in which he described Warden
Johnson as a humane, implacable man. I would not have chosen the
word "implacable," but I know what the writer meant. Only a stern
and humane man could have ruled a place like Alcatraz.

My time in California was drawing to an end. I decided to spend
my last two nights with the Burnses and amongst other things to
hear what they thought of my story. Then I would return east and
conclude my penological tour with visits to Denver, Omaha, To-
rorto, and New York. In preparation for my stay the Burnses picked
out their stoutest friends and gave them the task of looking after
Christopher and Hal for two nights. I think I should record that it
was this same Christopher, working as a young man for an airline,
who made it possible for his father to visit South Africa some
twenty years later.

So I returned to the Burnses. They had finished my story. There is
only one way to describe their reaction. They were overwhelmed by
it. Aubrey said to me, "This book will go on living long after you are
dead." I shall not repeat all that the Burnses said. Aubrey blew his
nose a great deal, and Marigold had recourse to her handkerchief. It
was clear that they had been through an emotional experience
which if not as deep as mine was akin to it. No writer in the world
could have asked for more from his first two readers.

The Burnses pointed out to me that the story had no title. One of
us suggested, and we all agreed, that it should be titled by secret

ballot. Three pieces of paper and three pens were produced. Three people wrote and they all wrote the same words: "Cry, the Beloved Country." So that is what it was called.

I have often been asked where the title came from. In one way it came from the house in Fairfax with the four redwood trees. But of course it came from the book itself.

Cry, the beloved country, for the unborn child that is the inheritor of our fear. Let him not love the earth too deeply. Let him not laugh too gladly when the water runs through his fingers, nor stand too silent when the setting sun makes red the veld with fire. Let him not be too moved when the birds of his land are singing, nor give too much of his heart to a mountain or a valley. For fear will rob him of all if he gives too much.

I suppose this could be regarded as some kind of hyperbole. One does not really wish that a child should not love the earth too deeply, but one is suggesting that if he loves it too deeply he cannot ask immunity from pain. That is what the visitors from America and Britain and Germany and other countries mean when they say to me, "Ah, but your country is beautiful." They mean, "But why is it so full of pain?" It is not true that fear will rob the child of all if he gives too much, but it is true that fear will temper his joy. I am sometimes astonished when I remember that these words were written in 1946, and that it took many of the white people of South Africa thirty years to acknowledge their truth, when black schoolchildren started rioting in the great black city of Soweto on June 16, 1976, on the day after which, of all the hundred thousand days of our written history, nothing would be the same again.

However, none of these thoughts was in our minds. The Burnses were insistent that we should find a publisher before I left the United States. They made a list of fifteen publishers and a list of friends who would type at least six of the chapters and send copies of them to all the publishers. I do not remember which were the six chapters, except for two, the first and the last of the book. If any publishers were interested they could write to me in the care of the South African High Commissioner in Ottawa, where I would be in twelve days' time. On Saturday, the eleventh day of January, 1947, my forty-fourth birthday, I left the Burnses and San Francisco and set out for Denver. Back in Fairfax the Burnses and their friends devoted themselves to the task of ensuring that Cry, the Beloved Country found a publisher.

I have visited California ten times since that first visit. When

Aubrey and Marigold parted company in 1958 I had visited them five times, and since that time I have visited Aubrey five times.

When he published his collected poems, *Out of a Moving Mist,* in 1977, to which I had written a foreword, he sent me a presentation copy. In this he wrote

> *Alan, who changed my life, again you have done*
> *a great kindness to me. I wish this book were better,*
> *but I give it to you, such as it is, with joy.*
> *Aubrey*
> *April 1, 1977*

On my birthday I took one of those fantastic trains to Denver, angry because I could see nothing of the great mountains. The outer glass of the double window was coated with thick ice. The whole world was under ice and snow. Denver was under ice and snow, and my hosts overwhelmed me with an Uno Eng type of hospitality. Boys Town, Omaha, founded by Father Edward Flanagan in 1917, had grown from its simple beginnings into a tremendous institution with grand buildings and an appearance of opulence. Boys Town choirs and bands toured the United States (and the world too maybe) to raise money to keep this colossus moving. A tremendous workshop, manned not by boys but by adult Nebraskans, daily turned out quantities of souvenirs, curios, and mementos, and those were marketed by high-powered executives. I had hoped to meet Father Flanagan, but he had retired because of ill health, and died the following year. I would like to have asked him what he thought of the new Boys Town, but perhaps he wouldn't have told me. In any case I was unable in the course of a one-day visit to form any sound judgement. All I can say in honesty is that it was the go-getting atmosphere that struck me most.

Then to Ottawa to plan my visit to schools and prisons in Ontario. After we had passed through Detroit the heating in the coaches failed. No one informed us about this, and I came to the naive conclusion that Canada was just very cold. Before I froze to death we reached Ottawa and the warmth of the station. Ottawa has a palatial hotel attached to the station, and one can walk to it in comfort but it was not for me. I took my two suitcases and struggled into the street, but I soon had to take refuge in a cafe because I was blinded by tears, my nose was running, my ears and hands were threatening to drop off. I was afraid that my tears would freeze and that I would be blinded. The temperature was −30°F, and it was colder than anything I had ever known. Eventually I found my modest hotel. To get off the freezing street and into the warm hotel partakes of the nature of ecstasy.

However, I forced myself out again in order to go to the offices of the High Commissioner for South Africa. After a pleasant talk I asked for my mail and saw that at least half of it was composed of letters from publishers. There was more pleasant talk upon which I could hardly concentrate. I was told that summer in Ottawa was hotter than anything in South Africa, and that in spite of these bitter winters the mosquitoes in Canada could out-bite and out-venom our mosquitoes back home. I was advised to buy earmuffs and was told terrible stories of toes and fingers and ears lost by frostbite. And all I wanted to do was to get back to the hotel and read my letters.

Eventually I got back to my room and my mail. The Burnses had written to fifteen publishers, sending each of them six chapters of my story. Nine of them had replied asking to see the rest of the book. One of these nine letters came from Maxwell Perkins, editor for Charles Scribner's Sons of New York. Not only was his letter extremely encouraging, but the idea of being published by the historic house of Scribner decided me to take the rest of the book to them. To the other eight publishers I wrote letters of regret.

The Burnses had meanwhile received copies of the letters, and they telephoned me and asked me to send the whole manuscript to them. Though I was afraid to part with it I sent it by airmail, but owing to snowstorms it went by train. I told the Burnses that they need not type nine copies, because I had already decided to go to Scribners, a decision they approved.

By this time I was in a state of extreme but controlled excitement. Was I about to join the noble company of published writers? Would I become rich? Or would I become famous? Which was preferable? Yet in spite of all this, I continued my dedicated progress to the goal of the Directorship of Prisons. I visited the prison at Kingston, and stayed in the La Salle Hotel, where I saw for the first time stout woolly-looking ropes by which one descended in case of fire. I have a note in my diary, "Car calls from Pen, visited Pen, Women's Section." I do not know whether Pen was a place, or whether Pen was short for "Penitentiary." It was a women's prison and it was man-starved. I am no Adonis, but from the moment of my entry I was the cynosure of all eyes. There was no attempt on the part of the women to hide their looks of admiration and invitation.

I shall mention one thing more, and that is that I visited Ontario

Reformatory at Guelph. This may have been an institution known for its educational programme, but its claim to fame was that it owned the champion milkers of the world, Frieslands whose food was brought to them, so to speak, on a plate so that not a fraction of their energy should be diverted from the task of making milk. On January 31 I took the train to Ottawa to find out from the High Commissioner whether he had been able to get me a passage to South Africa. And he had too. It was luck indeed. The Admiralty had decided that merchant ships need no longer carry two radio officers, and therefore a berth had become vacant on the S. S. *Fort Connolly,* bound from St. John, New Brunswick, to Cape Town, South Africa, at a cost of a hundred pounds.

On February 4 I reached New York and prepared to meet my destiny in the person of Maxwell Perkins, chief editor for Charles Scribner's Sons.

Chapter 33

Maxwell Perkins had not received any more chapters from the Burnses, but he said complimentary things about the six he had received. He also complimented me on my use of the English language, and I received his praise with modesty without and something quite different within.

Meanwhile the Burnses were encountering many difficulties in carrying out their task of launching a new writer. The arrival of my manuscript from Ottawa was delayed by the heavy snows, but the Burnses by their persistence located it in a nearby post office which had already closed for the weekend. By fervent supplications they persuaded the postmaster to open the post office and let them have the package. Then they and their friends typed day and night so that the whole typescript could arrive at Scribners before I had to leave for St. John, New Brunswick. A considerable part of the book arrived at Scribners while I was lunching with Maxwell Perkins.

I spent February 7, 1947, in saying good-bye to many of my New York friends, and in the afternoon went again to see Maxwell Perkins. The rest of the manuscript had arrived and the verdict was Yes. For the original edition of *Cry, the Beloved Country* I nominated Aubrey and Marigold Burns as my agents, which meant that they would receive one-tenth of my royalties. Perkins said it was extremely, perhaps overly generous, but I never regretted it. He did not suggest the change or the omission or the addition of any word in the book. Had circumstances been different he might have suggested some structural change, but that I shall write about later.

On February 10, full of joy and hope, I took the afternoon train to Boston, and from Boston I took the evening train to St. John, arriving there at noon. I need not have hurried for the S. S. *Fort Connolly* had been delayed for a week. That was the coldest week of my life. The trams ran in grooves of ice, and I was apprehensive that I might fall and break a leg. I was glad when on Saturday, February 15, the Captain of the S. S. *Connolly* invited me to take up my berth on the ship. We sailed at midnight on Tuesday, February 18, down the famous Bay of Fundy and its extraordinary tides, into the Atlantic Ocean. The cold was intense, and it would have been difficult to believe that the latitude of St. John was not very different from that of Madrid; yet within a few days we were nearing the tropics, and fish were flying over the surface of the sea.

On the first day out I began to write my report for the Union Department of Education. It was to occupy me for most of the four-week voyage, and it kept me out of the intrigues of this unhappy ship. The Captain, resplendent in whites, took us out of the Bay of Fundy and then retired to his cabin to be seen no more until he emerged some ten days later, resplendent in whites, to take us into the coaling harbour of St. Vicente in the Cape Verde Islands. After taking us out he again retired to emerge again to take us into Table Bay. The ship was run by the First Officer, who resented bitterly the fact that he had to do the work without getting the money. He in his turn destested the Chief Engineer, whom he accused of purposely letting out great clouds of black smoke while the First Officer was painting the ship. Everyone disliked the Chief Steward, who was said to be in cahoots with the Captain; they were said to buy nine-tenths of the standard rations, to indent the owners with ten-tenths, and to split the one-tenth with the chandlers. The crew were Chinese, and lived in a world apart. I made friends with the radio operator, and in the evenings we would play chess and discuss the goings-on, from which he held aloof. I asked him why no one reported the Captain, and he said because no one wanted to lose his job.

The day before we reached Cape Town, the Captain sent for me and asked me to sign a receipt for one shilling, for my work as a member of the crew. The exact reason for this I did not understand, but I accepted the shilling. My ability was rated "Very A 117 Good" and my general conduct as "Very A 117 Good." The next day I entered the harbour of Table Bay for the first time since 1924, with the same intense feelings as I had experienced as a young man of twenty-one. I caught the first train to Johannesburg, and was reunited with Dorrie and David and Jonathan.

It was a great reassurance to me to find that Diepkloof Reformatory was in a state of health, that my vice-principal looked happy and confident, and that absconding had remained low. I was given a warm welcome by my wards, nearly half of whom had never seen me before.

Of my book I said nothing except to Dorrie, but later in that year of 1947 the Johannesburg *Sunday Times* published an advance review by John Barkham, himself a South African and a reviewer of high repute in America. Barkham gave high praise to the novel, and it became impossible for me to keep quiet about it any longer.

The novel was to be published in America at the end of January 1948. Waiting for a book to be published is akin to an agony. There are some writers who say that they are immune to both the praise and adverse criticism of the reviewers. I am not one of these. Waiting for a book to appear strips me of all pretensions. I am shown to be a person avid for praise and wounded by disapprobation. This would not apply to my views on moral, social, and political issues, for here I expect adverse criticism, and am not wounded by it. But when it comes to writing, I am a poor creature.

I have found it most difficult to bring myself to write about the reception of *Cry, the Beloved Country*. There was no indication that it would become a best-seller, nor that it would still be selling well today, thirty-two years after its publication. It was chosen by no book club, and it had no prepublication publicity. Yet its critical reception was phenomenal. Of the hundreds of reviews published over the United States, hardly one was lukewarm. Its success was guaranteed by its first four reviews, two in the Sunday editions of *The New York Times* and the *New York Herald Tribune* on February 1 and two in the Monday editions of the same papers. Richard Sullivan in the Sunday edition of *The New York Times* said the novel was "An urgent, poetic and profound spiritual drama, universal in its implications. There is not much current writing that goes deeper than this." On the same day Margaret Carson Hubbard wrote in the *Herald Tribune*: "As a novel, a story of lives unfolding, *Cry, the Beloved Country* stands by any standards. But above all the quality of the style is a new experience." Orville Prescott in the *Times* of Monday wrote, "A beautiful and profoundly moving story, a story steeped in sadness and grief but radiant with hope and compassion. I believe it is certain to rank as one of the finest novels of the year." Lewis Gannett in the *Herald Tribune* of Monday wrote, "Beside the sprawling verbosity, the tawdry cleverness of currently touted novels, *Cry, the Beloved Country* shines with a quiet radiance."

And here one must stop. But I shall mention one other comment, because it came from Reinhold Niebuhr, who had held me in thrall at Friends' House in London in July 1946. He was talking to *The New York Times Book Review* in May 1948 and said: "The novels that aim directly at being Christian novels are pretty terrible, aren't they? Why do they so seldom succeed? I think, though, that Alan Paton in *Cry, the Beloved Country*, succeeds. The book has a genuine religious Christian content and has a nobly tragic element in it. It is about the only recent religious novel that succeeds."

Of letters from America there were hundreds. They poured into Diepkloof Reformatory day after day. The Burnses received a letter from Margaret Carroll Turnbull of Baltimore, who wrote, "I feel I must tell you that I know how you felt after Mr. Paton put his manuscript in your hands." Marcia Davenport, the novelist, wrote to Charles Scribner, "My God, don't send me any more such books (I doubt if there are any)—nobody would have the audacity to try another of her own." Leonard Huish wrote to me from Riverton, New Jersey, "I sell words for a living, but I have never sold any as beautiful as yours."

One of the letters I valued most was from Marjorie Bell, of the Probation and Parole Association, the woman who had done so much to plan my visits in America, and who now wrote, "Truly you have done a rare thing in writing this book and I am sure it will be widely read and for many years to come." She wrote also, "I marvel when I think how much of it you wrote in the midst of the tedium of day-coach travel, and the loneliness of a hotel room in a strange city." I marvelled a bit myself.

Margot, wife of John Barkham, wrote in April 1948 a piece for *The Outspan*, South Africa's popular magazine of those days, which greatly increased the interest of my compatriots. She reported that the first printing sold out on the first day, and that the book was in its sixth printing. In May the Book-of-the-Month Club, which had rejected it in January, made it an alternate choice, and this, while gratifying, meant the loss of a small fortune. She said I had joined General Smuts, our Prime Minister, and Bobby Locke, the world golfer, in the pantheon of South Africans known to the average New Yorker.

On March 2, 1948, Scribners cabled me that Sir Alexander Korda of London Films wanted to buy the world film rights, and a few days later cabled again that Maxwell Anderson, the distinguished American dramatist, wanted to buy the world dramatic rights. By now the work occasioned by the publication of the novel was becoming unmanageable, and I had more or less decided to resign the principalship of Diepkloof Reformatory and take my chance as a writer, a decision in which Dorrie wholly supported me. But Charles Scribner urged me not to take this step precipitately. He wrote, "The sales on your book are still relatively small to the furor that it has produced. Friends of mine who rarely read a book are enthralled by it. The Church (including R.C.s) are preaching about it and capitalists and leftists embrace it equally."

Charles Scribner went on to write some words which probably meant more to me than any others that were written at that time. He wrote, "You should be here—it is most exciting but exhausting. In my thirty-five years of publishing I have never known the like and if the book does not eventually sell into the hundreds of thousands I shall be equally at a loss." It only remains to add that he underestimated. It sold into the millions and has kept me alive to this day, enabling me to do many things that brought in less money, or indeed no money at all.

It was Charles Scribner who recommended Annie Laurie Williams to me as agent for the film and the play. She was a little elfish woman who had come from Texas when young, and had become by sheer industry and native ability one of the leading agents in New York. Her partner was her husband, Maurice Crain, who looked after the writers of books. Annie Laurie showered affection on me when we met later in 1948, and I was admitted to the ranks of her favourite clients, John Steinbeck, John Hersey, and Kathleen Windsor, the author of *Forever Amber.* We were later to be joined by Harper Lee, the writer of *To Kill a Mockingbird.* This unknown girl bowled Maurice Crain over when she submitted her manuscript to him, just as the Kilvert diaries had bowled William Plomer over when he first read them. Plomer likened himself to a pearl diver opening with eternally springing hope every dull oyster shell. So the reader "sits in his study knee-deep among the empty shells of disappointed expectation," and then suddenly, the pearl! So for Maurice Crain, *To Kill a Mockingbird.*

Maurice was an intellectual, Annie Laurie was not. Her lack of a conceptual language was intensely irritating to him, and his contempt could sometimes reduce her to tears. She had one great vanity. She concealed her age, and her sisters in the firm would never reveal it. She tried to look fifty, but in 1948 I guessed she was over sixty. When she died a few years ago she must have been ninety or very near it. She was reputed to be one of the sharpest of agents, but what I remember about her was her unfailing solicitude for myself.

Although she was a sharp agent, she concluded a deal with Sir Alexander Korda which brought me very little. She thought it was a victory to wrest from Korda the sum of one thousand pounds as an advance on royalties of two percent on gross receipts. However, the film was not successful; of this I shall write later. The truth is that I received the initial one thousand pounds and nothing more. At that time the reputation of the book was so high that Annie Laurie could have sold it outright to Korda for a sum greatly exceeding one thousand pounds. The deal with Maxwell Anderson was much more successful, but of that too I shall write later.

All these events strengthened my determination to resign the principalship of Diepkloof Reformatory. On March 30, 1948, I wrote to the department giving notice that I would leave the Public Service on June 30, 1948. My letter was primarily one of thanks, but I noted that I had "only one grievance" over the years. That was the failure of the authorities to break up Diepkloof into three totally separate institutions, on three noncontiguous pieces of land, under three separate principals. Approximately one quarter of our seven hundred pupils would have gone to a half-open, half-security institution; in general they would have been of the ages seventeen to twenty-one, and the majority of them would probably lead lives of conflict with the law. Approximately one quarter of the pupils, those of the ages eleven to fifteen or sixteen, those most likely to profit from schooling and the most likely to lead a law-abiding life, would have gone to an institution which would be predominantly open; the middle fifty percent would go to an institution very like Diepkloof Reformatory itself. The second part of my grievance was the failure of the authorities to provide the first working-boys' hostel, where boys ready to return to ordinary life would live, working by day in the city and returning by night to the hostel.

I expressed my thanks as follows:

If it is true that the child should be first, last, and always at the centre of any educational programme, it is equally true to say that the Department has always made that principle the foundation of its practice. No request, if it had been made in the interest of the child, has ever been denied; and I have never in all my thirteen years at Diepkloof felt hindered or frustrated in my attempts to perform the task allotted to me.

and I ended:

Whatever the degree of our success or failure, it is certain that we did what we could.

The news of my decision to resign had a mixed reception. There was a hard core of Afrikaner Nationalists who shared Dr. Verwoerd's views about the treatment of black delinquents, and who thought it a disgrace that a liberal English-speaking man should be in charge of any institution of national importance. Most of the younger Afrikaans-speaking staff members regretted my decision, two of them deeply. One was Lanky de Lange, with whom I had had long discussions of the difficulties facing an Afrikaner who acknowledged that he had become a servant of the delinquent sons of black people. Another was I. Z. Engelbrecht, six foot four inches, a genius with the wayward, who said to me, *"Meneer,* it has been my privilege to work for all these years under you as principal."

The reaction among the black staff was expectably stronger. They felt that they were facing an unknown future. What kind of principal would they get? Their salaries had improved, their hours of work, the amount of their annual leave, but for all that they felt they would now be more vulnerable. They gave me a scroll containing the words

This work, and the reforms which you have wrought here have been the salvation of many thousands of African delinquents who have passed through this Institution, and will remain as a lasting monument to your memory.

The publication and success of *Cry, the Beloved Country* changed my whole life. In fact it could justly be called one of the two decisive events of my life. The extraordinary thing is that the second decisive event happened soon after. On May 26, 1948, General Smuts, the Prime Minister, and J. H. Hofmeyr, his Deputy Prime Minister, fell from power, defeated by Dr. D. F. Malan and his National Party, and his ally Mr. N. C. Havenga of the Afrikaner Party. Malan came to power pledged to separate the different races of South Africa in every conceivable sphere of life, in schools, universities, trains, buses, hospitals, sports fields and sporting events, and above all, residential areas. Marriage between whites and persons not white would be forbidden, as well as sexual relations between whites and others, outside marriage.* And at last the Cape franchise, which offended against the sacred historical principle of "no equality in Church or State," and which the Cape had been allowed to retain when it entered the Union of South Africa in

---

* *This was done by the Immorality Amendment Act of 1950. The original Immorality Act of 1927 forbade extramarital sexual relations between whites and Africans.*

1910, would be abolished. There would be only one franchise for the whole country, and it would be for white people only.

In other words, reparation would at last be made to the Afrikaner nation, which had suffered so grievously under the British Government, and had lost its two republics and since 1910 had suffered so grievously under the Botha-Smuts-English-speaking alliance and under Hertzog the Afrikaner renegade. After the election Nationalist Afrikanerdom was filled with a jubilation that knew no bounds, while people like myself were struck dumb by this change in our fortunes. The coming to power of the National Party brought to a sudden stop the painfully slow progress made by the Hoernlés and the Rheinallt Joneses and the Hofmeyrs, and in thirty years it would make white South Africa the most hated country in the world, facing the possibility of total economic sanctions. The event of May 26, 1948, was cataclysmic, and it so affected the rest of my life and the life of South Africa that I am going to devote a brief last chapter to it. On April 30, 1948, I resigned my principalship with the firm intention of devoting the rest of my life to writing. But the event of May 26, 1948, brought my intention to nothing, and condemned me to a struggle between literature and politics that has lasted until now.

The victory of Malan and his National Party was received with jubilation by the Afrikaner Nationalists on my staff, though I will say they restrained it in my presence. But they knew that a new day had dawned in the history of the Afrikaner people. They knew also that they were entering a new dispensation, but they had no conception of the dangerous consequences that this would have, not only for South Africa but for Afrikanerdom itself.

Those Afrikaners who were not Nationalists received the news in stunned silence. Oubaas Fick, the gardening genius, said to me solemnly, "Sir, this is the end." The African staff were also stunned, for they knew that the future of black South Africans would be ruthlessly planned for them by an all-white parliament. This blow, following as it did so soon after the resignation of the Principal, left them bereft.

The thirtieth day of June 1948 was my last day at Diepkloof Reformatory. I attended to this and that, but in fact I had already withdrawn. I sat at my office table and suddenly the enormity of my action came home to me. Before I knew what had happened I had broken into a fit of desperate sobbing. I tried to control it but was unable to do so. Mr. Koos Verwey, my chief supervisor, one of the most faithful public servants that ever was, came and shut the door.

When the fit was over I pulled myself together, and got up and opened the door.

The afternoon of that day was given over to a grand farewell parade, at which I had to take the salute, and a grand farewell tea in the pine plantation above the parade ground. Seven hundred boys passed me, under the almost silent command of Supervisor Grobler, and again I had great difficulty in controlling myself. The Chief Magistrate of Johannesburg and the Chief Inspector of Special Education made laudatory speeches. Then we adjourned to the tea tables, where a bitter shock awaited me. The function was to be strictly segregated.

It would have been impossible to hold a completely integrated function at Diepkloof. But the Board of Management was opposed to completely segregated functions. Therefore such functions were held on one site, not two, and only the discerning would have noted that a white person who so wished could be served by white women and rub shoulders only with white people, while a black person who so wished could be served by black women. The tables were usually drawn up on three sides of a square, and the middle tables were unsegregated. It was to these tables that most of our guests made their way. It was a device, but the appearance of segregation was avoided.

But my vice-principal had made my farewell a totally segregated function. The black guests were diverted to tables in another part of the pine plantation, perhaps fifty to a hundred metres away. Mr. Laas was an Afrikaner Nationalist, and his Government had triumphed on May 26, 1948. His Government was pledged to the rigid separation of the races, and that was the way things were going to be. Had he any notion that the great farewell was ruined for the guest of honour? To this day I do not know.

I was full of anger, and sick at heart. I drank my white tea and then went over to the black tables. Moloi said to me, "Well, at least we know how things are going to be." In my anger I could have spent the rest of the afternoon at the black tables, but I had white guests to consider, so I returned to them.

I sometimes wonder what would have happened to me if circumstances had compelled me to continue at Diepkloof Reformatory. What would have happened to me when the instructions began to arrive from Pretoria to change this and to change that, to abandon this and to abandon that? For thirteen years I had never received any instructions to alter anything in the educational policy of the reformatory. Would it have broken my heart? Yes it would. But I had the great luck of being able to return to schoolmastering. I was only forty-five years old, and I could have returned to Natal and resumed the career that I had given up thirteen years earlier.

So we left Diepkloof Reformatory, where we had spent thirteen years, not necessarily the happiest but certainly the fullest years of our lives. I had been a public servant for twenty-four years, secure and cared for, looked after in illness, and a pension at the end of it. Any fear for the future was far exceeded by the excitement of the new life. The first royalty cheque from Scribners had already arrived, and it was the largest sum of money I had ever received in my life. I was also due to receive money from the Book Find Club, and from the Book-of-the-Month Club, which made *Cry, the Beloved Country* a supplementary choice after its favorable critical reception. And lastly, I would soon receive a refund of all my payments to the pension fund for nearly twenty-five years. We were rich, very, very rich. Why worry then about the future?

Did all this excitement go to our heads? To some extent, undoubtedly. But we did not embark on a fast and luxurious life. We decided to return to Natal, not to Pietermaritzburg, but to the small village of Anerley on the south coast. I entertained one foolish notion, and that is that I would never wear a formal suit of clothes again, but would lead the independent and unconventional life of a writer. It came to nothing. I did not have it in me to become a Bohemian.

The second great event of my life, the coming to power of the National Party on May 26, 1948, was to make the affliction worse. It was to pull me away from the idyllic life of Anerley, and set me back on the road to the holy mountain where they neither hurt nor destroy, towards which one travels, not always hopefully, and at which one never arrives.

But before that happened we had four and a half years of the idyllic life.

Chapter 34

The birth and rise of Afrikaner nationalism is one of the most powerful subthemes of my life story. My childhood and boyhood in the city of Pietermaritzburg, an intense love of nature, the discovery of literature, the influence of Railton Dent, and the conscious adoption of service as the proper watchword for life, love and marriage and family life, the slow awakening to the real nature of South African society, and the opportunity granted to few of creating a new institution out of an old, all these have been subthemes of my life.

In an earlier chapter I gave a brief history of the country into which I had been born. Different people would give different dates for the birth of Afrikaner nationalism. To me the cardinal event in the making of it was the Anglo-Boer War of 1899–1902, which gave to Afrikaners throughout South Africa the sense that they were a people. When the Union of South Africa came into being in 1910 many Afrikaners rejected the conciliation policies of Botha and Smuts. In their view there was only one thing for Afrikaners to do, and that was to use the franchise and their numerical superiority over the English-speaking to capture Parliament, and then to entrench white superiority and black subordination. In 1914 the National Party was founded for that purpose.

In 1924 the National Party had grown so strong that General Hertzog, with the aid of the largely English-speaking Labour Party, captured the Government. But in 1933, in the depths of the recession Hertzog alienated the "true" Afrikaners by reuniting with his old enemy Smuts to form the United Party. The leadership of "true" Afrikanerdom passed into the hands of Dr. D. F. Malan. Malan's group was small but fierce, and when the Centenary of the Great Trek was celebrated in 1938, with all its pride in that achievement and all its nostalgia for the heroic past, his type of Afrikaner nationalism received a great infusion of enthusiasm and a considerable accession of strength.

What were the causes of this burgeoning of Afrikanerdom? I shall give only two: the memories of the Anglo-Boer War and the immense influence of the Afrikaner schools and universities, which taught that the most important possession of Afrikaners was their Afrikanerhood. Afrikaner nationalism used many agencies in its struggle for domination, but the most powerful was the *Afrikaner Broederbond* ("alliance of brothers"), which in time came to control the overwhelming majority of important positions in the country.

In an earlier chapter (Chapter 24) I described my participation in the great Centenary celebrations of the Great Trek, held on December 16, 1938. I grew a beard, I wore Voortrekker clothes, I travelled to the site of the future Monument in a wagon flying the flag of the Transvaal Republic, the Vierkleur. For the first time I saw Afrikaner nationalism in its extreme form, and it was its extreme form that captured that tremendous gathering. The Afrikanerdom of Hertzog, with its two streams, its scrupulous recognition of English-speaking rights, its tenderness (in spite of indiscretions) for English susceptibilities, was ebbing. The Afrikanerdom of Malan was coming in. Malan held only 27 seats in a House of 153, but if an election had been held in 1938, he would have increased his number of representatives.

It was on that day, December 16, 1938, that I became anti-Nationalist. With Malan's brand of exclusive nationalism, and particularly with his race theories, I wished to have nothing to do. I went back to Diepkloof and said to Dorrie, "I'm taking off this beard, and I shall never wear another."

The further growth of Afrikaner nationalism was halted by a tremendous extraneous event, the outbreak of the Second World War in 1939. It split the great United Party in two, with Hertzog in favour of neutrality and Smuts in favour of declaring war on Germany. Smuts won by eighty votes to sixty-seven, and by the force of his overpowering personality ruled successfully and firmly over a divided country. Nationalist Afrikanerdom fell into disarray, and this disguised for many the strength of its determination to free itself forever of the obligations of belonging to a Commonwealth that twice in the century had gone to war over issues which many Afrikaners considered were no concern of theirs.

The defeat of Smuts on May 26, 1948, astounded the country. It astounded even the leaders of the National Party. Smuts had gone into the election with a majority over all comers of 25 in a house of 153, but he had lost 25 seats to Malan and 7 to Malan's ally, Havenga. Malan and Havenga drove Smuts out of virtually every Afrikaans-speaking constituency in the country, and Smuts lost his own seat at Standerton, which he had held for twenty-five years. Malan and Havenga won 79 seats, and Smuts 65, although he had polled fifty percent of the vote, and they only forty percent. This was because of the provision made in the constitution of the Union of South Africa by which an urban seat could be overloaded fifteen percent and a rural seat underloaded fifteen percent, a provision to which Smuts himself had agreed in 1909.

When the results were known, Smuts's son, J. G. Smuts, Jr., drove his father down to his beloved bushveld, hoping "he would find solace." But Smuts found no solace. He was in a mood of the deepest depression and hardly spoke a word. There was a great deal of talk that the Nationalist Government could not last. Their majority was small, and they had never learned to stand together. Even my friend and fallen Minister J. H. Hofmeyr said, "There's no hope for this country," then he hesitated and added, "unless they fight amongst themselves." Then he said, "They always do, don't they?"

But they did not fight amongst themselves. Their small majority grew steadily with one minor setback, for thirty years, until in fact they occupied more than three quarters of the seats in the lower house, so that the whole plan of seating had to be drastically altered.

It was a new era that had begun. The task before the new Government was nothing less than to fashion not only the perfect society, but one which would endure into foreseeable time, one in which every race would be allotted its place and its function, and would pursue its own separate destiny, preserve its own culture, love its own language. Malan presided over all the freedom fighters of Afrikaner nationalism, all imbued with the same ideal of the perfect society, to be presided over by the Afrikaner Government. One day the world, so hostile to the idea of racial discrimination, would come to respect the justice and the efficacy of the race doctrines of Afrikaner nationalism. So noble was the end pursued by Malan's Government, so sublime the goal, that almost any means became justifiable. The Christian rulers of Afrikanerdom began to observe the un-Christian precept that the end justified the means.

In the first few years of my new freedom, the success of the novel and the play, and to a lesser extent the film, tended to stand between me and a realisation of the real meaning of the new era, that its principles were in fact totally alien to me. Or should I say that my success made the new era easier to endure? But it did not last. The time came when I could no longer close my eyes to the injustices that were essential to the creation of a Nationalist utopia.

I have told the story of the six-year-old boy who pushed a six-year-old girl off the pavement because he was afraid to disobey the orders of bigger boys. This was the same boy whose hat was snatched from his head and thrown into the drain by a drunken soldier and who retrieved his hat and then pursued the soldier in order to punish him. He was now a man and had decided to live the privileged life of a writer. Against his will he was drawn into public life. He was drawn into doing the one thing he had no desire to do. He felt that he and others had to challenge the morality of this new era. For the first time in his life he had to challenge the State, and he had been brought up to respect, almost revere, the law. After all the State had been good to him. In a way Mr. Hofmeyr had been the State, but now Mr. Hofmeyr had been replaced by a new breed of Afrikaners who were going to make fierce laws to achieve utopian purposes, and woe betide any who got in the way. That was the plain meaning of the new security laws, which would abolish for many the right of appeal to the courts.

This second part of my life I hope to write before I die.

Index

Index

Index

Index

Index

MORE ABOUT PENGUINS, PELICANS, PEREGRINES AND PUFFINS

For further information about books available from Penguins please write to Dept EP, Penguin Books Ltd, Harmondsworth, Middlesex UB7 0DA.

In the U.S.A.: For a complete list of books available from Penguins in the United States write to Dept DG, Penguin Books, 299 Murray Hill Parkway, East Rutherford, New Jersey 07073.

In Canada: For a complete list of books available from Penguins in Canada write to Penguin Books Canada Ltd, 2801 John Street, Markham, Ontario L3R 1B4.

In Australia: For a complete list of books available from Penguins in Australia write to the Marketing Department, Penguin Books Australia Ltd, P.O. Box 257, Ringwood, Victoria 3134.

In New Zealand: For a complete list of books available from Penguins in New Zealand write to the Marketing Department, Penguin Books (N.Z.) Ltd, Private Bag, Takapuna, Auckland 9.

In India: For a complete list of books available from Penguins in India write to Penguin Overseas Ltd, 706 Eros Apartments, 56 Nehru Place, New Delhi 110019.

18498